U.S. Consultant
Susan F. Resnick

Author
Susan D'Souza

PRIMARY MATHEMATICS
Home Instructor's Guide

Grade 3B

 **Marshall Cavendish**
Education

© 2022 Marshall Cavendish Education Pte Ltd

Published by Marshall Cavendish Education
Times Centre, 1 New Industrial Road, Singapore 536196
Customer Service Hotline: (65) 6213 9688
US Office Tel: (1-914) 332 8888 | Fax: (1-914) 332 1082
E-mail: cs@mceducation.com
Website: www.mceducation.com

First published 2022

ISBN 978-981-49-1321-8

Printed in Singapore

Table of Contents

Table of Contents

6 AREA AND PERIMETER

Chapter Overview

In this chapter, your student's knowledge of measuring length using metric and standard units and multiplying using an area model from Grade 2 will be extended to understanding finding area and perimeter. Your student will:

- use square units to find the areas of figures made of squares and half-squares.

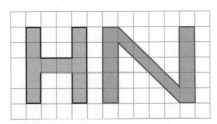

(a) Area of Letter H = __12__ square units

(b) Area of Letter N = __14__ square units

- use multiplication and addition to find the areas of squares and rectangles.

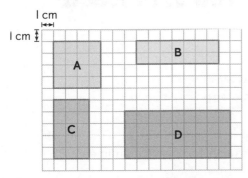

(a) Area of Square A = __4__ × __4__

                   = __16__ square cm

(b) Area of Rectangle B = __7__ × __2__

                        = __14__ square cm

- find perimeter of 2-D shapes using different units of measure and by adding given side lengths.

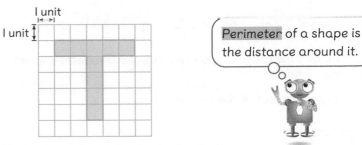

Perimeter of a shape is the distance around it.

Perimeter = 5 + 1 + 2 + 4 + 1 + 4 + 2 + 1

          = __20__

The distance around the shape or its perimeter is __20__ units.

- find an unknown side length given the perimeter.

The perimeter of the figure is 120 feet.
Find the unknown length.

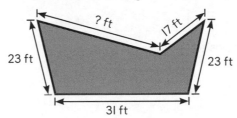

120 − 31 − 17 − 23 − 23 = 26

The unknown length is __26__ feet.

- find unknown sides and the areas of composite figures made of rectangles and squares.

What is the unknown length q?
Find the area of the figure.

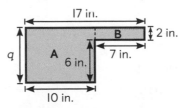

q = __8__ in.
80 + 14 = 94
The area of the figure is __94__ square inches.

Draw lines to divide the figure into rectangles.
Then find the area of the figure.
Answers vary for method of dividing the figure.

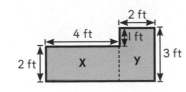

Key Ideas

- We can multiply the length and width to find the area of a rectangle.

$6 \times 3 = \underline{\quad 18 \quad}$

The area of the rectangle is $\underline{\quad 18 \quad}$ square feet.

- We can add the lengths of all sides to find the perimeter of a shape.

  Find the perimeter of the figure.

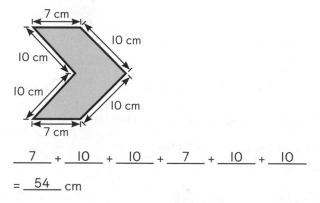

$\underline{\quad 7 \quad} + \underline{\quad 10 \quad} + \underline{\quad 10 \quad} + \underline{\quad 7 \quad} + \underline{\quad 10 \quad} + \underline{\quad 10 \quad}$

$= \underline{\quad 54 \quad}$ cm

- We can decompose composite figures into squares and rectangles to find its area.

  Find the area of the figure.

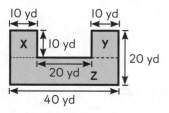

Area of Square X = Area of Square Y

$\qquad = \underline{\quad 10 \quad} \times \underline{\quad 10 \quad}$

$\qquad = \underline{\quad 100 \quad}$ square yd

Area of Rectangle Z = $\underline{\quad 10 \quad} \times \underline{\quad 40 \quad}$

$\qquad = \underline{\quad 400 \quad}$ square yd

Area of figure = $\underline{\quad 100 \quad} + \underline{\quad 100 \quad} + \underline{\quad 400 \quad}$

$\qquad = \underline{\quad 600 \quad}$ square yd

- We can find an unknown side of a composite figure by using the lengths of its known sides.

  The figure is made up of rectangles and squares.

  What is the unknown length?

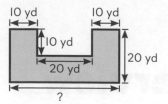

$10 + 20 + 10 = 40$

Unknown length = $\underline{\quad 40 \quad}$ yd

- We can solve real-world problems involving area and perimeter.

  Maria wants to sew decorative lace around her L-shaped rug. How much lace does Maria need?

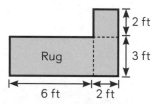

$2 + 3 + 2 + 6 + 3 + 6 + 2 + 2 = 26$

Maria needs $\underline{\quad 26 \quad}$ feet of lace.

Materials You Will Need

- 3 paper bags
- 1 measuring stick
- 1 pack of sticky notes
- 1 piece of square meter poster board
- 1 piece of string
- 1 set of rubber bands
- 1 set of index cards (inch, foot, yard, centimeter, and meter)
- 1 set of square centimeter tiles
- 1 set of square counters
- 1 stack of different colored paper strips
- 1 timer
- 1 dual scale ruler
- 1 geoboard
- 1 number cube
- 1 set of connecting cubes
- Number Cards from 0 to 30 (TR03)
- Square Grid Paper (TR05)
- Square and Triangle Cutouts (TRI9)
- Grid Paper (TR20)
- Tangrams (TR21)
- Paper Squares (TR22)
- Centimeter Square Grid (TR23)
- Inch Square Grid (TR24)
- Playroom Square Grid (TR25)

Chapter at a Glance

	Day	Learning Objective(s)	Vocabulary	Resource(s)	Material(s)
Chapter Opener / Recall Student Book, pp. 1–4	1 of 16				• 1 piece of string • 1 set of index cards (inch, foot, yard, centimeter, and meter) • 1 timer • 1 dual scale ruler • 1 copy of Number Cards from 1 to 10 (TR03) • 1 copy of Square and Triangle Cutouts (TR19) • 1 copy of Grid Paper (TR20) • 1 copy of Tangrams (TR21)
Section 6A Area (1): Area in Square Units Student Book, pp. 5–10	2 of 16	• Find the areas of figures in square units. • Compare the areas of figures in square units. • Understand that figures with different shapes can have the same area.	• area • square unit	• **Additional Practice 3B,** Exercise 6A (1) • **Reteach 3,** Exercise 6A (1) • **Extension 3,** Exercise 6A (1)	• 1 pack of sticky notes • 1 set of square counters • 1 timer • 1 number cube • 1 set of connecting cubes • 4 copies of Square Grid Paper (TR05) • 3 copies of Paper Squares (TR22)
Section 6A Area (2): Area in Square Centimeters and Square Inches Student Book, pp. 11–16	3 of 16	• Find the areas of figures in square centimeters or in square inches. • Compare the areas of figures in square centimeters or in square inches.	• square centimeter • square inch	• **Additional Practice 3B,** Exercise 6A (2) • **Reteach 3,** Exercise 6A (2) • **Extension 3,** Exercise 6A (2)	• 1 set of square centimeter tiles • 1 dual scale ruler • 5 copies of Centimeter Square Grid (TR23) • 6 copies of Inch Square Grid (TR24)

Section	Day	Learning Objective(s)	Vocabulary	Resource(s)	Material(s)
Section 6A Area (3): Area in Square Meters, Square Feet, and Square Yards Student Book, pp. 17–22	4 of 16	• Find the areas of figures in square meters, square feet, or square yards. • Compare the areas of figures in square meters, square feet, or square yards.	• square meter • square yard • square foot	• **Additional Practice 3B,** Exercise 6A (3) • **Reteach 3,** Exercise 6A (3) • **Extension 3,** Exercise 6A (3) • **Mastery and Beyond 3B,** Chapter 6, Practice 1	• 1 measuring stick (centimeters, inches, feet, yards, and meters) • 1 piece of square meter poster board • 1 copy of Number Cards from 0 to 10 (TR03) • 1 copy of Square Grid Paper (TR05)
Section 6B Area of Squares and Rectangles Student Book, pp. 23–28	5 of 16	• Find the area of a rectangle given its length and width. • Find the area of a square given its side length.		• **Additional Practice 3B,** Exercise 6B • **Reteach 3,** Exercise 6B • **Extension 3,** Exercise 6B • **Mastery and Beyond 3B,** Chapter 6, Practice 2	• 1 copy of Number Cards from 0 to 10 and from 11 to 20 (TR03) • 4 copies of Square Grid Paper (TR05)
Section 6C Perimeter (1): Perimeter Student Book, pp. 29–32	6 of 16	• Find the perimeter of a figure given the side lengths.	• perimeter	• **Additional Practice 3B,** Exercise 6C (1) • **Reteach 3,** Exercise 6C (1) • **Extension 3,** Exercise 6C (1)	• 1 set of rubber bands • 1 geoboard • 1 set of connecting cubes • 1 copy of Number Cards from 11 to 30 (TR03) • 1 copy of Inch Square Grid (TR24)
Section 6C Perimeter (2): Word Problems: Perimeter Student Book, pp. 33–36	7 of 16	• Find an unknown side length given the perimeter. • Solve real-world problems involving finding perimeters of figures.		• **Additional Practice 3B,** Exercise 6C (2) • **Reteach 3,** Exercise 6C (2) • **Extension 3,** Exercise 6C (2) • **Mastery and Beyond 3B,** Chapter 6, Practice 3	• 1 rubber band • 1 geoboard
Section 6D Composite Figures Student Book, pp. 37–40	8 of 16	• Find unknown side lengths of composite figures. • Find the areas of composite figures.	• composite figures	• **Additional Practice 3B,** Exercise 6D • **Reteach 3,** Exercise 6D • **Extension 3,** Exercise 6D • **Mastery and Beyond 3B,** Chapter 6, Practice 4	• 1 set of index cards • 1 stack of different colored paper strips • 1 copy of Square Grid Paper (TR05)

Section	Lesson	Learning Objectives	Practice / Resources	Materials
Section 6E Word Problems Student Book, pp. 41–46	9 of 16	• Solve real-world problems involving composite figures.	• **Additional Practice 3B,** Exercise 6E • **Reteach 3,** Exercise 6E • **Extension 3,** Exercise 6E • **Mastery and Beyond 3B,** Chapter 6, Practice 5	• 3 paper bags
Chapter Wrap Up / Performance Task Student Book, pp. 47–51	10 of 16			
STEAM Project Work Student Book, p. 52	11 of 16			• 1 copy of Playroom Square Grid (TR25)
Chapter Practice Student Book, pp. 53–56	12–13 of 16		• **Additional Practice 3B,** Chapter Practice	
Chapter Test	14–15 of 16		• **Assessment Guide Teacher Edition,** Chapter Test 6	
Solve! Heuristics Student Book, pp. 57–58	16 of 16			

Chapter Opener (Student Book, page 1)

Consider the picture and the questions on the page. Discuss them with your student. Prompt him/her to consider the information given in the picture and what is being asked. You may wish to ask the following questions:

🗨 **What do you notice about the picture? What are the people doing? How do you know? What is everything you know from the picture?** *They are gardening; they have a vegetable garden and a flower garden; the tulip garden is smaller than the pumpkin garden.* **Why do you think they would want to know how big their gardens are?** *They could figure out how many plants or how much mulch they need, or how much produce (vegetables or flowers) they will grow.* **What should they do to compare sizes?** *Your student may not know how to answer this at this point, but can offer a few ideas to explore later on.*

For Additional Support

To connect this to real life, you may wish to talk about other things that require knowing area, for example, the size of a room for arranging furniture or purchasing paint. This will help your student find a real-world context for studying area and perimeter.

Recall (Student Book, pages 2 to 4)

Material(s)

- 1 piece of string
- 1 set of index cards (inch, foot, yard, centimeter, and meter)
- 1 timer
- 1 dual scale ruler
- 1 copy of Number Cards from 1 to 10 (TR03)
- 1 copy of Square and Triangle Cutouts (TR19)
- 1 copy of Grid Paper (TR20)
- 1 copy of Tangrams (TR21)

Before moving on to the problems on pages 2 to 4 of the Student Book, have your student model similar tasks using strings and rulers, Square and Triangle Cutouts (TR19), and Grid Paper (TR20).

- To practice measurement, you may wish to play the game suggested in **Make it a Game**.
- To practice composing and decomposing 2-D shapes, you may wish to play with Tangrams (TR21).
- To practice the area model of multiplication, your student may either draw or build models from multiplication facts you present or determine multiplication facts from models you draw or build for your student.

Teaching Tip

When given more hands-on activity and real-world context, your student will grasp area and perimeter better. Starting with the first page of the Student Book, invite your student into a place of actively imagining and visualizing the problems so that he/she can relate.

For the **Chapter Opener**, if possible, look at some real flower and vegetable gardens.

🗨 **Which is larger? Why do you think that flower gardens are often not as big as vegetable gardens?** *We need a lot of veggies to live; flowers are more for pleasure so we need fewer.* **How do you think we might measure the areas of these gardens?** *Answers vary.*

Digging Deeper

🗨 **Why might a carpenter need to know area?** *for purchasing materials in the right sizes* **Why might a quilter need to know area?** *so that the designs come out correctly* **What other professions might need to know area? Why?** *Painters; landscapers; architects; designer; firemen; people who build cars or fill ballpoint pens with ink, etc., all need to know area in some context or other.*

Bigger or Smaller?

Practice comparing lengths using different units of measurement and measuring lengths.

Invite your student to turn over a number from Number Cards (TR03) and two units of measure from the index cards with familiar units of measure written on them such as inch, foot, yard, centimeter, and meter.

Your student chooses the smaller or larger unit by saying "Bigger!" or "Smaller!," and lays down the larger or smaller unit of measure next to the Number Cards (TR03).

Your student then runs to find an object in the house that is about the length as the measurement he/she chooses.

Use a timer to limit time allowance if you wish.

When your student returns, have him/her measure to see if the object is about the right size.

Award a point for each object that is close to the chosen measurement.

Play until your student tires or you are convinced he/she understands how to measure and compare as in Questions 1 and 2 on page 2 of the Student Book.

After this review, your student should be able to complete the tasks on pages 2 to 4 of the Student Book independently.

- **QUESTION 1** assesses your student's ability to measure the lengths of three lines and determine which line is the longest/shortest given the same start point.
- **QUESTION 2** assesses your student's ability to reason about the appropriate measurement for the length of each object.
- **QUESTION 3** assesses your student's ability to create composite shapes.
- **QUESTION 4** assesses your student's ability to partition 2-D shapes.
- **QUESTIONS 5** and **6** assess your student's ability to find the total number using an area model.

Recall Answers

(Student Book, pages 2 to 4)

1. 8; 7; 9; C; B

2. (a) 26 cm
   (b) 2 m
   (c) 2 ft
   (d) 17 in.

3.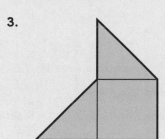

4.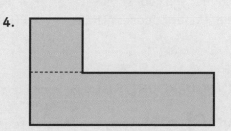

5. 32

6. 16

6A Area (1)

Learning Objective(s)
- Find the areas of figures in square units.
- Compare the areas of figures in square units.
- Understand that figures with different shapes can have the same area.

Vocabulary
- area
- square unit

Material(s)
- 1 pack of sticky notes
- 1 timer
- 1 set of connecting cubes
- 3 copies of Paper Squares (TR22)
- 1 set of square counters
- 1 number cube
- 4 copies of Square Grid Paper (TR05)

Focus Question

🗨 **How can you use unit squares to find the area of figures?**
Invite your student to ponder this question as you go through the lesson. Revisit this question when you reach the end of the lesson to check his/her understanding.

AREA IN SQUARE UNITS (Student Book, pages 5 to 10)

Lesson Opener
Task (Student Book, page 5)

Show your student the **Lesson Opener** and cover the rest of the page. Discuss the question with your student. Do not show your student how to do the task and allow him/her to explore the concept of finding the area of the different figures.

Refer your student to **Learn** and **Learn Together** in the Student Book for reflection after your student has explored the concepts. Use questions to build understanding and direct instruction to refine understanding.

Teaching Tip

You may wish to use concrete objects such as connecting cubes, square counters, and sticky notes then move on to pictorial drawings on Square Grid Paper (TR05). Your student will continue to use the visual model of grid paper for the duration of lesson 6A in order to solidify understanding of area.

Lesson Development
Learn (Student Book, page 5)

Invite your student to explore the idea of area using 4 connecting cubes. As he/she builds the given shapes, discuss with your student if the area changes or remains the same. You may wish to ask these questions:

🗨 **What is a unit?** *a measurement* **What is area?** *The amount of surface a 2-D shape covers.* **What is a square unit?** *A measure of area that has equal sides.* **Tell me about the shapes you made. What can you say about the area they cover?** *Each area is 4 square units.* **How do you know?** *Each figure is made up of 4 connecting cubes, and each connecting cube is one unit square, so the area of each figure is 4 square units.* **Do the figures cover the same amount of surface area?** *yes* **What is the mascot asking us?** *what we notice about the shapes and their areas* **What do you notice?** *The shapes of the figures are different but they have the same area.*

Learn Answers
(Student Book, page 5)

4; 4

Activity! (Student Book, page 6)

Invite your student to cover the surface of a book with Paper Squares (TR22) or square counters. Allow your student a time of productive struggle to try to figure out the surface area of the math book.

🗨 **What are you asked to do?** *I must cover the surface of my book with squares and find how many pieces of squares are used.* **How might you figure it out? What have you seen before that reminds you of all these squares arranged in a rectangle? Is there anything you have done before that allows you to know how many squares there are when they are arranged in this way? How many square units does it take to cover your math book?** *Answers will vary depending on the size of the squares your student used.* **What is another way to find out?** *I can multiply, count, or add the numbers in each row.*

Learn Together (Student Book, pages 6 and 7)

Invite your student to observe each picture before proceeding with the problems in **Learn Together**. Provide Square Grid Paper (TR05) and Paper Squares (TR22) for drawing or modelling so that your student can re-create the pictures to build concrete understanding.

Through questioning, lead your student to find the area of shapes in **Learn Together**. As you go through the problems with your student, you may wish to ask the following questions:

🗨 **How is this like the one you did before, and how is it different? How might you model or measure half units? Why does multiplication help you find area?**

After your student has explored the concepts in the **Lesson Opener, Learn,** and **Learn Together**, you may wish to ask these questions to encourage further reflection:

🗨 **What is new learning for you? What is difficult? What did you know before that helped you with this? What do you want to remember about this lesson?**

You may wish to have your student summarize his/her learning in a math journal. Invite your student to write his/her own area problem along with an explanation of how he/she can find the area of a figure using square units and half units.

- **QUESTION 1** requires your student to use unit squares and half-squares to find the area of a shape.
  🗨 **What shapes do you see?** *two squares and two triangles* **What do you notice about the triangles?** *Each seems to be exactly half of a square.* **What do you think the area of the figure is?** *3 square units* **How can we figure it out?** *We can count the squares and then add the two half-squares to make one more.* **What is the mascot saying?** *Two triangles make one square.* **Is that true?** *yes*

Activity! Answers

(Student Book, page 6)

Answers vary.

Learn Together Answers

(Student Book, pages 6 and 7)

1. 3

2. 14; 10; Q

3. Answers vary.

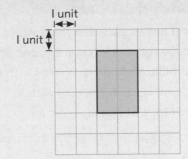

- **QUESTION 2** requires your student to record and compare the areas of two figures.
  - 💬 **How can you tell what the square unit is?** *On the grid, it shows me one square unit.* **Are all the units in these two figures one square units?** *No. Some are half units.* **How will you count the half units to find area?** *Every two half units makes one square unit.* **How many half units are in Figure P and Figure Q?** *There are no half units in Figure P and there are two half units in Figure Q.* **Which do you think has the smaller area?** *Answers vary.*

- **QUESTION 3** requires your student to draw a figure with 6 square units using the given square grid.
- 😊😊 Invite your student to think about how figures of different shapes can give the same area.
  - 💬 **Draw a different figure with an area of 6 square units and compare it with your figure in Question 3. What do you notice? What is different about these figures? What is the same about these figures? Which figure do you like best? What is the area of each of these figures? How do you know? If you were to make another figure how would you make it?**

For Additional Support

If your student has trouble with the concept of square units and area, provide connecting cubes or square counters and Square Grid Paper (TR05). Have your student build, then draw figures with the same area in different ways until the concept is solid. You may wish to turn this into a game such as the one in the **Do More at Home**.

Digging Deeper

💬 **What do you observe about area?** *It looks like multiplication.* **Can you find the surface area of anything? Why or why not?** *Answers vary.* **Is there a pattern to finding area? How do you use the squares in each figure to find its area?** *We count the squares to find its area.* **Why do we call the units in area square units?** *We are looking at all the space covered by each unit, not just a measurement of a line, such as a line that is 1 centimeter long.*

Lesson Debrief

- Conclude the lesson and facilitate your student's reflection by asking him/her to answer the **Focus Question** and share his/her thinking.
- Extend the discussion by posing the following questions.
  - 💬 **How do you determine area? What do square units have to do with it? What about half units? What can you do to figure out area when half units are involved? What happens to the total area when you rearrange units?**

- Allow time for your student to reflect on what he/she has learned and ask questions about what he/she may be unsure of.
- Encourage him/her to share anything that was confusing or difficult, and how thinking about it differently and perseverance helped the process of learning.
- Ask your student to answer a reflection question or draw a picture to show his/her reflection. You may offer these prompts:

  🗨 **Tell me everything you know about square units and area. What is important to know in order to figure out the area of a figure? What would you tell someone who had never determined the area of a figure before? Why do we talk about area in square units? Does every unit have to be square in order to figure out square units? Why or why not? What would you tell someone who doesn't know anything about measuring area in square units?**

What to look for:
- an explanation that shows your student understands how to find area using square units and understands the definitions for area and square unit
- to see that two half units make one unit and can be counted as 1 square unit
- ability to produce drawings to show area using square units, figure area from square units and half units, and answer the problems

Practice On Your Own (Student Book, pages 8 to 10)

- **QUESTION 1** assesses your student's ability to count the unit squares to find the area of each figure.
- **QUESTION 2** assesses your student's ability to count the unit squares and half-squares to find the area of each figure.
- **QUESTION 3** assesses your student's ability to count the unit squares and half-squares on a square grid to determine the area of each figure, then compare the areas.
- **QUESTION 4** assesses your student's ability to draw two figures using unit squares and half-squares for the given area.

Think!

- **QUESTION 5** assesses your student's understanding of the concept of area using the same figure made up of different-sized square units.

Practice On Your Own Answers

(Student Book, pages 8 to 10)

1. (a) 6
   (b) 8

2. (a) 12
   (b) 14

3. (a) 9
   (b) 8
   (c) 8
   (d) A

4. Answers vary; 7

Think! Answers

5. 8; 8
   No. Figure B has a greater area because the unit squares are bigger than those used in Figure A.

More Resources

- Refer to **Do More at Home** below and **Reteach 3, Exercise 6A (I)** if your student needs additional support.
- When your student is ready, have him/her work on **Additional Practice 3B, Exercise 6A (I)**.
- To provide your student with a challenge, have him/her work on **Extension 3, Exercise 6A (I)**.

Do More at Home

Invite your student to roll a number cube to get a number. Using the number shown on the number cube as the area, both you and your student use connecting cubes or Paper Squares (TR22) to build as many shapes with the given area. Then you and your student each choose one of the shapes to draw on Square Grid Paper (TR05). Using a timer set for 2 minutes, you and your student will draw as many modifications as you can to your chosen shapes using squares units and half units while keeping the same area. When the timer goes off, the player with the most correct variations gets a point for each additional and correct variation he/she has over the other player. You may wish to ask the following questions:

💬 **Is it the same area? How do you know? How many variations do you think there are?**

Caution

Your student will recognize that the areas of the figures in Question 5 are not the same, but he/she may not be able to explain his/her thinking. Help your student process this by offering an item he/she enjoys, but a very tiny version of it. For example, if your student enjoys relaxing with a book while wrapping up in a cuddly blanket, you might offer a doll-sized version of the same blanket or you can use pretend food, such as a tiny square of pretend pizza compared to a huge square of pretend pizza. You may wish to ask the following questions:

💬 **What do you think of this blanket?** *It is a tiny cuddly blanket. It is a great blanket to wrap yourself in while you read.* **Why are you not happy with the tiny cuddly blanket? Isn't it a blanket, just like the other?** *Answers vary.*

Hold up a full-sized notebook paper and a sticky note as your square units.

💬 **What can we say about the size of the blankets in relation to the size of the units we use to measure them?** *A tiny blanket measured with tiny units is not all that cuddly!* **What can you say about the area of each blanket?** *They are not the same.* **What does it tell you about measuring with square units?** *The size of each unit must be the same in order to compare areas accurately.*

6A Area (2)

Learning Objective(s)
- Find the areas of figures in square centimeters or in square inches.
- Compare the areas of figures in square centimeters or in square inches.

Vocabulary
- square centimeter
- square inch

Material(s)
- 1 set of square centimeter tiles
- 1 dual scale ruler
- 5 copies of Centimeter Square Grid (TR23)
- 6 copies of Inch Square Grid (TR24)

AREA IN SQUARE CENTIMETERS AND SQUARE INCHES
(Student Book, pages 11 to 16)

Lesson Opener
Task (Student Book, page 11)

Show your student the **Lesson Opener** and cover the rest of the page. Discuss the question with your student. Do not show your student how to do the task and allow him/her to explore the concept for finding the area in square centimeters.

Refer your student to **Learn** and **Learn Together** in the Student Book for reflection after your student has explored the concepts. Use questions to build understanding and direct instruction to refine understanding.

Lesson Development
Learn (Student Book, page 11)

Invite your student to determine the area of the rectangle. Allow your student to use square centimeter tiles or Centimeter Square Grid (TR23) to support thinking if needed. Discuss with your student ways to find the area. You may wish to ask these questions:

🗨 **What can you say about the area of each tile in the picture?** *Each tile has an area of 1 square centimeter.* **How do you know that?** *Each side has a length of 1 centimeter. Since they are squares, each tile is 1 square centimeter.* **What are some different ways to figure out the area of the tiles?** *We can count the tiles to find out the surface area they cover.* **What do you think is the surface area?** *5 square centimeters*

Focus Question

🗨 **When do you find areas in square centimeters or square inches?**
Invite your student to ponder this question as you go through the lesson. Revisit this question when you reach the end of the lesson to check his/her understanding.

Teaching Tip

Your student will apply concepts involving square units and half units to square centimeters and square inches using visual models on grid paper. It is best if you use both Centimeter Square Grid (TR23) and Inch Square Grid (TR24), along with a ruler that measures both centimeters and inches. This will help your student establish a good sense of what centimeters and inches look like in linear measurement and measurement of area.

Learn Answer
(Student Book, page 11)

5

Learn Together (Student Book, pages 12 and 13)

Invite your student to observe each picture before proceeding with the problems in **Learn Together**. Provide Centimeter Square Grid (TR23) and Inch Square Grid (TR24) for drawing so that your student can move into pictorial understanding.

Through questioning, lead your student to find the area of shapes in square centimeters and square inches in **Learn Together**. As you go through the problems with your student, you may wish to ask the following questions:

🗨 **How do you measure square centimeters?** *the same way as measuring square units; count the number of squares that show 1 square centimeter* **How do you measure half units using square centimeters?** *the same way as measuring half units using square units; use half units by putting two triangles together to make 1 square centimeter* **Are square inches different than square centimeters?** *Yes, square inches are larger than square centimeters.* **How do you know?** *We can tell by the size of the grid paper. Also, I can measure a square inch with my centimeter ruler and see that it is about $2\frac{1}{2}$ centimeters.* **Is the area of one square inch different than one square centimeter?** *Yes, it is larger because an inch is larger than a centimeter.* **What is the same about square inches and square centimeters?** *We measure area with them in the same manner, by counting square units.*

After your student has explored the concepts in the **Lesson Opener, Learn,** and **Learn Together**, you may wish to ask these questions to encourage further reflection:

🗨 **How is measuring square centimeters or square inches similar to measuring square units? How can you tell which unit of measure a problem is using?**

You may wish to have your student summarize his/her learning in a math journal. Invite your student to write his/her own question along with an explanation of how he/she can find the area of a figure using square centimeters or square inches, along with the abbreviations for centimeter and inch.

- **QUESTION 1** requires your student to use 1-centimeter squares to create a bigger square and find the area.
- **QUESTION 2** requires your student to find the area of the figure made up of 1-centimeter squares and half-squares.
- **QUESTION 3** introduces your student to area in square inches. Point out that the "square inch" is another standard unit of area.
- **QUESTION 4** requires your student to find the area of the figure made up of 1-inch squares and half-squares.

Activity! (Student Book, page 13)

Invite your student to practice measuring square inches by estimating the area of the surface of his/her hand. Allow your student to trace his/her hand on Inch Square Grid (TR24) and approximate its area.

🗨 **Are all the squares whole squares or half-squares?** *no* **How will you measure the area of the squares that are not quite half-squares?** *I can estimate or add a few partial squares together.* **How do you think a mathematician would state the area of the surface of your hand?** *Answers vary.*

Learn Together Answers

(Student Book, pages 12 and 13)

1. 4

2. 11

3. 1

4. 4

For Additional Support

If your student still struggles with determining area of figures using standard measures, provide Centimeter Square Grid (TR23) and Inch Square Grid (TR24) to re-create the figures in the Student Book. If needed, modify the figures to exclude half units until your student is ready. Allow your student to double check the size of each grid box with a ruler if he/she is not convinced. You may wish to ask the following questions:

🗨 **How do you know the unit of measure?** *I see it on one square of the figure.* **How do you find square centimeters or inches?** *We can determine the number of square units by counting them.*

Activity! Answers

(Student Book, page 13)

Answers vary.

Lesson Debrief

- Conclude the lesson and facilitate your student's reflection by asking him/her to answer the **Focus Question** and share his/her thinking.
- Extend the discussion by posing the following questions.
  - 💬 **What are centimeters and inches?** *units of measure* **How might you determine a square centimeter or a square inch?** *The unit of measure is marked at the side of each square in the figure.* **What can you tell me about measuring area using square inches or square centimeters? How are they the same and how are they different? How is measuring in square inches and square centimeters similar to measuring in square units? How is it different? How can you estimate area?** *I can measure as closely as possible and combine partial units in what is about I square unit in order to estimate area.*

Reflect and Connect

- Allow time for your student to reflect on what he/she has learned and ask questions about what he/she may be unsure of.
- Encourage him/her to share anything that was confusing or difficult, and how thinking about it differently and perseverance helped the process of learning.
- Ask your student to answer a reflection question or draw a picture to show his/her reflection. You may offer these prompts:
  - 💬 **What do you notice about finding area? What can you say about estimating area? What did you learn about finding area in square units? Tell me something you learned about finding area in square centimeters and square inches.**

What to look for:
- an explanation that shows your student understands how to find area using square centimeters
- an explanation that shows your student understands how to measure and estimate area in square inches

Digging Deeper

Extend your student's thinking by having him/her measure his/her hand in both square inches and square centimeters. Encourage him/her to estimate to predict which measurement will be greater and why. Your student should determine that it is important to note which unit of measure was used when the answer is recorded. Here are some questions to extend thinking:

- 💬 **What do you imagine the area of your hand will be in square inches? What about square centimeters? Which will be the greater number?** *centimeters* **Why?** *Square centimeters will be the larger number because more centimeters can fit in a smaller space.*

You measured the same area with different units and you got two different numbers.

- 💬 **Is the area the same or different?** *The area is the same, but one measurement number is larger than the other because the units of measure are different.* **What can you say about units of measure?** *It is important to tell which unit of measure you use in order to accurately describe the area.*

Practice On Your Own (Student Book, pages 14 to 16)

- **QUESTIONS 1(a) to (d)** assess your student's ability to count the number of squares and half-squares with side lengths in centimeters to find the area of figures.
- **QUESTIONS 1(e) and (f)** assess your student's ability to compare the areas of the figures in square centimeters.
- **QUESTIONS 2(a) to (c)** assess your student's ability to count the number of squares and half-squares with side lengths in inches to find the area of figures.
- **QUESTION 2(d)** assesses your student's ability to compare the areas of the figures in square inches and identify figures with the same area.
- **QUESTION 3** assesses your student's ability to draw a figure that has an area of 5 square inches on a square grid.

More Resources

- Refer to **Do More at Home** below and **Reteach 3, Exercise 6A (2)** if your student needs additional support.
- When your student is ready, have him/her work on **Additional Practice 3B, Exercise 6A (2)**.
- To provide your student with a challenge, have him/her work on **Extension 3, Exercise 6A (2)**.

Do More at Home

If your student needs help consolidating the idea of measuring in inches and centimeters, either linear distance or area, provide practice using measuring tapes you make out of strips from grid paper. This will reinforce the idea that one box of the grid paper is one unit. Moreover, it provides an easier step into understanding the relation of square units to linear units. Practice measuring area of various household items in square inches and square centimeters using the Centimeter Square Grid (TR23) and Inch Square Grid (TR24). Here are some ideas of items to measure: cereal or pasta boxes, business cards, quilt squares, playing cards, books, photos or photo frames, small table tops, CDs or DVDs, sugar cube, square cracker, passport, driver's license, and cell phone.

You may wish to ask the following questions:

💬 **Which unit of measure do you find the easiest to use? Inches or centimeters? Why do you think so? What is easy or difficult about measuring this item? Which objects are easier to get an accurate measurement, and which objects do you find yourself estimating?** *Anything square or rectangular will give more accurate measurements than oddly shaped items.*

Practice On Your Own Answers

(Student Book, pages 14 to 16)

1. (a) 10
   (b) 7
   (c) 9
   (d) 6
   (e) D
   (f) A

2. (a) 5
   (b) 6
   (c) 6
   (d) Q; R

3. Answers vary.

Caution

In Question 2, your student might not be able to tell the areas of figures Q and R are the same. If your student struggles with this, offer a little more practice using Inch Square Grid (TR24) to measure the area of different figures. You may wish to modify the **Do More at Home** from the first day of Lesson 6A to focus solely on your student's trouble area, be it square inches or square centimeters.

6A Area (3)

Learning Objective(s)
- Find the areas of figures in square meters, square feet, or square yards.
- Compare the areas of figures in square meters, square feet, or square yards.

Vocabulary
- square meter
- square yard
- square foot

Material(s)
- 1 measuring stick (centimeters, inches, feet, yards, and meters)
- 1 copy of Number Cards from 0 to 10 (TR03)
- 1 piece of square meter poster board
- 1 copy of Square Grid Paper (TR05)

AREA IN SQUARE METERS, SQUARE FEET, AND SQUARE YARDS
(Student Book, pages 17 to 22)

Lesson Opener
Task (Student Book, page 17)

Show your student the **Lesson Opener** and cover the rest of the page. Discuss the question with your student. Do not show your student how to do the task and allow him/her to explore finding the area in square meters.

Refer your student to **Learn** and **Learn Together** in the Student Book for reflection after your student has explored the concepts. Use questions to build understanding and direct instruction to refine understanding.

Lesson Development
Learn (Student Book, page 17)

Discuss with your student how he/she might determine area for large spaces. Invite him/her to investigate how to use area to determine the size of Mr. Mark's garden. It might be helpful to provide your student with a large-scale concrete example, such as 1 piece of square meter poster board. You may wish to ask the following questions:

💬 **What is the unit of measure that Mr. Mark used?** *He used square meters.* **How do you know?** *Each grid in Mr. Mark's garden is a square with equal sides. The length of each side is 1 meter.* **How do you know it is a meter?** *The abbreviation m means meter.* **Tell me two ways to find the area covered by Mr. Mark's garden.** *I can count the grid squares, or I can add 7 two times to find the area.* **What is the mascot thinking?** *The area of a square centimeter is much smaller than the area of a square meter.* **What is the area of Mr. Mark's garden?** *14 square meters*

Focus Question

💬 **When do you find areas in square meters, square feet, or square yards?**

Invite your student to ponder this question as you go through the lesson. Revisit this question when you reach the end of the lesson to check his/her understanding.

Teaching Tip

Take some time to bring this lesson into the real world and make the idea of a square meter come alive to your student. First, have your student cut out a 1-centimeter square, along with a rectangle that is 2 centimeters high and 7 centimeters wide. Next, go outside with a meter stick and together mark off a space that is 1 meter high and 1 meter wide.

💬 **This is a square meter. It is 1 meter high and 1 meter wide.**
Finally, measure off the area of Mr. Mark's garden, 2 meters high and 7 meters wide. You may wish to ask these questions:

💬 **How does one square centimeter compare to one square meter? How does Mr. Mark's garden compare to your rectangle? What is the area of your rectangle? What is the area of Mr. Mark's garden? How are they different? In what ways are they the same?**

If you have extra time, invite your student to build a square meter using square centimeters. Your student can make a square meter by measuring 100 centimeters by 100 centimeters, then marking the area off with yarn or on a poster board so the size comparison is evident. (There are 100 centimeters in each meter, so 100 × 100 square centimeters in each square meter— or 10,000 square centimeters per square meter.)

Learn Answer
(Student Book, page 17)

14

Learn Together (Student Book, pages 18 and 19)

In this section, your student will apply conceptual understanding previously built to measuring area with larger units, including feet, yards, and meters. Invite your student to observe each picture before proceeding with the problems in **Learn Together**.

Through questioning, lead your student to find areas in square meters and square yards in **Learn Together**. As you go through the problems with your student, you may wish to ask the following questions:

💬 **How can you tell whether the grid you are measuring is square meters, yards, centimeters, or inches? Is the area of one square meter different from the area of one square yard? How is measuring area the same no matter what unit is used?**

After your student has explored the concepts in the **Lesson Opener, Learn,** and **Learn Together**, you may wish to ask these questions to encourage further reflection:

💬 **When would you use square feet, yards, or meters? How do all the units of measure you have used so far compare to each other?**

You may wish to have your student summarize his/her learning in a math journal. Invite your student to write his/her own question along with an explanation of how you can measure the area of very big spaces.

- **QUESTIONS 1(a)** to **(d)** require your student to count the number of squares and half squares to find the area of each figure in square meters.
- **QUESTIONS 1(e)** and **(f)** require your student to compare the areas of the figures.
- **QUESTION 2** requires your student to count the number of squares to find the area in square yards. Point out that "square yard" is another standard unit of area.
- **QUESTION 3** requires your student to count the number of squares and half squares to find the area in square yards.
- **QUESTION 4** requires your student to compare two different units used to measure area and identify the larger area.

Learn Together Answers

(Student Book, pages 18 and 19)

1. (a) 6
   (b) 5
   (c) 7
   (d) 7
   (e) B
   (f) C; D

2. 1; 3

3. 3

4. (a) (1 square meter) or 1 square centimeter

   (b) 1 square foot or (1 square yard)

   (c) 1 square inch or (1 square foot)

Activity! (Student Book, page 20)

Invite your student to measure 1 square foot, figure out how many square inches are in 1 square foot, and use his/her 1 square foot paper to measure a room. Allow your student to draw a square inch in the corner of the square foot, and compare the two. Then move on to the Math Talk.

💬 **How many inches are in a foot?** *12* **How many square inches are in a square foot?** *There are 12 inches on each side of a square foot.* **How might you figure it out?** *I could add 12 twelve times, I could make a grid and count all the square inches, I could multiply 12 by 12.*

😃 Invite your student to think about the intersection of area with multiplication.

💬 **How many 1-inch squares can fill the 1-foot square without gaps and overlaps? How many square inches are there in a square foot?** *144* **What else do you know that is 144?** *12 × 12* **Is there a relationship between 12 × 12, 144, and the number of square inches in a square foot? Why or why not? What might you do to estimate the area of the room?** *I can use my square foot paper to measure how many feet there are on each side of the room, then make a diagram to solve it.*

Lesson Debrief

• Conclude the lesson and facilitate your student's reflection by asking him/her to answer the **Focus Question** and share his/her thinking.
• Extend the discussion by posing the following questions.

💬 **What sorts of things do you measure with square meters, square yards, or square feet?** *large things, like gardens or rooms* **How can you estimate area?** *I can use what I know to find what I do not know. If I know the number of tiles and I know the measurement of each tile, I can determine the area by counting tiles.*

Activity! Answers

(Student Book, page 20)

(b) Answers vary.
(c) Answers vary.

Teaching Tip

Take advantage of the connections your student can make between area and multiplication in preparation for Lesson 6B. If he/she can discover it on his/her own before you teach it, he/she will conceptualize it on a much deeper level. Do not spoon-feed it, though. Do your best to set your student up for discovery, even if it means allowing him/her to count each square inch on the square foot of paper.

In **Activity** Questions b and c, your student will find two items that have an area of about a square foot in order to get a good sense of the measurement, then he/she will estimate the area of a room. You may wish to ask this question:

💬 **What might you do to estimate the area of the room?** *I can use my square foot paper to measure how many feet there are on each side of the room.*

- Allow time for your student to reflect on what he/she has learned and ask questions about what he/she may be unsure of.
- Encourage him/her to share anything that was confusing or difficult, and how thinking about it differently and perseverance helped the process of learning.
- Ask your student to answer a reflection question or draw a picture to show his/her reflection. You may offer these prompts:
  - 💬 **What do you notice about finding area in square meters, feet or yards? What, if anything, surprised you about measuring in square units such as square feet, yards, or meters? What have you learned about finding area in square units? What would you tell someone who does not know anything about measuring area in yards, meters, or feet?**

What to look for:
- an explanation that shows your student understands how to find, compare, and estimate area

Practice On Your Own (Student Book, pages 21 and 22)

- **QUESTION 1** assesses your student's ability to count the number of squares to find the area of each figure in square feet or square yards.
- **QUESTIONS 2(a) to (c)** assess your student's ability to count the number of squares covered by each figure on the grid to find the area in square meters.
- **QUESTION 2(d)** assesses your student's ability to compare the areas of the figures in Questions 2(a) to (c).

Think!

- **QUESTION 3** assesses your student's ability to explain how he/she would draw a figure with the same area as a given figure.

In Question 2, your student might measure the area of Figure *X* incorrectly by including the two square units in the middle, which are not part of the figure.

Have your student create a 4-square or box ball court using square feet as the measure. Make a grid to determine the area of the court before you paint it, then enjoy teaching your student how to play this fun game.

Practice On Your Own Answers

(Student Book, pages 21 and 22)

1. (a) 10
   (b) 10
   (c) 10
   (d) 12

2. (a) 9
   (b) 10
   (c) 9
   (d) W; Y

Think! Answers

3. Answers vary.
   I could draw a rectangle that is made up of ten 1-m squares.

More Resources

- Refer to **Do More at Home** below and **Reteach 3, Exercise 6A (3)** if your student needs additional support.
- When your student is ready, have him/her work on **Additional Practice 3B, Exercise 6A (3)**.
- To provide your student with a challenge, have him/her work on **Extension 3, Exercise 6A (3)**.
- You may also assign **Mastery and Beyond 3B, Chapter 6, Practice I** to provide further support and development to sustain learning.

Do More at Home

Help your student solidify understanding of different sizes of each unit of measure by carrying out this activity in an outdoor area. Invite your student to choose a number from Number Cards – I to IO (TRO3) and a unit of measure such as centimeters, meters, inches, feet, or yards. Encourage your student to use chalk to draw the chosen measurement with the appropriate measuring stick (centimeters, meters, inches, feet, or yards). You may wish to ask the following questions:

💬 **Which unit of measure is largest? Smallest? What do you need to know before writing a measurement of area?** *The units that are used.* **Why?** *If you do not write the unit, the actual area is anybody's guess. Once you write the unit of measure, you can tell how big the area is.* **Compare 20 square inches to 20 square feet. Show 20 square feet in two different ways, then show 20 square inches beside it.**

6B Area of Squares and Rectangles

Learning Objective(s)
- Find the area of a rectangle given its length and width.
- Find the area of a square given its side length.

Material(s)
- 1 copy of Number Cards from 0 to 10 and from 11 to 20 (TR03)
- 4 copies of Square Grid Paper (TR05)

AREA OF SQUARES AND RECTANGLES (Student Book, pages 23 to 28)

Lesson Opener

Task (Student Book, page 23)

Show your student the **Lesson Opener** and cover the rest of the page. Discuss the question with your student. Do not show your student how to do the task and allow him/her to explore the concept in finding the area of a rectangle.

Refer your student to **Learn** and **Learn Together** in the Student Book for reflection after your student has explored the concepts. Use questions to build understanding and direct instruction to refine understanding.

Lesson Development
Learn (Student Book, page 23)

Invite your student to consider the picture and discuss it together. If needed, provide Square Grid Paper (TR05) so your student can determine the square footage of the bathroom. Hide the rest of the page until your student has determined the area. You may wish to ask these questions:

🗨 **What can you say about this picture?** *It is a grid of 3 feet width and 6 feet length.*
Draw it on your Square Grid Paper (TR05).

🗨 **What do you know about the floor in the bathroom?** *The tiles are square and have a side length of 1 foot.* **How might you figure its area?** *We can count; we can multiply 3 and 6 to get the area of 18 square feet.* **How is this similar to the picture of the bathroom?** *It is the same; it is 18 square feet.* **What is the mascot saying? What does it mean?** *We can treat this as a multiplication problem.*

Focus Question

🗨 What strategies can you use to find the area of a rectangle or a square?

Invite your student to ponder this question as you go through the lesson. Revisit this question when you reach the end of the lesson to check his/her understanding.

Teaching Tip

In this lesson, your student will learn to apply concepts of area learned in Lesson 6A to finding the area of rectangles and squares using multiplication. This is an excellent opportunity to solidify shaky multiplication facts. You can take advantage of it by changing measurements to numbers your student finds more difficult to recall as multiplication facts. In the concrete-pictorial-abstract learning progression, your student will start this lesson using gridlines and end it looking at figures without gridlines, featuring measurements only. This is an important step toward the abstract, which appears in this lesson through problem-solving.

Learn Answers

(Student Book, page 23)

18; 18

Learn Together (Student Book, pages 24 to 26)

Invite your student to observe each picture before proceeding with the problem in **Learn Together**. Encourage your student to determine the area of rectangles and square by multiplying their lengths by their widths.

Through questioning, lead your student to find the areas of square and rectangles by multiplying in **Learn Together**. As you go through the problems with your student, you may wish to ask the following questions:

🗨 **How will you find out the area? What are two ways you can solve this? How can you determine the length of each side? How can multiplication help you solve this problem?**

After your student has explored the concepts in the **Lesson Opener, Learn,** and **Learn Together**, you may wish to ask these questions to encourage further reflection:

🗨 **How can you use multiplication to figure out area? What is important to know about the units when you do that? What did you learn about finding area from these problems?**

You may wish to have your student summarize his/her learning in a math journal. Invite your student to write his/her own question along with an explanation of how you can find area by multiplying.

- **QUESTION 1** requires your student to multiply the length and width to find the area of a rectangle. The rectangle shows the unit squares.

  🗨 **What do you see?** *A green rectangle that says one side is 2 inches and the other is 9 inches.* **How is this different from problems you have seen before?** *Usually the problem only gives the length of 1 square, not the whole figure.* **What can you tell me about the area of 1 square in this rectangle?** *It is 1 square inch.* **How can you prove it is 1 square inch?** *2 squares are 2 inches, so one side of a square must be 1 inch. 9 squares are 9 inches, so the other side must be 1 inch. The square must be 1 square inch.* **What are some different ways you could figure the area of this rectangle?** *I could count the squares, or I could add 9 + 9, or I could multiply 9 by 2.* **Do all of those ways give you the same answer? Check it.** *Yes, they do.* **What is the area of the green rectangle?** *It is 18 square inches.*

- **QUESTION 2** requires your student to find the area of the rectangle in Question 1 by decomposing it into two rectangles.

  🗨 **How is this picture like the picture in the last problem?** *It has two rows that are each with sides one inch. The units are square inches.*
  Tell me about the other side of the picture? How wide is it? *9 inches, like Question 1.* **What do you know about the area of this rectangle just by comparing it with Question 1?** *Its area is the same.* **How is this figure different than the last?** *It has two colors, yellow and teal. It is broken up into lengths of 3 and 6 inches.* **What is a way you could figure out the area by using the two different rectangles created by the two different colors?** *I could figure out the area of the yellow part and the area of the teal part and add them.*

Learn Together Answers

(Student Book, pages 24 to 26)

1. 9; 2; 18; 18

2. 3; 2; 6
   6; 2; 12
   6; 12; 18
   18

3. (a) 4; 4; 16
   (b) 7; 2; 14
   (c) 3; 5; 15
   (d) 9; 4; 36

4. (a) 4; 2; 8
   (b) 3; 2; 6
   (c) 7; 2; 14
   (d) 4; 3; 7

For Additional Support

If your student has trouble with the concept of multiplying to find area, or decomposing rectangles to make finding area easier, invite him/her to draw rectangles on Square Grid Paper (TR05). Split them in two different, smaller rectangles. Find the areas of the smaller rectangles, then add them together to see if it equals the same area as the larger rectangle. Your student may have to prove it to himself/herself several times before truly believing that there is a relationship among the area of the three rectangles.

- **QUESTION 3** requires your student to determine the side lengths of each rectangle or square and find the area.
- **QUESTION 4** requires your student to find the area of rectangles by multiplying.

😀 Invite your student to look at the three rectangles and identify the relationship between their areas.

💬 **What is the relationship between the areas of the three rectangles?** *Rectangle A plus Rectangle B equals Rectangle C.* **Do you notice anything else that is an interesting relationship?**

If your student does not see the connection with 4 + 3 = 7, have him/her complete Question (d) and discuss together how you can break apart a number to help you multiply it.

💬 **Is it true that (4 × 2) + (3 × 2) is the same as (7 × 2)?** *yes*

Lesson Debrief

- Conclude the lesson and facilitate your student's reflection by asking him/her to answer the **Focus Question** and share his/her thinking.
- Extend the discussion by posing the following questions.

💬 **What are some strategies you know for finding area?** *I can count the unit squares; I can find the area of different shapes and add them; I can multiply side lengths of squares and rectangles.* **What is the relationship between multiplication and area?** *We can use multiplication of the sides to find the area.* **What are the two different ways you can use multiplication to find area?** *I can multiply the entire rectangle, or I can decompose figure into smaller rectangles, multiply to find the area of each part, then add their areas.*

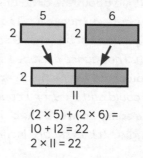

Reflect and Connect

- Allow time for your student to reflect on what he/she has learned and ask questions about what he/she may be unsure of.
- Encourage him/her to share anything that was confusing or difficult, and how thinking about it differently and perseverance helped the process of learning.
- Ask your student to answer a reflection question or draw a picture to show his/her reflection. You may offer these prompts:
  - 💬 **What have you learned about finding area by multiplying? What would you tell someone who doesn't know anything about multiplying to find area?**

What to look for:

- can multiply side by side to find the area of a figure, and that he/she must pay attention to units to know the size of the area
- to show how to find area of rectangles by multiplying and by decomposing the figure into smaller shapes to find the area of each of those, and then add them together

Practice On Your Own (Student Book, pages 27 and 28)

- **QUESTION 1** assesses your student's ability to find area of a rectangle given the side lengths.
- **QUESTION 2** assesses your student's ability to find the area of a rectangle and square by multiplying the given side lengths.
- **QUESTION 3** assesses your student's ability to find the area of a rectangle by decomposing it into two rectangular figures in different ways.

Think!

- **QUESTION 4** assesses your student's ability to identify the figure with the given area.

Caution

In Question 4, your student might mistakenly find the area of Figure A to be 80 square inches by adding 40 inches plus 40 inches instead of multiplying 40 inches by 40 inches to get 1600 square inches. The areas of Figures B and C are both 80 square inches.

Practice On Your Own Answers

(Student Book, pages 27 and 28)

1. $9 \times 6 = 54$; 54

2. (a) 45
    (b) 36

3. (a) 9; 5
        45; 25
        70
    (b) 6; 8
        30; 40
        70
        9; 5
        6; 8

Think! Answers

4. Figures B and C are possible sizes. Both figures have an area of 80 square inches.

More Resources

- Refer to **Do More at Home** below and **Reteach 3, Exercise 6B** if your student needs additional support.
- When your student is ready, have him/her work on **Additional Practice 3B, Exercise 6B**.
- To provide your student with a challenge, have him/her work on **Extension 3, Exercise 6B**.
- You may also assign **Mastery and Beyond 3B, Chapter 6, Practice 2** to provide further support and development to sustain learning.

Do More at Home

Break It Up!

If your student continues to struggle with the idea of breaking apart rectangles to help determine area, invite your student to choose one number from the first stack of Number Cards – 2 to 9 (TR03) and another from the second stack of Number Cards – 10 to 20 (TR03).

Encourage your student to draw a rectangle using the chosen numbers as length and width on Square Grid Paper (TR05).

Do this activity with your student:

One of you calculates the area of the drawn rectangle.

The other breaks apart the larger number from your student's chosen numbers and draws two smaller rectangles matching the decomposition. (See visual in the **Digging Deeper** for an example.)

Multiply to find the area of each smaller rectangles before adding the results together to find the area of the entire figure. Take turns to switch roles.

Each person who finds the total area correctly using either method earns a point. The first person to 5 points wins. You may wish to ask the following questions:

💬 **Is it the same area? How do you know?** Answers vary.

6C Perimeter (1)

Learning Objective(s)
- Find the perimeter of a figure given the side lengths.

Vocabulary
- perimeter

Material(s)
- 1 set of rubber bands
- 1 set of connecting cubes
- 1 copy of Inch Square Grid (TR24)
- 1 geoboard
- 1 copy of Number Cards from 11 to 30 (TR03)

PERIMETER (Student Book, pages 29 to 32)

Lesson Opener

Task (Student Book, page 29)

Show your student the **Lesson Opener** and cover the rest of the page. Discuss the question with your student. Do not show your student how to do the task and allow him/her to explore the picture to find the perimeter of the shape.

Refer your student to **Learn** and **Learn Together** in the Student Book for reflection after your student has explored the concepts. Use questions to build understanding and direct instruction to refine understanding.

Lesson Development
Learn (Student Book, page 29)

Discuss the picture with your student. Invite him/her to use a geoboard to re-create the picture and determine the distance around the figure. Hide the answer in the Student Book and allow your student to engage in productive struggle to figure it out. You may wish to ask these questions:

- 💬 **What shape did Noah make?** *It is a T.* **What measure is here on the grid?** *units* **What is the mascot saying?** *The distance around a shape is the perimeter.* **Does every shape have a perimeter?** *yes* **How can we determine the perimeter of this figure?** *Add the side lengths.*

Show your student the rest of **Learn** and ask:

- 💬 **Is there anything different or similar about how they did it and how you did it?** *Answers vary.*

💬 **How do you find the perimeter of a figure?**

Invite your student to ponder this question as you go through the lesson. Revisit this question when you reach the end of the lesson to check his/her understanding.

Teaching Tip

Today, your student will apply concepts of area to finding perimeter. Encourage your student to use actual geoboards and rubber bands. Your student should find more than one way to determine perimeter in order to promote flexible thinking. Drawing some of the problems on grid paper will ease the transition into more abstract problem-solving in tomorrow's lesson.

Learn Answers

(Student Book, page 29)

20; 20

Learn Together (Student Book, page 30)

In this section, your student will solidify understanding of perimeter. Make room for him/her to begin putting together all conceptual understanding built so far. Invite your student to observe each picture before proceeding with the problems in **Learn Together**.

Through questioning, lead your student to find the perimeters of the figures and compare the perimeters of the figures in **Learn Together**. As you go through the problems with your student, you may wish to ask the following questions:

🗨 **What do you notice about this picture?** *The sides are made up of squares that are all 1 inch each.*

Ensure your student recognizes how to determine the unit of measure for each problem.

🗨 **How could we find the perimeters of each figure?** *We can count to find each side length and then add them together.* **Is there another way?** *Sometimes there are two sides of the same length. In that case, I can multiply that side by two and add.* **Predict which shape has the longest and shortest perimeter. Why do you think that?**

After your student has explored the concepts in the **Lesson Opener, Learn,** and **Learn Together**, you may wish to ask these questions to encourage further reflection:

🗨 **How do you find perimeter? What else do you need to know in order to show exactly how long the perimeter is? How is perimeter different from area?**

You may wish to have your student summarize his/her learning in a math journal. Invite your student to write his/her own question along with an explanation of how you can find perimeter of shapes.

- **QUESTION 1(a)** requires your student to count along the square edges to find the perimeter of the given figures.
- **QUESTIONS 1(b)** and **(c)** require your student to compare the perimeters of the figures.

> ### For Additional Support
>
> If your student struggled with **Learn Together**, write the length of each side and, then add them to find the perimeter. Have your student check that he/she does not miss out on any sides.

Learn Together Answers

(Student Book, page 30)

1. **(a)** 16; 16; 18; 20
   (b) Z
   (c) W; X

Activity! *(Student Book, page 31)*

In activity (a), invite your student to create two shapes on the geoboard and find the perimeters and areas. Encourage your student to compare the perimeters and areas.

👥 Invite your student to look the figures and find the perimeter and area of the figures.

💬 **How do the perimeters of the figures compare?** *They are the same.* **How do the areas of the figures compare?** *The area of the square is greater than the area of the rectangle.* **Does a figure with a greater area always have a longer perimeter?** *no* **Are area and perimeter related at all?** *They are related in the sense that we can find both area and perimeter from side length. However, greater area does not necessarily mean longer perimeter.*

In activity (b), invite your student to create two shapes with the same area on the geoboard and find the perimeters and compare. Encourage your student to compare the perimeters.

👥 Invite your student to look at the figures to find the perimeters and compare.

💬 **Compare the perimeters of the two figures. What do you notice about the areas and perimeters of the figures?** *The areas of both the figures are the same but the perimeters are different.*

Lesson Debrief

- Conclude the lesson and facilitate your student's reflection by asking him/her to answer the **Focus Question** and share his/her thinking.
- Extend the discussion by posing the following questions.

  💬 **Have you ever walked on a walking track? How do you know how far you walked?** *Answers vary.* **How do you measure the distance around something like a track?** *Answers vary.* **How might we find the distance around shapes like squares and rectangles?** *Answers vary.* **What must you know to solve the perimeter of shapes?** *You must be able to find the length of the sides and add them together. Sometimes the sides have the same length, and you can multiply them. For example, we can multiply the side of a square by 4 to find perimeter, since all 4 sides are of equal length.*

Activity! Answers

(Student Book, page 31)

(a) 12; 8; 12; 9

(b)

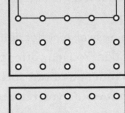

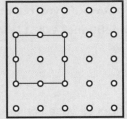

Digging Deeper

Have fun playing geoboards with your student. Take turns making shapes on them, the more complicated the better, and challenging each other to figure out perimeter and area. You may wish to ask the following questions:

💬 **Which types of figures have the greatest areas? Which have the longest perimeters? Does a long perimeter guarantee a large area?** *no* **How are perimeter and area related?** *Both use side lengths, but with area we multiply, and with perimeter we add.*

- Allow time for your student to reflect on what he/she has learned and ask questions about what he/she may be unsure of.
- Encourage him/her to share anything that was confusing or difficult, and how thinking about it differently and perseverance helped the process of learning.
- Ask your student to answer a reflection question or draw a picture to show his/her reflection. You may offer these prompts:

  🗨 **What have you learned about solving problems involving perimeter? What would you tell someone who does not know how to solve such problems? What is important to know? How do you find perimeter?**

What to look for:
- creating different figures based on perimeter or area and compare areas and perimeters of figures
- an understanding that the perimeter and area are not necessarily related to each other, except for the fact that we use the side length to figure both

Practice On Your Own (Student Book, page 32)

- **QUESTIONS 1** and **2** assess your student's ability to find the perimeter and area of each figure. Then compare the perimeters and areas.

Practice On Your Own Answers

(Student Book, page 32)

1. 12; 7
    14; 6
    B; A
    greater

2. 18; 8
    12; 8
    D; C
    same

More Resources

- Refer to **Do More at Home** below and **Reteach 3, Exercise 6C (I)** if your student needs additional support.
- When your student is ready, have him/her work on **Additional Practice 3B, Exercise 6C (I)**.
- To provide your student with a challenge, have him/her work on **Extension 3, Exercise 6C (I)**.

Do More at Home

If your student needs some extra practice, offer an Inch Square Grid (TR24) and invite him/her to create some problems for you to "solve," the more complicated the better. Have your student provide the answers on the back of the grid for you to "check your work."

In doing this, your student will create various shapes and determine their perimeters, as well as have fun checking your work.

If it is a struggle to create odd shapes, turn this activity into a game by allowing your student to choose a Number Card (TR03) between 15 and 25, and then draw the figures that match that perimeter on the grid paper.

If your student needs to make this a concrete experience first, allow him/her to build figures with connecting cubes, re-create them on 1-inch grid paper, and then determine their areas.

6C Perimeter (2)

Learning Objective(s)
- Find an unknown side length given the perimeter.
- Solve real-world problems involving finding perimeters of figures.

Material(s)
- 1 rubber band
- 1 geoboard

WORD PROBLEMS: PERIMETER (Student Book, pages 33 to 36)

Lesson Opener

Task (Student Book, page 33)

Show your student the **Lesson Opener** and cover the rest of the page. Discuss the question with your student. Do not show your student how to do the task and allow him/her to explore the concept to find the perimeter of a shape in a real-life situation.

Refer your student to **Learn** and **Learn Together** in the Student Book for reflection after your student has explored the concepts. Use questions to build understanding and direct instruction to refine understanding.

Lesson Development
Learn (Student Book, page 33)

Invite your student to look at the sign and engage in a period of productive struggle to determine the perimeter of the pentagon. Discuss with your student what he/she knows about finding perimeter and how that will help him/her to solve this problem. You may wish to ask these questions:

🗩 **What do you know from this picture?** *This is a pentagon. There are different side lengths: two are 21 inches, two are 15 inches, and one side is 30 inches.* **What do you need to find out?** *I need to find the perimeter of the sign.* **How will you do that?** *I can add all the sides together.* **Is there anything else you know from the picture that is important?** *The units are inches.*

After your student has solved the problem, uncover **Learn** in the Student Book.

🗩 **What is the mascot saying?** *He says to check that we added all the sides.* **Is there more than one way to solve this problem?** *Answers vary.*

Focus Question

🗩 How can you find the perimeter given the side lengths?

Invite your student to ponder this question as you go through the lesson. Revisit this question when you reach the end of the lesson to check his/her understanding.

Teaching Tip

In this lesson, your student will consolidate understanding about perimeter to solve problems, including finding the lengths of unknown sides. Your student will continue to use concrete materials with geoboards and rubber bands but encourage him/her to draw every problem he/she builds, in order to transfer the concept to long-term visual memory.

Learn Answers

(Student Book, page 33)

102; 102

Activity! (Student Book, page 33)

Invite your student to create a square with sides of 3 units and find the perimeter.

🗨 **What is it asking you to do?** *I must create a square with a side of 3 units and find the perimeter.* **How might you figure it out?** *Answers vary.* **What do you know about the sides of squares?** *All sides of a square are equal.*
Tell me two ways to find the perimeter. *I can find the perimeter by adding the same number four times or multiplying the number by four.*

Learn Together (Student Book, page 34)

Invite your student to observe each figure before proceeding with the problems in **Learn Together**. Encourage your student to check that all side lengths are correct in the equation.

Through questioning, lead your student to find the perimeter of the figure and find the unknown side length of the figure in **Learn Together**. As you go through the problems with your student, you may wish to ask the following questions:

🗨 **What do you notice about this picture? What do you know? What is this asking you to find? What is one way you can do it? What is your solution? What other ways are there to find the unknown side? What do you know about rectangles that can help you?**

After your student has explored the concepts in the **Lesson Opener, Learn,** and **Learn Together,** you may wish to ask these questions to encourage further reflection:

🗨 **How can you find the length of an unknown side? What do you know that can help you? How is finding perimeter different than finding area? What can you say about finding perimeter for any shape?**

You may wish to have your student summarize his/her learning in a math journal. Invite your student to write his/her own question and include information about how to find a missing side when you are trying to find perimeter.

- **QUESTION 1** requires your student to find the perimeter of the figure by adding the given side lengths.
- **QUESTION 2** requires your student to find an unknown side length given the perimeter.

Activity! Answers
(Student Book, page 33)

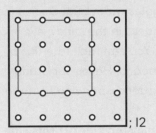
; 12

Learn Together Answers
(Student Book, page 34)

1. 7; 10; 10; 7; 10; 10; 54; 54

2. 3; 8; 4; 7; 12; 4; 4

Digging Deeper

Take advantage of the opportunity to extend your student's thinking and solidify principles of geometry that will continue to serve through high school. Have your student use regular geometric shapes to create problems involving missing side lengths.

🗨 **How can you determine the length of this side?** *I know that each side in a square is the same length, so I can determine every side from one side.*

Lesson Debrief

- Conclude the lesson and facilitate your student's reflection by asking him/her to answer the **Focus Question** and share his/her thinking.
- Extend the discussion by posing the following questions.
  🗨 **How do you find perimeter?** *Add together the side lengths.* **Do you know anything about squares and rectangles that can help you find a side length if you do not know it?** *Yes, rectangles have two sides that are the same length, and squares have four sides that are the same length.*
  How can that help you find perimeter if you do not know one of the sides? *You can use the known side to help you find a part of an unknown side.*
  What are the two ways to find a missing side length when you are solving for perimeter? *I can take the perimeter and subtract all the other sides, or I can think about the relationships that side lengths of rectangles have to the figure and look for clues to determine the missing side length.*

- Allow time for your student to reflect on what he/she has learned and ask questions about what he/she may be unsure of.
- Encourage him/her to share anything that was confusing or difficult, and how thinking about it differently and perseverance helped the process of learning.
- Ask your student to answer a reflection question or draw a picture to show his/her reflection. You may offer these prompts:

  💬 **What have you learned about solving problems involving perimeter? What would you tell someone who does not know how to solve such problems? What is important to know?**

What to look for:
- an explanation that shows your student understands the process of finding perimeter
- an explanation that shows your student understands the process of finding the unknown side lengths given the perimeter

Practice On Your Own (Student Book, pages 35 and 36)

- **QUESTION 1** assesses your student's ability to find the perimeter of each figure given the side lengths.
- **QUESTION 2** assesses your student's ability to find the unknown side length given the perimeter and the other side lengths.

Think!

- **QUESTION 3** assesses your student's ability to use the picture to find the side length and the perimeter of the figure.

In Question 3, your student may forget to multiply the number of squares on the chess board by 2 (the length of each square).

Practice On Your Own Answers

(Student Book, pages 35 and 36)

1. $6 + 3 + 6 + 3 = 18$; 18
   $4 \times 10 = 40$; 40

2. $120 - 31 - 17 - 23 - 23 = 26$; 26

Think! Answers

3. **(a)** Since the chess board is made up of 8 small squares on each side and each small square has a side length of 2 inches, the length of one side of the chess board is $2 \times 8 = 16$ in.
   (b) Perimeter of chess board
   $= 16 + 16 + 16 + 16 = 64$ in.
   The perimeter of the chess board is 64 inches.

More Resources

- Refer to **Do More at Home** below and **Reteach 3, Exercise 6C (2)** if your student needs additional support.
- When your student is ready, have him/her work on **Additional Practice 3B, Exercise 6C (2)**.
- To provide your student with a challenge, have him/her work on **Extension 3, Exercise 6C (2)**.
- You may also assign **Mastery and Beyond 3B, Chapter 6, Practice 3** to provide further support and development to sustain learning.

Do More at Home

You can help your student prepare for the next lesson by combining concepts from Lesson 6C, Day 1 and Day 2 into an interesting activity. A little observation now will provide helpful thinking time.

Offer your student a geoboard and rubber band. Create a few shapes on the board as in **Learn Together** Question 1 on page 30 of the Student Book. Shapes W and Z will work very well as a start. You may wish to ask the following questions:

💬 **What do you notice about this shape? What different smaller shapes can you see inside the larger shape?** *Rectangles, squares, etc.* **What do you notice about the sides of the larger shape compared to the smaller shapes?** *Since the smaller shapes are rectangles and squares, I can see that some sides are equal to other sides.* **How would you be able to find a missing side length? What do you have to know?** *If I know one side of a rectangle, I can tell the opposite side.* **Look at the side lengths in this rectangle. Prove that the opposite sides are the same.**

6D Composite Figures

Learning Objective(s)
- Find unknown side lengths of composite figures.
- Find the areas of composite figures.

Vocabulary
- composite figures

Material(s)
- 1 set of index cards
- 1 stack of different colored paper strips
- 1 copy of Square Grid Paper (TR05)

COMPOSITE FIGURES (Student Book, pages 37 to 40)

Lesson Opener
Task (Student Book, page 37)

Show your student the **Lesson Opener** and cover the rest of the page. Discuss the question with your student. Do not show your student how to do the task and allow him/her to explore how to divide the figures into rectangles and squares in different ways.

Refer your student to **Learn** and **Learn Together** in the Student Book for reflection after your student has explored the concepts. Use questions to build understanding and direct instruction to refine understanding.

Lesson Development
Learn (Student Book, page 37)

Discuss with your student different ways to decompose the composite figures, then show your student **Learn** on page 37 of the Student Book and read it together. You may wish to ask these questions:

- **What are the shapes called?** *They are composite figures.* **Did you divide the shapes in the same way the book divided the shapes?** *Answers vary.* **What smaller shapes are in these composite shapes?** *Rectangles and squares.*

- Invite your student to decompose the shapes in several different ways.

- **Is there another way to divide the shapes? How many different ways are there? If you were dividing these shapes in order to figure out area, what would be the most efficient way to divide them?** *The most efficient way would be the way that makes me do the fewest number of calculations.* **Among all the ways that you have seen, choose the most efficient way for each figure.** *Answers vary.*

Focus Question

How do you find the area of a composite figure?
Invite your student to ponder this question as you go through the lesson. Revisit this question when you reach the end of the lesson to check his/her understanding.

Teaching Tip

Today, your student will apply concepts of area and perimeter to find the areas of composite figures. Encourage your student to decompose the figures in various ways to promote flexible thinking. If your student finds this difficult, you may wish to have a small stack of paper strips in various colors. Your student can fold and combine these to re-create the shapes in the book, providing the concrete boost your student needs to access the pictorial models in this lesson.

Learn Together (Student Book, pages 38 and 39)

In this section, your student will learn how breaking apart composite shapes into smaller, known shapes can help him/her solve area. Invite your student to observe each picture before proceeding with the problems in **Learn Together**.

Through questioning, lead your student to find the area of composite figures with or without gridlines in **Learn Together**. As you go through the problems with your student, you may wish to ask the following questions:

💬 **What do you know from the problem? Is there any missing information? How can you find the missing information? How does breaking apart the composite figure into smaller shapes help you solve these problems? How would you break apart this composite shape? What do you know about shapes that can help you find unknown sides? How does knowing side length help you find area? How can you find the units of measure to use in this figure?**

After your student has explored the concepts in the **Lesson Opener, Learn,** and **Learn Together,** you may wish to ask these questions to encourage further reflection:

💬 **Which of these is your favorite problem so far? What do you like about it? How many different ways can you think to solve for area in this figure?**

You may wish to have your student summarize his/her learning in a math journal. Have your student create and then decompose a composite figure into squares and rectangles in order to determine the area of the entire figure.

For Additional Support

In Question I, if your student uses the gridlines to count square units to find area, allow it. Then advance his/her thinking by requiring that your student find the area of both parts by multiplying side lengths and adding their areas to determine the area of the entire composite shape. Your student will already know the answer, having counted the squares. You may wish to ask the following questions:

💬 **Are both answers the same? Which way is most efficient? Which way can you use on every problem? Do all area problems show little square units you can count?**

Through such questioning, you will help your student to see that using multiplication to solve area is generalizable to all problems, and most efficient. At this point, you are not so much concerned with answer-getting as you are with building your student's understanding of the process to find such answers in any composite shape— with or without gridlines.

- **QUESTION 1** requires your student to find the area of the composite figure by partitioning the figure.
  - 💬 **What do you see?** *Two shapes, a rectangle and a square, with side measurements marked in centimeters.* **What are two ways to find the area of this figure?** *1) Use the gridlines; 2) Use side lengths to find the area of each shape and then add those areas together to find the total area of the figure.*

- **QUESTION 2(a)** requires your student to find the unknown side length of a composite figure.
  - 💬 **What do you notice about this picture?** *We do not know the length of one of the sides.* **How could we figure it out?** *We can add the lengths of the opposite sides: 10 + 20 + 10 = 40 yards.*

- **QUESTION 2(b)** requires your student to find the area of the composite figure.
  - 💬 **How is the picture of this figure different than the last?** *It has a dotted line showing us where to decompose the figure.* **Do you like how they decomposed it?** *Answers vary.*

Invite your student to decompose the shapes in other ways.
- 💬 **Is there another way to divide the figure?** *yes* **How else could you divide it?** *Answers vary.* **Is your result the same as before?** *Yes, it should be.*

Lesson Debrief

- Conclude the lesson and facilitate your student's reflection by asking him/her to answer the **Focus Question** and share his/her thinking.
- Extend the discussion by posing the following questions.
  - 💬 **What must you know to solve the area of composite figures?** *You must be able to find the length of unknown sides and the area of smaller squares and rectangles. You must also know to add the area of the smaller figures together to find the total area.*

Learn Together Answers

(Student Book, pages 38 and 39)

1. 2; 5; 10; 3; 3; 9; 10; 9; 19; 19

2. **(a)** 10 + 20 +10 = 40
    40
   (b) 10; 10; 100; 10; 40; 400; 100; 100; 400; 600

Digging Deeper

Challenge your student to create his/her own composite shapes to solve area.
You can make this a game by having your student draw different composite figures on Square Grid Paper (TR05). Cut them out, glue them on index cards, and shuffle them.
Take turns turning over a card from the stack and racing to see who can decompose the figure and solve for total area first.
Compare how you and your student decided to decompose each figure, and decide which method was most efficient.
Save the composite figure cards for use in Lesson 6E, Do More at Home.

- Allow time for your student to reflect on what he/she has learned and ask questions about what he/she may be unsure of.
- Encourage him/her to share anything that was confusing or difficult, and how thinking about it differently and perseverance helped the process of learning.
- Ask your student to answer a reflection question or draw a picture to show his/her reflection. You may offer these prompts:
  💬 **What have you learned about finding area of composite figures? What would you tell someone who does not know anything about decomposing a figure to find area?**

What to look for:
- an explanation for how we can multiply side lengths to find the area of each part of a composite figure, then add their areas together to determine the area of the entire figure
- be able to show how to find area of composite figures by decomposing the figure into smaller squares and rectangles, solve to find the area of each, and then add the areas together to determine the area of the entire figure

Practice On Your Own (Student Book, pages 39 and 40)

- **QUESTION 1** assesses your student's ability to find the area of the composite figure shown on a square grid.
- **QUESTION 2** assesses your student's ability to find an unknown side length and then find the area of the composite figure.
- **QUESTION 3** assesses your student's ability to partition a composite figure to find its area.

If your student does not read Question 2 carefully, he/she might mistakenly assume that the unknown side q is actually a measurement of 9.

Practice On Your Own Answers

(Student Book, pages 39 and 40)

1. Area of Rectangle A = 6 × 2 = 12 square cm
   Area of Square B = 2 × 2 = 4 square cm
   Area of figure = 12 + 4 = 16 square cm
   16

2. 6 + 2 = 8; 8;
   Answers vary for method of dividing the figure.

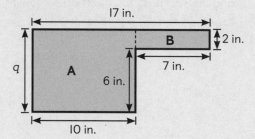

   Area of rectangle A = 10 × 8 = 80 square in.
   Area of rectangle B = 7 × 2 = 14 square in.
   Area of figure = 80 + 14 = 94 square in.
   94

3. Answers vary for method of dividing the figure.

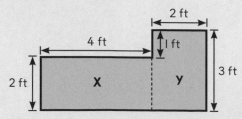

   Area of rectangle X = 4 × 2 = 8 square ft
   Area of rectangle Y = 2 × 3 = 6 square ft
   Area of figure = 8 + 6 = 14 square ft.
   14

More Resources

- Refer to **Do More at Home** below and **Reteach 3, Exercise 6D** if your student needs additional support.
- When your student is ready, have him/her work on **Additional Practice 3B, Exercise 6D**.
- To provide your student with a challenge, have him/her work on **Extension 3, Exercise 6D**.
- You may also assign **Mastery and Beyond 3B, Chapter 6, Practice 4** to provide further support and development to sustain learning.

Do More at Home

Encourage your student to spend some time engaged in productive struggle to solve for the perimeter of the composite shape in **Learn Together** Question 2a on page 38 of the Student Book. Encourage him/her to find different ways to decompose the shapes to find the perimeter. There are two missing values for side lengths in the figure. You may wish to ask the following questions:

💬 **What do you know about squares and rectangles that can help you solve for unknown side lengths? What is the perimeter of the figure?**
140 yards

This exercise will set up Lesson 6E by extending thinking to finding perimeter in a composite figure with unknown side lengths.

6E Word Problems

Learning Objective(s)
- Solve real-world problems involving composite figures.

Material(s)
- 3 paper bags

Lesson Opener
Task (Student Book, page 41)

Show your student the **Lesson Opener** and cover the rest of the page. Discuss the question with your student. Do not show your student how to do the task and allow him/her to examine the picture and think about the measurements he/she sees and solve real-world problems involving composite figures.

Refer your student to **Learn** and **Learn Together** in the Student Book for reflection after your student has explored the concepts. Use questions to build understanding and direct instruction to refine understanding.

Lesson Development
Learn (Student Book, pages 41 and 42)

Invite and discuss with your student how to find the area of the sleep and play areas of Sally's room, keeping step three covered. You may wish to ask these questions:

🗨 **Does your thinking match the thinking in the book? What did you do the same or differently? How would you like to change your thinking? Is there more than one way to solve this problem? How will you check your work? What is the total area of the room?** *90 square feet* **How do you know?** *One side is 10 feet, and I can see that the other side is 6 + 3 feet. 10 × 9 = 90.* **How can you use the area of the room to check your work?** *Answers vary.* **Use the total area of the room to find the area of the sleep and play areas. What do you have to take away in order to do that?** *I have to take away the area of the reading corner.* **Are the answers the same?** *yes* **What is the mascot thinking?** *He says that by checking the area of the sleep and play areas, we can find the area of the whole room and subtract the area of the reading corner.* **Is there another way to check your work?** *We can add back all the parts of the room to see if we get a total area of 90 square feet.*

Focus Question

🗨 When do you solve real-world problems involving composite figures?

Invite your student to ponder this question as you go through the lesson. Revisit this question when you reach the end of the lesson to check his/her understanding.

Teaching Tip

In this lesson, your student will use what he/she learned about finding area and perimeter of composite shapes to solve two-step problems with the four operations: addition, subtraction, multiplication, and division. Each of the three problem-solving steps taught in this lesson can be used to help your student learn to break apart tough problems in order to solve them. Encourage your student to use the following steps to unravel any problem, along with one or more of the suggested questions at each step.

Step 1: Understand the Problem
Ask yourself: What do I know from the problem? What do I need to find? Is there any missing information? How can I find the missing information?

Step 2: Solve it (using a plan!)
Ask yourself: Can I estimate to predict an answer? How can I think logically about it to determine a reasonable possible answer? Have I solved any similar problems that will help me solve this one? How can I use simpler numbers to make solving it with more complicated numbers possible?

Step 3: Check my work
Ask yourself: Can I solve it a different way that will prove if my answer is correct? How can I prove my thinking? Can I solve it backwards or reverse operations?

Learn Together (Student Book, pages 43 and 44)

Invite your student to observe each picture before proceeding with the problem in **Learn Together**. Encourage your student to solve for area and perimeter of composite figures.

Through questioning, lead your student to find the unknown lengths and area in **Learn Together**. As you go through the problems with your student, you may wish to ask the following questions:

🗩 **What do you notice about this picture? What do you know? What is this asking you to find? Underline it. What kind of problem is this? Is there any missing information you need to find in order to solve it? What is the next step? What is your solution? Where will you write it? How will you check your work to know if you are correct? What methods could you use?**

After your student has explored the concepts in the **Lesson Opener, Learn,** and **Learn Together**, you may wish to ask these questions to encourage further reflection:

🗩 **What types of information can you discover by looking at composite figures such as the ones in the book? How does breaking apart the larger composite figures into smaller shapes that you know help you solve this problem? What shapes can you see in this composite figure? Is the place that you decomposed the figure helpful to you? Why or why not? Is there another way you can decompose the figure that is more helpful?**

You may wish to have your student summarize his/her learning in a math journal. Invite your student to write his/her own question to include the three problem-solving steps and some helpful questions to remind yourself.

- **QUESTION 1(a)** requires your student to find the perimeter of the composite figure with unknown side lengths.
- **QUESTION 1(b)** requires your student to find the area of the composite figure.
- **QUESTION 2(a)** requires your student to find the perimeter of a composite figure with some unknown side lengths.
- **QUESTION 2(b)** requires your student to find the area of the composite figure.

Learn Answers

(Student Book, pages 41 and 42)

60; 6
60 + 6; 66; 66
90; 24
90; 24
66

Learn Together Answers

(Student Book, pages 43 and 44)

1. **(a)** 20; 10; 100; 100
   (b) 30; 10; 300
   10; 10; 100
   300; 100; 400
   400

2. **(a)** 3; 1; 13; 8; 44; 44
   (b) 4; 8; 32
   6; 5; 30
   3; 6; 18
   32; 30; 18; 80
   80

Teaching Tip

Your student might miss the fact that a fence marks a perimeter. In real-world application, secure buffers are often called perimeters—for example the perimeter of a flight line at an airport, or the perimeter of a military base. Prompt self-discovery of this idea by asking the following questions.

🗩 **Where is a fence located? How can you measure a fence? How is the amount of fencing different than the surface amount of land inside the fence? Mathematically, what does the land inside the fence represent?** *area* **What does the fence mark?** *perimeter*

Lesson Debrief

- Conclude the lesson and facilitate your student's reflection by asking him/her to answer the **Focus Question** and share his/her thinking.
- Extend the discussion by posing the following questions.
  - 🗨 **What questions can you ask yourself to help solve complicated problems? What question did you find most helpful to ask yourself when solving word problems?** *What do I know? What do I need to find? Is there any information I am missing?* **How does asking questions help you think about it?**

Reflect and Connect

- Allow time for your student to reflect on what he/she has learned and ask questions about what he/she may be unsure of.
- Encourage him/her to share anything that was confusing or difficult, and how thinking about it differently and perseverance helped the process of learning.
- Ask your student to answer a reflection question or draw a picture to show his/her reflection. You may offer these prompts:
  - 🗨 **What have you learned about solving problems involving perimeter and area? What would you tell someone who does not know how to solve such problems? What is important to know?**

What to look for:

- an explanation that shows your student understands how to use the three-step model to solve area problems

Practice On Your Own (Student Book, pages 45 and 46)

- **QUESTION 1** assesses your student's ability to solve a problem that involves finding the perimeter of a composite figure with unknown sides.
- **QUESTION 2(a)** assesses your student's ability to solve a problem that involves finding the area of a composite figure.
- **QUESTION 2(b)** assesses your student's ability to solve a problem that involves finding the perimeter of a composite figure with unknown sides.
- **QUESTION 3** assesses your student's ability to solve a problem that involves finding and comparing the areas of two composite figures.

Practice On Your Own Answers

(Student Book, pages 45 and 46)

1. $2 + 3 + 2 + 6 + 3 + 6 + 2 + 2 = 26$; 26

2. (a) $5 \times 10 = 50$
   $35 \times 20 = 35 \times 2 \times 10$
   $\qquad\qquad = 700$
   $50 + 700 = 750$
   750

   (b) $10 + 5 + 10 + 35 + 20 + 40 = 120$
   120

3. $4 \times 8 = 32$
   $4 \times 12 = 48$
   $32 + 32 + 48 = 112$

   $5 \times 9 = 45$
   $5 \times 14 = 70$

   $45 + 70 = 115$
   $115 - 112 = 3$

   Doreen should choose Design B.
   It is 3 square yards bigger than Design A.

More Resources

- Refer to **Do More at Home** below and **Reteach 3, Exercise 6E** if your student needs additional support.
- When your student is ready, have him/her work on **Additional Practice 3B, Exercise 6E**.
- To provide your student with a challenge, have him/her work on **Extension 3, Exercise 6E**.
- You may also assign **Mastery and Beyond 3B, Chapter 6, Practice 5** to provide further support and development to sustain learning.

Do More at Home

Reinforce problem-solving with area and perimeter by playing the following game.

Using three paper bags, you and your student should fill the first paper bag with slips of paper containing units of measure such as centimeters, meters, inches, feet, and yards. Fill the second paper bag with slips of paper naming objects or locations. These should be objects or locations that have a surface area, for example, the ocean or a math book. The third paper bag will contain slips of paper with names. Your student may enjoy using the names of family members, friends, pets, or even famous people or characters from a favorite book. (Optional: If you did the **Digging Deeper** in Lesson 6D, you may wish to use the composite figure cards your student created. Otherwise, create your own composite figures as you go.)

Take turns to draw a slip of paper from each bag to create a word problem for each other to solve. The word problem should include questions on both area and perimeter.

For example, your student might choose the following slips: meters; cookies; Aunt Bertha. He/she would choose or create a composite shape and make a word problem to go with it using the slips:

Aunt Bertha baked a cookie that looked like this:

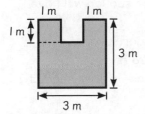

What were the area and perimeter of the cookie?

Aunt Bertha's cookie had an area of 8 square meters and a perimeter of 14 m.

Check each other's work and wrap up by deciding together which was the silliest problem.

Digging Deeper

For Question 3, you can extend the question by asking these questions:

🗩 **Doreen wants to spend as little money as possible on fencing. Which design should she choose? Why?** *Doreen should choose Design B. Design A is 64 yards in perimeter. Design B's perimeter is 56 yards. Doreen will spend less on fencing if she chooses the design with the smaller perimeter, Design B.* **Do figures with the greatest perimeter always have the greatest area?** *no* **Do figures with the greatest area always have the greatest perimeter?** *no*

Chapter Wrap Up

Before your student works on the **Performance Task**, help him/her recap the key learning objectives and develop a concept map to reflect the concepts and skills of the chapter. Use the following key terms to start constructing the concept map:

- Area
- Area of squares and rectangles
- Perimeter
- Composite figures

Encourage your student to complete the **Chapter Self-Reflection** on page 51 as a form of self-reflection.

Performance Task (Student Book, pages 47 to 50)

Refer your student to the **Performance Task** to consolidate and deepen his/her understanding of the chapter through tasks that require him/her to show, explain, and/or apply thinking. You may use the rubric on page 48 to encourage your student to set his/her own goals.

QUESTION (a) requires your student to find the area of the indoor section of the chicken coop which is in the shape of a rectangle.

💬 **What do you know?**

QUESTION (b) requires your student to reason about the areas of two rectangles and explain which rectangle has a greater area.

💬 **What is an idea you have? What do you know? How might you solve this in a different way?**

QUESTION (c) requires your student to find the perimeter of a rectangle to determine if the given length of wooden planks is enough to frame the outdoor section.

💬 **How might you calculate this problem? Does he have enough wood?**

Performance Task Answers

(Student Book, pages 47 to 50)

(a) Area of indoor section = 5×4
$$= 20 \text{ square ft}$$
The area of the indoor section is 20 square feet.

(b) **Way 1**—Area of outdoor section
$$= 10 \times 4 = 40 \text{ square ft}$$
Comparing it with the area of the indoor section found in (a), the outdoor section of the coop has a greater area.

Way 2—The two sections have the same width of 4 feet. The outdoor section has a longer side than the indoor section, so when both sides are multiplied by 4 feet, the outdoor section will have a greater area.

(c) Perimeter of outdoor section
$$= 10 + 4 + 10 + 4 = 28 \text{ ft}$$
Total length of wooden plank needed
$$= 28 + 28 = 56 \text{ ft}$$
Since 55 feet is less than 56 feet, Jill's father does not have enough wooden planks to build the frame.

QUESTION (d) requires your student to draw a rectangular model with the same area as the given outdoor section but with a smaller perimeter.

🗨 **What might you do to the shape of the outdoor area so that they have enough wood but maintain the same area? How might you calculate this problem?**

QUESTION (e) requires your student to determine if Jill's father will have enough wooden planks and explain the reasoning.

🗨 **How can you find out if your plan works?**

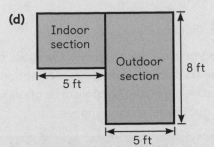

(d)

Answers vary. Example:

$40 = 1 \times 40$

Perimeter:

$1 + 40 + 1 + 40 = 82$ ✗

$40 = 2 \times 20$

Perimeter:

$2 + 20 + 2 + 20 = 44$ ✗

$40 = 5 \times 8$

Perimeter: $5 + 8 + 5 + 8 = 26$

(e) $26 + 26 = 52$

Since 55 feet is more than 52 feet, Jill's father now has enough wooden planks to build the frame.

Teaching Tip

As your student works through the **Performance Task**, engage with the first idea your student offers and help him/her explore the chosen method before investigating other ways. Encourage your student to evaluate given information, even if it is not explicitly stated, such as comparing the two areas and considering how changing parameters for area might affect perimeter. You may wish to ask the following questions:

🗨 **What do you know about the inside and outside sections? How do they compare in area? Perimeter? Does changing one affect the other? Why or why not? How does what you know about multiplication help you?** *I can use different factors to multiply to get the same area but different perimeters.*

Rubric (Student Book, page 51)

Use the scoring guide to help you give feedback on your student's work. Use the comments section to provide information about what was done well and what could be improved. Write words of encouragement to let your student know what he/she has done well.

	Description	**Point(s)**
Scoring Rubric		
(a)	Your student: • correctly finds the area of the indoor section of the coop. (20 sq ft)	1
(b)	Your student: • correctly compares the areas of the two sections by finding the area of the outdoor section. (40 sq ft)	1
	• correctly reasons that the outdoor section shares the same width but has a longer side, and hence has a greater area.	1
(c)	Your student: • correctly finds the perimeter of the outdoor section. (28 ft)	0.5
	• correctly finds the length of wooden plank needed. (28 + 28 = 56 ft)	1
	• determines that there is not enough wooden planks.	0.5
(d)	Your student: • correctly determines the area needs to be 40 square feet.	1
	• correctly draws a rectangle with a perimeter of less than 55 ÷ 2 = 27.5 feet. (5 ft by 8 ft)	1
(e)	Your student: • correctly explains why the new design would work. (26 + 26 = 52 ft, 52 ft < 55 ft)	1
	Total	**8**

Use this table as a guide to help you relate your student's scores to his/her performance levels.

Level	Score
😊 😊 😊	7–8
😊 😊	2.5–6.5
😊	0–2

STEAM Project Work (Student Book, Chapter 6, page 52)

- Your student is given an opportunity to make connections between engineering and mathematics in this project work.
- At the end of **Chapter 6**, your student should be able to complete **Part 1**.
- **Part 1** requires your student to use a Playroom Square Grid (TR25) to design and draw a plan for a playroom that has a total floor area of 200 square feet.

Chapter Practice (Student Book, pages 53 to 56)

- Have your student work on **Chapter Practice** in the Student Book independently to help him/her consolidate and extend understanding of the chapter.
- You may find a summary of the chapter learning objectives and the difficulty level of the questions below.
- Teaching prompts are provided for Levels 2 and 3 questions.
- When your student is ready, have him/her work on **Additional Practice 3B, Chapter Practice**.

Chapter Practice Answers

(Student Book, pages 53 to 56)

1. Option A

2. Option B

3. Option C

4. Answers vary.

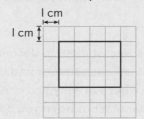

5.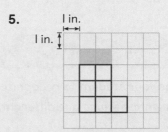

6. 50; 30; 36; 30
    Rectangles with the same perimeter can have different areas.

Question	Level	Chapter 6 Learning Objective(s)	Section(s)	Day(s)
1	1	Find the areas of figures in square inches.	6A	3
2	1	Find the areas of figures in square feet.	6A	4
3	1	Find the perimeter of a figure given the side lengths.	6C	6
4	1	Find the areas of figures in square centimeters.	6A	3
5	1	Find the areas of composite figures.	6D	8
6	1	Compare the areas of figures in square centimeters. Find the area of a rectangle given its length and width. Find the perimeter of a figure given the side lengths.	6A, 6B, 6C	3, 5, 6
7	2	Find unknown side lengths of composite figures. Find the areas of composite figures.	6D	8
8	3	Find the perimeter of a figure given the side lengths. Solve real-world problems involving finding perimeter of figures.	6C	6, 7
9	3	Find unknown side lengths of composite figures. Find the areas of composite figures. Solve real-world problems involving composite figures.	6D, 6E	8, 9

QUESTION 7 requires your student to partition a composite figure to find its area in two ways.

💬 Does the answer make sense? Why or why not? How can you justify your answer? What convinced you that your answer is correct?

QUESTION 8 requires your student to find the perimeter of a swimming pool surrounded by 2-feet square tiles.

💬 What have you done before that is similar? What questions might you ask to help get started? Does the answer make sense? Why or why not? How can you justify your answer? What convinced you that your answer is correct?

QUESTION 9 requires your student to decompose a figure into identical squares, then find the side length of each square and the area of the composite figure.

💬 Can you describe where or why you are stuck? What is another way to solve this problem? What have you done before that is similar? What questions might you ask to help get started?

Caution

Question 8 requires your student to recognize that the area of the pool and the area of the entire figure are different, and account for the path around the figure.

Days 14–15 of 16

Chapter Test

- Assign **Chapter Test 6** in **Assessment Guide Teacher Edition** to assess your student's understanding of the chapter.

7.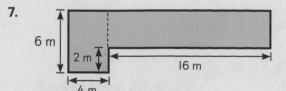

Way 1
$6 \times 4 = 24$
$4 \times 16 = 64$
$24 + 64 = 88$

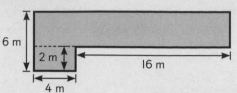

Way 2
$4 \times 2 = 8$
$20 \times 4 = 80$
$80 + 8 = 88$
88

8. $2 \times 10 = 20$
$5 \times 2 = 10$
$20 + 10 + 20 + 10 = 60; 60$

9. (a)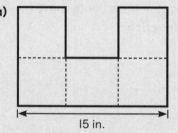

15 in.

Side length of each square is 5 inches. There are 3 squares at the base of the pentomino.
$15 \div 3 = 5$

(b) $5 \times 5 = 25$
$25 \times 5 = 125$
The area of the pentomino is 125 square inches.

Chapter Self-Reflection

Check (✓) to show what I can do.

I Can	Yes	Not Sure	No
find the areas of figures in square units.			
compare the areas of figures in square units.			
understand that figures with different shapes can have the same area.			
find the areas of figures in square centimeters and square inches.			
compare the areas of figures in square centimeters and square inches.			
find the areas of figures in square meters, square feet, and square yards.			
compare the areas of figures in square meters, square feet, and square yards.			
find the area of a rectangle given its length and width.			
find the area of a square given its side length.			
find the perimeter of a figure given the side lengths.			
find an unknown side length given the perimeter.			
solve real-world problems involving finding perimeters of figures.			
find unknown side lengths of composite figures.			
find the areas of composite figures.			
solve real-world problems involving composite figures.			

MY JOURNAL

I can show...

I still wonder...

Solve! Heuristics (Student Book, pages 57 and 58)

Heuristic: Make a supposition

Go through the four-step problem-solving model to guide your student to solve the problem.

 Step 1 Understand

Show the problem only. Have your student read the problem and begin to engage in productive struggle.

🗨 **What do you know?** *There are 18 shapes and 62 sides. Some are triangles, some are squares.* **What do you need to find out?** *We must find out how many of the 18 shapes are squares.* **Is there anything else you know that might help you, even if it is not stated in the problem?** *Triangles have 3 sides; squares have 4 sides.*

 Step 2 Plan

🗨 **How could you start to solve the problem?** *Answers vary. I could make a model; I could make a list; I could make a supposition.*

Step 3 Do

Give your student a chance to engage in productive struggle to answer the question before looking at the solution. Do not show the book's solution until your student has generated one of his/her own.

🗨 **What is a supposition you might make that could tell you how many squares there are?** *Answers vary.*

Display the book's solution.

🗨 **Why do you think making this supposition that all the shapes are triangles, when we know that some are definitely squares, helps us figure out the actual number of squares?** *By assuming they are all triangles, we can see how many extra sides there are. Each square has one more side than a triangle, so the number of extra sides tells us the number of squares.*

 Step 4 Look Back

Guide your student to check the answer.

🗨 **How might you check the answer? Is the answer correct? What is another way to solve the problem?** *Answers vary.*

Alternative strategy
Heuristic: Make a List

Encourage your student to share alternative ways to solve the problem. In this example of making a list, the student stopped calculating as soon as he/she saw the pattern, circled below:

Triangles	Squares	Sides Tri + Squares	Total Sides	Total shapes
18 × 3 = 54	0	54 + 0	54	18
17 × 3 = 51	1 × 4 = 4	51 + 4	55	18
16 × 3 = 48	2 × 4 = 8	48 + 8	56	18
15			57	18
14			58	18
13			59	18
12			60	18
11			61	18
10 × 3 = 30	8 × 4 = 32	30 + 32	62	18

Solve! (page 58)

QUESTION 1 requires your student to make a supposition to solve for the number of stars, given the number of craft sticks used to make a total number of 17 stars and triangles.

🗨 **What do you know?** *100 craft sticks, 17 stars and triangles, 10 sticks per star, and 3 sticks per triangle.* **What do you need to find?** *How many stars Ben made?* **How is this problem different from the example?** *There is not just one extra side. There are seven extra sides for each star. Also, sides = craft sticks.* **What should your supposition be, and why?** *If I suppose they are all triangles, I will find out how many extra sides there are. Then I can divide that by 7 to find out the number of stars.* **How might you check your work?** *I can multiply out the number of sides for each shape and add them together to see if I get 100 sticks. (7 stars × 10 sticks) + (10 triangles × 3 sticks) = 100*

Alternative strategy
Heuristic: Make a list
As with the previous example, your student can also make a systematic list to solve this problem.

QUESTION 2 requires your student to make a supposition to solve for the number of each shape, given the number of blocks used to make a total number of 30 squares and rectangles.

🗨 **What do you know?** *Mary used 86 blocks to make 30 shapes. Squares used 2 blocks and rectangles used 4 blocks.* **What do you need to find out?** *The number of each shape Mary made.* **What do you know that might help you?** *If I make a supposition that all the shapes are squares, I can find the number of extra blocks. Since each rectangle has 2 extra blocks, I can divide the leftovers by 2 to find out the number of rectangles I will need.*

Solve! Heuristics Answers

(Student Book, page 58)

1. Suppose there are 17 triangles:
    $17 × 3 = 51$
    Ben would need 51 craft sticks.
    $100 − 51 = 49$
    Since each star needs 7 more sticks than each triangle, there are $49 ÷ 7 = 7$ stars.
    Ben made 7 stars.

2. Suppose there are 30 square shapes:
    $30 × 2 = 60$
    Mary would need 60 rectangular blocks.
    $86 − 60 = 26$
    Since each rectangle shape takes 2 more rectangular blocks to make than each square shape, there are $26 ÷ 2 = 13$ rectangle shapes.
    $30 − 13 = 17$
    Mary made 13 rectangle and 17 square shapes.

Alternative strategy
Heuristic: Act It Out
In addition to the alternative strategy of making a list, your student could use connecting cubes to model this problem and see the relationship between the total number of rectangular blocks and the composition of the shapes needed to solve this problem.

7 FRACTIONS

Chapter Overview

In this chapter, your student's knowledge of breaking apart shapes into equal parts from Grade 2 will be extended to understanding fractions as equal parts of a whole or equal parts of a set of objects. Your student will:

- work with **unit fractions** such as halves, thirds, fourths, sixths, and eighths specified for Grade 3. To build flexible thinking about fractions, understanding is then extended to additional unit fractions such as fifths, sevenths, ninths, and tenths.
- introduce each fraction concept using **concrete materials** such as fraction circles and fraction bars or tiles.

  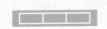

fraction circle   fraction tiles

- learn to use **pictorial models** to further help his/her understanding of fractions. Models are used to show fractions and help your student visualize the size of each fraction. Drawing these models helps your student internalize the concepts.

This model shows thirds.   This model shows $\frac{2}{3}$ of a whole.

- grapple with the idea that fractions are parts that represent **something less than one whole**. Fractions can be added and subtracted to make other wholes or parts of wholes. For example, $\frac{2}{3}$ is formed by 2 parts that are $\frac{1}{3}$ of the whole (2 one-thirds).

$$\frac{2}{3} = \frac{1}{3} + \frac{1}{3}$$

- learn about how fractions can represent **intervals on a number line**, for building upon the understanding of fractions as parts of 1 or more wholes. The interval from 0 to 1 is the whole and it is decomposed into 3 equal parts. Each part has a size of $\frac{1}{3}$. $\frac{2}{3}$ is 2 times the distance of $\frac{1}{3}$ from 0.

0      $\frac{1}{3}$ $\frac{2}{3}$ 1

- learn to represent fractions in a variety of ways, he/she will learn to **compare fractions** by comparing the size of fractions. Draw models to explain thinking and use symbols (>, =, or <) to record the results of these comparisons. It is important to show the whole each time a fraction of a whole is drawn.

I whole

$\frac{1}{4}$	$\frac{1}{4}$	$\frac{1}{4}$	$\frac{1}{4}$

$\frac{1}{4}$	$\frac{1}{4}$	$\frac{1}{4}$	$\frac{1}{4}$

$$\frac{3}{4} > \frac{1}{4}$$

$$\frac{1}{4} < \frac{3}{4}$$

Key Ideas

- We can read, write, and identify fractions between 0 and 1, and fractions greater than 1. These fractions are expressed using the notation in the form $\frac{a}{b}$.

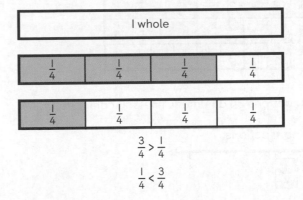

I whole = 2 halves = $\frac{2}{2}$

$$\frac{2}{2} = \frac{1}{2} + \frac{1}{2}$$

2 wholes = 4 halves = $\frac{4}{2}$

$$\frac{4}{2} = \frac{1}{2} + \frac{1}{2} + \frac{1}{2} + \underline{\frac{1}{2}}$$

We can write $\frac{2}{2}$ as a sum of unit fractions.

- We can compare and order fractions.

$\frac{1}{6}$	$\frac{1}{6}$	$\frac{1}{6}$	$\frac{1}{6}$	$\frac{1}{6}$	$\frac{1}{6}$

$\frac{1}{6}$	$\frac{1}{6}$	$\frac{1}{6}$	$\frac{1}{6}$	$\frac{1}{6}$	$\frac{1}{6}$

$\frac{1}{6}$	$\frac{1}{6}$	$\frac{1}{6}$	$\frac{1}{6}$	$\frac{1}{6}$	$\frac{1}{6}$

Order the fractions from least to greatest.

$$\underline{\frac{3}{6}} , \quad \underline{\frac{4}{6}} , \quad \underline{\frac{5}{6}}$$

least   greatest

- We can identify and find equivalent fractions.

Look at the fraction bars. Which fractions are equivalent to $\frac{3}{4}$?

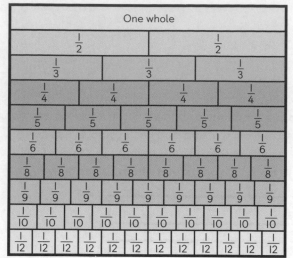

$\frac{3}{4} = \boxed{\frac{6}{8}} = \boxed{\frac{6}{12}}$

- We can show fractions on a number line and compare them.

Fill in the missing fractions.

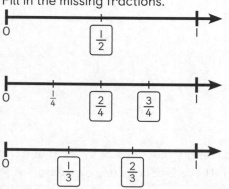

Write <, =, or > to compare the fractions.

$\frac{1}{4}$ ⟨ < ⟩ $\frac{1}{3}$ ⟨ < ⟩ $\frac{1}{2}$

- We can identify fraction of a set.

There are 8 stickers.

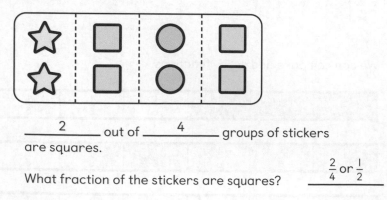

_____2_____ out of _____4_____ groups of stickers
are squares.

What fraction of the stickers are squares? $\frac{2}{4}$ or $\frac{1}{2}$

Materials You Will Need

- 1 paper bag
- 1 piece of graph paper
- 1 piece of paper plate
- 1 set of colored pencils
- 1 set of construction paper
- 15 colored cubes (6 red, 3 yellow, 3 green, and 3 blue)
- 2 number cubes
- 1 set of connecting cubes (two colors)
- 1 set of counters
- 1 set of fraction circles
- 1 set of fraction tiles
- Number Cards (TR03)
- Paper Squares (TR22)
- Inch Square Grid (TR24)
- Rectangular Paper Strips (TR26)
- Unit Fraction Cards (TR27)
- Ten Frame (TR28)
- Paper Square (TR29)
- Fraction Cards (TR30)
- Fraction Bars (TR31)
- Fraction Strips (TR32)
- Number Line Template (TR33)

Chapter at a Glance

	Day	Learning Objective(s)	Vocabulary	Resource(s)	Material(s)
Chapter Opener / Recall Student Book, pp. 59–60	1 of 17				• 1 number cube with the numbers 2, 3, and 4 • 1 set of fraction circles • 1 copy of Number Cards from 2 to 4 (TR03)
Section 7A Unit Fractions Student Book, pp. 61–70	2 of 17	• Read, write, and identify unit fractions as part of a whole.	• one-half • one-fourth • one-third • unit fractions • one-fifth • one-sixth • one-seventh • one-eighth • one-ninth • one-tenth • one-eleventh • one-twelfth	• **Additional Practice 3B,** Exercise 7A • **Reteach 3,** Exercise 7A • **Extension 3,** Exercise 7A • **Mastery and Beyond 3B,** Chapter 7, Practice 1	• 1 set of connecting cubes (two colors) • 1 set of fraction circles • 1 set of fraction tiles • 2 copies of Paper Squares (TR22) • 1 copy of Inch Square Grid (TR24) • 2 copies of Rectangular Paper Strips (TR26) • 1 copy of Unit Fraction Cards (TR27) • 1 copy of Ten Frame (TR28)
Section 7B More Fractions Student Book, pp. 71–76	3 of 17	• Read, write, and identify fractions within 1 whole as part of a whole.	• numerator • denominator	• **Additional Practice 3B,** Exercise 7B • **Reteach 3,** Exercise 7B • **Extension 3,** Exercise 7B • **Mastery and Beyond 3B,** Chapter 7, Practices 2 and 3	• 1 paper bag • 1 number cube • 1 set of fraction circles • 1 set of fraction tiles • 1 copy of Number Cards (TR03) • 1 copy of Rectangular Paper Strips (TR26) • 1 copy of Paper Square (TR29)

Section	Day	Learning Objective(s)	Vocabulary	Resource(s)	Material(s)
Section 7C Fractions Greater Than 1 Student Book, pp. 77–82	4 of 17	• Read, write, and identify fractions greater than 1.		• **Additional Practice 3B**, Exercise 7C • **Reteach 3**, Exercise 7C • **Extension 3**, Exercise 7C • **Mastery and Beyond 3B**, Chapter 7, Practice 4	• 2 number cubes • 1 set of fraction circles • 1 set of fraction tiles • 1 copy of Unit Fraction Cards (TR27)
Section 7D Compare and Order Fractions (1): Compare Two Fractions Student Book, pp. 83–86	5 of 17	• Compare like and unit fractions. • Compare fractions with the same numerators.		• **Additional Practice 3B**, Exercise 7D (1) • **Reteach 3**, Exercise 7D (1) • **Extension 3**, Exercise 7D (1)	• 1 paper bag • 1 number cube • 1 set of fraction circles • 1 set of fraction tiles • 1 copy of Number Cards (TR03)
Section 7D Compare and Order Fractions (2): Compare and Order Fractions Student Book, pp. 87–90	6 of 17	• Compare and order like and unit fractions. • Compare and order fractions with the same numerators.		• **Additional Practice 3B**, Exercise 7D (2) • **Reteach 3**, Exercise 7D (2) • **Extension 3**, Exercise 7D (2) • **Mastery and Beyond 3B**, Chapter 7, Practice 5	• 1 number cube • 1 set of fraction circles • 1 set of fraction tiles • 1 copy of Fraction Cards (TR30)
Section 7E Equivalent Fractions Student Book, pp. 91–94	7 of 17	• Identify equivalent fractions. • Find equivalent fractions.	• equivalent fractions	• **Additional Practice 3B**, Exercise 7E • **Reteach 3**, Exercise 7E • **Extension 3**, Exercise 7E • **Mastery and Beyond 3B**, Chapter 7, Practice 6	• 1 piece of graph paper • 1 set of colored pencils • 1 set of fraction circles • 1 set of fraction tiles • 2 copies of Rectangular Paper Strips (TR26) • 1 copy of Fraction Cards (TR30) • 2 copies of Fraction Bars (TR31)

Section	Lesson	Objective	Resources	Materials
Section 7F Fractions on a Number Line Student Book, pp. 95–100	8 of 17	• Show fractions as numbers on a number line.	• **Additional Practice 3B,** Exercise 7F • **Reteach 3,** Exercise 7F • **Extension 3,** Exercise 7F • **Mastery and Beyond 3B,** Chapter 7, Practices 7 and 8	• 1 set of fraction tiles • 1 copy of Rectangular Paper Strips (TR26) • 1 copy of Fraction Cards (TR30) • 1 copy of Fraction Strips (TR32) • 3 copies of Number Line Template (TR33)
Section 7G Fractions of a Set Student Book, pp. 101–106	9 of 17	• Identify fractions of a set.	• **Additional Practice 3B,** Exercise 7G • **Reteach 3,** Exercise 7G • **Extension 3,** Exercise 7G • **Mastery and Beyond 3B,** Chapter 7, Practices 9 and 10	• 1 paper plate • 1 pack of construction paper • 15 colored cubes (6 red, 3 yellow, 3 green, and 3 blue) • 1 set of connecting cubes • 1 set of counters
Chapter Wrap Up / Performance Task Student Book, pp. 107–110	10 of 17			• 1 set of connecting cubes
STEAM Project Work Student Book, p. 52	11 of 17			
Chapter Practice Student Book, pp. 111–114	12–13 of 17		• **Additional Practice 3B,** Chapter Practice	
Chapter Test / Cumulative Assessment	14–17 of 17		• **Assessment Guide Teacher Edition,** Chapter Test 7 • **Assessment Guide Teacher Edition,** Cumulative Assessment 3	

Chapter Opener (Student Book, page 59)

Consider the picture and the questions on the page. Discuss them with your student. Prompt him/her to think of the times he/she had to share food. You may wish to ask the following questions:

🗨 **What shapes do you see here? What happens to the shapes when they are divided?** *They can form other equal shapes sometimes if they are divided equally.* **Did you divide the cake equally?** *Answers vary.* **Why might Wendy want to make equal pieces?** *to share equally* **How did you divide the cake into 4 equal pieces?** *Vertically, horizontally, diagonally, and other ways.* **How do you know the pieces are all equal?** *They are all the same.* **Is there a way to prove if the pieces are equal?** *We might fold them or cut and stack them on each other.* **What are some different ways Wendy can cut the cake and still have equal parts? What about the pizza? Is there a difference between equal pieces from a square and equal pieces from a circle?**

Teaching Tip

Make sure your student is able to explain that halves, thirds, and fourths can only be called such if the pieces are equal. Understanding that a fraction is an equal piece of the same whole is critical to understanding the content in this chapter. In order to process that idea, offer your student plenty of opportunities similar to the ones suggested in the **Recall** as you begin the chapter.

If your student does not understand equal parts, now is the time to make sure the concept becomes clear. Your student will have a short review in lesson one, but the foundation of what an equal part is should be solid before beginning chapter content. You may wish to play fraction games such as **Make it a Game** in order to review prior knowledge and correct possible misunderstanding.

For Additional Support

If your student finds thinking of fractions as "a part of a whole" too abstract, start by exploring with concrete fraction circles. In this way, your student can make connections between what he/she already knows about equal parts and the concept of fractions as equal parts of the same whole. Eventually, your student can also draw different representations of wholes to explain thinking.

🗨 **What are different ways to talk about wholes and parts?** *A whole might be a number like 1 or 10, or an object like your body. For example, when you get sick, you might say your whole body hurts. A part might be a piece of a whole, like on a car. For example, part of a car can have a problem, such as a flat tire, while the rest of the vehicle is fine.* **What are some different wholes and parts you can think of?** *A whole family; a whole paycheck.* **What are some examples of different wholes that are easily broken into equal parts?** *Food like pizza or a candy bar; payment for a chore like weeding the garden, etc.*

Recall (Student Book, page 60)

Material(s)
- 1 number cube with the numbers 2, 3, and 4
- 1 set of fraction circles
- 1 copy of Number Cards from 2 to 4 (TR03)

Before moving on to the problems on page 60 of the Student Book, have your student do similar tasks using real-world objects, such as pieces of paper. Once you are convinced of his/her proficiency, move on to drawing shapes on a whiteboard and having your student subdivide or shade them according to your instructions.

Halves, thirds, and fourths should be familiar at this point. You may want to role-play with real-world experiences to help surface any prior knowledge your student has. Sharing a sandwich with a sibling or friend can help your student recall halves, for example. Provide opportunities as you cook or divide toys, etc., to support the concept as you go about daily life.

Recall Answers

(Student Book, page 60)

1.

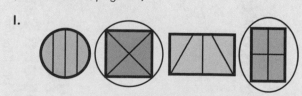

2. Answers vary. Example:

(a)

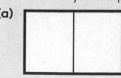

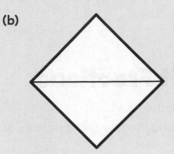

Make it a Game!

Using a whiteboard and markers, each of you draw a regular shape, such as a circle, square, or rectangle, then toss a number cube or pull Number Cards (TRO3) with the numbers 2, 3, and 4. The other person needs to subdivide the shape into that many parts, and then the person who drew the shape decides if the parts are equal. Be sure to make some of each, equal and not equal, and use vocabulary including halves, thirds, and fourths when you draw your Number Cards (TRO3) or toss the number cube.

Variation: shade $\frac{1}{2}$, $\frac{1}{3}$, or $\frac{1}{4}$ after subdividing. You may wish to ask the following questions:

🗨 **Are they equal? How do you know? If they are not equal, can we call these fourths (or thirds, or halves)? Why or why not? When can we call something a fourth (or a third, or a half)?**

3. Answers vary. Example:

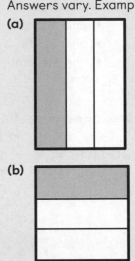

After this review, your student should be able to complete the tasks on page 60 of the Student Book independently.

- **QUESTION 1** assesses your student's ability to recognize equal shares.
- **QUESTION 2** assesses your student's ability to show an equal share of a whole.
- **QUESTION 3** assesses your student's ability to color one equal share of a whole.

For Additional Support

If your student has difficulty with visual processing and/or visual memory, he/she will need extra support in this chapter. Start by having him/her build models and then, when he/she is sure the model is built to his/her liking, draw it on a whiteboard exactly as he/she built it. Prompt your student to self-correct by asking:

🗨 **Is this drawing exactly the same as the model you built? Are you sure? How is it the same and how is it different?**

Digging Deeper

If your student is ready to extend the concept, invite him/her to share what he/she thinks about other equal pieces that are more than fourths.

🗨 **What if we divided it into five equal pieces? What would we call each piece?**

Repeat for fifths, sixths, sevenths, eighths, ninths, and tenths. Your student may enjoy saying the word twelfths, as well. When you get a few covered, you may wish to ask the following questions:

🗨 **Can you see a pattern?** *4 fractions are fourths, 5 fractions are fifths.* **What do you predict the name of this fraction will be?** *6 will be sixths.*

7A Unit Fractions

Learning Objective(s)

- Read, write, and identify unit fractions as a part of a whole.

Vocabulary

- one-half
- one-fourth
- one-third
- unit fractions
- one-fifth
- one-sixth
- one-seventh
- one-eighth
- one-ninth
- one-tenth
- one-eleventh
- one-twelfth

Material(s)

- 1 set of connecting cubes (two colors)
- 1 set of fraction tiles
- 1 copy of Inch Square Grid (TR24)
- 1 copy of Unit Fraction Cards (TR27)
- 1 set of fraction circles
- 2 copies of Paper Squares (TR22)
- 2 copies of Rectangular Paper Strips (TR26)
- 1 copy of Ten Frame (TR28)

UNIT FRACTIONS (Student Book, pages 61 to 70)

Lesson Opener

Task (Student Book, page 61)

Show your student the **Lesson Opener** and cover the rest of the page. Discuss the questions with your student. Do not show your student how to do the task and allow him/her to explore and discover one or more possibilities to fold Paper Squares (TR22) into halves and fourths.

Refer your student to **Learn** and **Learn Together** in the Student Book for reflection after your student has explored the concepts. Use questions to build understanding and direct instruction to refine understanding.

Lesson Development

Learn (Student Book, page 61)

Guide your student, when folding the Paper Squares (TR22), to start with halves and then move on to fourths. After sufficiently exploring equal halves and fourths, draw your student's attention back to the parts. Hold up half a square at first, then one-fourth. You may wish to ask these questions:

🗨 **What do we call this piece?** *One-half; one-fourth* **How do you know?** *It is 1 out of 2 equal pieces; it is 1 out of 4 equal pieces.* **How could we write that?** $\frac{1}{2}$; $\frac{1}{4}$ **What are equal parts of a whole called?** *fractions* **What is a fraction?** *a part of a whole* **What does the top number in a fraction mean? What does the bottom number mean?**

Your student may not realize yet that the top number represents the number of parts and the bottom number represents the parts that make the whole, but it will become clearer in a little while.

Focus Question

🗨 **What is a unit fraction?**
Invite your student to ponder this question as you go through the lesson. Revisit this question when you reach the end of the lesson to check his/her understanding.

Teaching Tip

Make sure your student can prove to himself/herself that each half (or fourth) is exactly the same size as the other half (or fourths). Making a visual comparison will help later on in the lesson. You may wish to ask these questions:

🗨 **Is there a way to know for sure that each piece is precisely the same? How might we prove it? How many different ways are there to make equal halves (or fourths)?**

Learn Together (Student Book, pages 62 to 66)

Using fraction circles and fraction tiles, you will extend your student's understanding to other types of fractional parts. Place a whole fraction circle and a fraction circle in 3 thirds in front of your student.

💬 **What do you notice about these circles?** *One is whole, one is in three equal pieces.* **What else do you see?** *3 of three pieces is the same as a whole—they match up.*

Exchange the fraction circles for two equal-sized, matching Rectangular Paper Strips (TR26). Invite your student to pretend that one of the Rectangular Paper Strips (TR26) is something he/she can relate to cutting in three exact equal pieces (such as a candy bar shared with two other siblings or friends).

💬 **How might we fold this into three exact equal parts?**

After exploration, take another Rectangular Paper Strips (TR26) and fold it as equal thirds. This will support bar modeling later in the chapter. Encourage your student to lightly draw a line to show 3 thirds and to shade in one of the thirds.

💬 **How many parts did you shade?** *one* **How do we say that as a fraction?** *I out of 3 equal parts is one-third.* **How would we write that?** $\frac{1}{3}$ **What does the I stand for?** *I colored part.* **What does the 3 tell us?** *The number of equal parts we have in all.* **We have seen a few different types of fractions. What can you say about the number of pieces in the whole and what can we call them?** *I out of 2 equal pieces is $\frac{1}{2}$, I out of 3 equal pieces is $\frac{1}{3}$, I out of 4 equal pieces is $\frac{1}{4}$.* **Do you see a pattern?** *Answers vary.* **What other types of fractions do you think there might be?** *fifths, sevenths, and twelfths*

Hold up a fraction circle or fraction tiles with eighths.

💬 **What would we call one piece of this strip?** *I out of 8 equal pieces, $\frac{1}{8}$.* **How can we know what to call a fraction just by looking at it in relationship to the whole?** *The total number of equal pieces tells us the number at the bottom of the fraction and the name of the fraction.* **How many pieces make up the whole?** *8 out of 8 equal pieces, $\frac{8}{8}$* **Is there a pattern?** *Yes. $\frac{3}{3}$, $\frac{5}{5}$, etc., all are I whole.*

Through questioning, lead your student to understand what a unit fraction is and how to write the fractions in **Learn Together**. As you go through the problems with your student, you may wish to ask the following questions:

💬 **How do you write the fraction of each piece?** *The total number of equal pieces tells us the number at the bottom of the fraction and the name of the fraction. $\frac{1}{2}$, one half; $\frac{1}{3}$, one third; $\frac{1}{4}$, one quarter; and $\frac{1}{8}$, one eighth are all examples of unit fractions.* **Why do you think we call them that?**

The number at the top is I and represents I part of that type of fraction, a standard.

After your student has explored the concepts in the **Lesson Opener**, **Learn**, and **Learn Together**, you may wish to ask these questions to encourage further reflection:

💬 **How does your thinking compare to the book? Do you see anything the book is telling us that helps you understand better? What is the same? What is different?**

You may wish to have your student summarize his/her learning in a math journal. Have your student choose a unit fraction and explain everything he/she knows about that fraction using drawings and numbers.

Learn Together Answers
(Student Book, pages 62 to 66)

1. I; 3

Unit fraction	Name		Unit fraction	Name
$\frac{1}{5}$	one-fifth		$\frac{1}{9}$	one-ninth
$\frac{1}{6}$	one-sixth		$\frac{1}{10}$	one-tenth
$\frac{1}{7}$	one-seventh		$\frac{1}{11}$	one-eleventh
$\frac{1}{8}$	one-eighth		$\frac{1}{12}$	one-twelfth

2. (a) I; 5
    (b) I; 7

3. (a) $\frac{1}{8}$
    (b) I; 9; $\frac{1}{9}$

4. (a)
    (b)

5. 2; 2; 2; $\frac{1}{8}$

6. $\frac{1}{3}$; $\frac{1}{3}$; $\frac{1}{3}$

- **QUESTION 1** requires your student to demonstrate an understanding of what a unit fraction is.
- **QUESTION 2** requires your student to relate the fraction notation to the number of colored parts and the total number of parts in the whole.

  💬 **What do you notice? What can you say about the pieces?** *They are equal within each shape; each shape has a different number of equal pieces.* **How many pieces are colored?** *1*

- Work with your student to discover Question 2(a): $\frac{1}{5}$ of the shape is colored; $\frac{1}{5}$ is 1 out of 5 equal parts. Vary your questioning until your student can prove his/her thinking, explain that $\frac{1}{5}$ is 1 out of 5 equal pieces and generate the fraction, $\frac{1}{5}$.

  💬 **How do you know it is true?** *Answers vary.*

- Work through the rest of the questions, allowing your student increasing independence, but checking for understanding.

  💬 **How do you know this piece is called one-seventh?** *It is 1 out of 7 equal pieces. The name of the fraction has to match the total number of equal pieces.*

- Wrap up this section by going back to the chart on the top of page 63 of the Student Book and having your student fill in the blanks to summarize understanding.
- **QUESTION 3** requires your student to express the number of colored parts as a fraction of the whole.
- **QUESTION 4** requires your student to consider each shape and identify the shapes that show the given fraction.

  💬 **What is different about these problems?** *We need to figure out which ones show the fraction the questions ask for.* **What types of pieces do they need to be to represent fractions?** *equal*

- Allow your student to work as independently as possible, supporting with questions where needed.
- Encourage your student to prove his/her thinking.

  💬 **How do you know that is true?** *Answers vary.*

- **QUESTION 5** requires your student to recognize that a shape divided in different ways can represent the same fraction.
- You may wish to copy square B onto Inch Square Grid (TR24) and have your student cut and fold the triangles so that he/she can see that each triangle can fit into 2 squares of grid paper. The tip of each triangle fits exactly next to its base.

  💬 **How might you prove that each triangle would fit into 2 squares without cutting one of them?** *A triangle is half the rectangle. Since the rectangle covers 4 squares of the grid, each triangle is two squares.*

Teaching Tip

Use questioning and exploration with manipulatives to lead your student into deeper understanding. The key ideas in this lesson include:

- understand that the top number tells the number of colored pieces, and the bottom number tells the total number of equal pieces in one whole;
- see the pattern relating the total number of equal pieces in the whole to the name of the fraction and the number in the bottom;
- make the connection that there are many different types of fractions depending on how many equal pieces we use to represent the whole; and
- see that fractional pieces must be equal parts.

Digging Deeper

💬 **What do you notice about the relationship between size of the piece and the number in the bottom? What pattern do you see?** *As the size of the piece gets smaller, the number in the bottom gets larger.* **Why?** *Because you are cutting the whole into more pieces, so the size gets smaller.* **Convince me.** *Allow student to prove it.*

😊😀 How can you tell if each part is exactly $\frac{1}{8}$ of the whole?

💬 **What visual tools do you see on the problem to help you solve it?** *There is a grid I can use to see if all pieces are the same.* **What makes it tricky?** *Some squares are halved.* **How can you use what you know to help you determine whether the pieces are equal?** *I know two halves make a whole, so two half-squares make one whole square.*

- **QUESTION 6** requires your student to identify that fractions are equivalent only if the wholes are the same.
- Your student will determine that fractions are equal if the original wholes are equal.
  - 💬 **What do you notice about these pictures?** *Each has three equal parts.* **How is each figure divided?** *Into three equal parts; into thirds.*

😊😀 Invite your student to look at $\frac{1}{3}$ of each shape to share whether the areas are the same.

💬 **How can you tell if each third is equal to every other third?** *We cannot tell because the wholes are not the same and they are not the same size.* **How is this one-third the same or different from that of the other one-third?** *They are both 1 out of 3 equal parts, but they are $\frac{1}{3}$ of different-sized wholes.* **Are they equal?** *no* **What needs to be true for the pieces to be equal?** *The wholes must be the same size.* **Can you make a rule?** *Fractions are equal, they are the same size, and come from the same-size whole.*

Lesson Debrief

- Conclude the lesson and facilitate your student's reflection by asking him/her to answer the **Focus Question** and share his/her thinking.
- Extend the discussion by posing the following questions.
  - 💬 **How can you show a unit fraction in different ways? Can you divide a whole into unequal parts and name each part as a fraction of the whole? Why?** *No, because to use a fraction to name each part of a whole, all the parts of the whole must be equal.*

For Additional Support

Your student who cannot see which shapes form an exact fraction can trace the shapes and cut them out to see if they can lay exactly one on top of the other. This will not work in every case (for example, the **Think!** on page 70 of the Student Book), but it is a good starting point for your student who is not convinced or who has difficulty rotating the shapes in his/her mind. Having proved that certain shapes are identical, such as the triangle in Question 4(a), encourage your student to close his/her eyes and try to flip the colored side onto the uncolored side in his/her mind's eye. This ability to use spatial reasoning is a useful skill in many areas, not just in mathematics. It may take a while for your student to begin to "see" the math.

Practice On Your Own (Student Book, pages 67 to 70)

- **QUESTION 1** assesses your student's ability to identify unit fractions in different shapes divided into a different number of equal parts.
- **QUESTIONS 2** and **3** assess your student's ability to identify fractional parts.
- **QUESTION 4** assesses your student's ability to show unit fractions in different shapes divided into equal parts.
- **QUESTION 5** assesses your student's ability to show $\frac{1}{6}$ on two different shapes in different ways.
- **QUESTION 6** assesses your student's ability to divide identical rectangles into equal parts in two other ways. Your student then identifies the fraction of the area of each part in relation to the area of the whole.
- **QUESTION 7** assesses your student's ability to determine the total number of parts in wholes divided into different-sized parts.

Think!

- **QUESTION 8** assesses your student's ability to reason that the square is divided equally by drawing to show his/her reasoning. The square is divided into 2 halves. One half is divided into 2 equal squares. The other half is divided into 2 equal triangles. Each square and triangle is "half of half."
- This interesting problem requires your student to see fourths in two different ways and then prove each fourth, being $\frac{1}{4}$ of the same whole, is exactly the same size even though shapes are different. You may wish to ask the following questions:
  - 💬 **What have you done before that can help you solve this question? Is there another way? How can you prove your thinking? What heuristic might you use to help you solve this?**

Caution

This sequence of practice questions requires your student to use visual reasoning. If your student misidentifies the shapes, which show $\frac{1}{2}$ and $\frac{1}{4}$ in Questions 2 and 3, have him/her go back to the concrete paper shapes. Your student can trace, cut, and place pieces on top of each other to prove congruency, then close his/her eyes to try to see that before returning to Questions 2 and 3.

Practice On Your Own Answers
(Student Book, pages 67 to 70)

1.

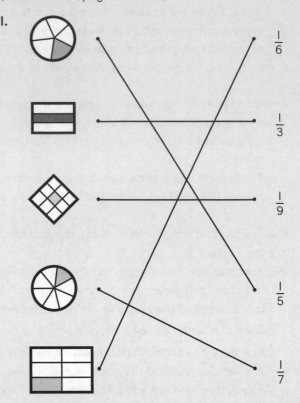

2.

3.

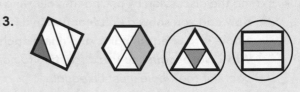

4. Answers vary. Example:

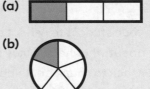

(a)

(b)

(c)

(d)

5. Answers vary. Example:

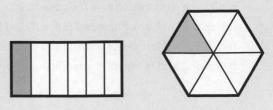

More Resources

- Refer to **Do More at Home** below and **Reteach 3, Exercise 7A** if your student needs additional support.
- When your student is ready, have him/her work on **Additional Practice 3B, Exercise 7A**.
- To provide your student with a challenge, have him/her work on **Extension 3, Exercise 7A**.
- You may also assign **Mastery and Beyond 3B, Chapter 7, Practice I** to provide further support and development to sustain learning.

Do More at Home

Where is It?

Invite your student to play this version of memory using Unit Fraction Cards (TR27). Place the Unit Fraction Cards (TR27) and their matching models face down. Be sure to include models using fraction circles and fraction tiles.

Player I turns over one card and one model. If they match (a unit fraction with its model), the player keeps the card and the model. If they do not match, the player turns the card and the model again.

Player 2 turns over a card and guesses where the matching model might be.

You and your student take turns until all the cards and models are gone. The player with the most pairs wins!

Use both models (fraction circles and fraction tiles for each unit fraction) and find a triple match for extra challenge!

6.

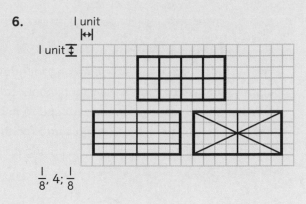

$\frac{1}{8}$, 4; $\frac{1}{8}$

7.   2; 4; 3; 10

Think! Answers

8.   Answers vary. Example:

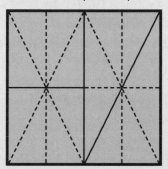

Each of the 4 equal parts is made up of 4 triangles of the same size. So, the whole is divided into 4 parts with equal area.

If your student does not have a strong foundation of breaking apart numbers and recombining them (commonly called decomposition and composition of number), he/she will tend to find working with fractions difficult. The ability to break 1 whole into fractional pieces rests on a foundation of breaking apart 10 and being able to use the numbers found within it.

It is critical that you take care of this number sense gap now, as future mathematics, pre-Algebra and Algebra, relies on understanding of fractions and (eventually) the proportional reasoning they represent. Ideas for bridging the number sense gap include:

• Use connecting cubes to show the combinations that make 10 and all the numbers within 10. Offer only two colors to your student for each number to prevent visual confusion. Your student should build 10 as number trains of two parts for all the possible combinations. Here is a sample train for 7 + 3 = 10:

Your student can make a "Ten Wall" by stacking the different number trains that form 10 (9 + 1; 8 + 2, etc.)

• Have your student draw representations of all the numbers within 10 on Ten Frame (TR28). He/she should be able to recognize at a glance how many more cubes are needed to make ten.

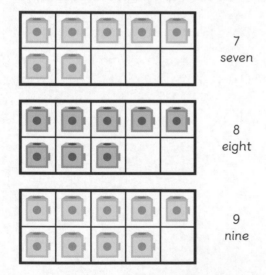

7
seven

8
eight

9
nine

• Familiarize yourself with number bonds (a visual model that highlights numerical relationships) and have your student begin to use them to show how to break apart numbers. Here is one way to make a number bond of 10:

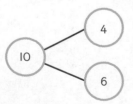

Use the following problems to challenge your student to extend and deepen his/her thinking about unit fractions.

💬 **True or False, and Why? 2 is less than 3, so $\frac{1}{2}$ is less than $\frac{1}{3}$.** *The statement is false. $\frac{1}{2}$ is larger than $\frac{1}{3}$ because there are fewer equal pieces in the whole. 1 out of 2 equal pieces is larger than 1 out of 3 equal pieces.*

You may also wish to extend the **Think!** Question on page 70. Offer your student Paper Squares (TR22) and invite him/her to find as many different ways as possible to divide it into equal parts. Encourage your student to prove his/her thinking.

💬 **How many ways are there?**

7B More Fractions

Learning Objective(s)
- Read, write, and identify fractions within 1 whole as part of a whole.

Vocabulary
- numerator
- denominator

Material(s)
- 1 paper bag
- 1 set of fraction circles
- 1 copy of Number Cards (TR03)
- 1 copy of Paper Square (TR29)
- 1 number cube
- 1 set of fraction tiles
- 1 copy of Rectangular Paper Strips (TR26)

MORE FRACTIONS (Student Book, pages 71 to 76)

Lesson Opener

Task (Student Book, page 71)

Show your student the **Lesson Opener** and cover the rest of the page. Discuss the question with your student. Do not show your student how to do the task and allow him/her to explore and discover one or more possibilities to figure out how to cut the pizza, so that Ron can eat $\frac{2}{3}$ of it.

Refer your student to **Learn** and **Learn Together** in the Student Book for reflection after your student has explored the concepts. Use questions to build understanding and direct instruction to refine understanding.

Lesson Development
Learn (Student Book, page 71)

Allow your student to continue his/her exploration with fraction circles while you watch to see what fractions he/she generates. Look for fractions with more than one piece, such as $\frac{3}{4}$ or $\frac{2}{3}$. You may wish to ask these questions:

💬 **What is a fraction?** *a part of a whole* The whole must be represented by the same equal pieces. **Do you remember what we named one piece of the whole when the whole was three pieces?** $\frac{1}{3}$ **Do you remember what we named one piece of the whole when the whole was four pieces?** $\frac{1}{4}$

If your student makes a fraction with more than one piece, point to one of those nonunit fractions.

💬 **What could we name the fraction when it is more than one piece, like this one?** *Answers vary.*

Focus Question

💬 **How can you show fractions in different ways?**

Invite your student to ponder this question as you go through the lesson. Revisit this question when you reach the end of the lesson to check his/her understanding.

Teaching Tip

In this lesson, your student will learn that a whole is the sum of unit fractions. He/she will discover that the number 1 can be written in a variety of ways, depending on the fractional pieces in a whole—such as $\frac{3}{3}$ or $\frac{5}{5}$. Finally, your student will learn to add fractional pieces to make a whole with both unit and nonunit fractions.

As much as possible, it is important to question your student into understanding. Do not just say what he/she needs to know; allow your student a chance to discover it. Using concrete fraction tiles or circles, then drawing the fractions, will help establish foundational understanding as the concept eventually builds into adding and subtracting fractions. You may wish to ask these questions:

💬 **How do you know this represents $\frac{2}{3}$? How might we prove it?**
What different ways are there to represent thirds?

Continuing to work with fraction circles, you may wish to ask the following questions:

🗨 **Ron wants to eat $\frac{2}{3}$ of his pizza. How should he cut it to show $\frac{2}{3}$?**
Use fraction circles to help you show Ron's pizza and the amount of pizza Ron wants to eat. How many equal-sized pieces would Ron's pizza need to have? *3 equal pieces* **If Ron ate $\frac{1}{3}$ of the pizza, how many pieces would he eat?** *One out of 3 equal pieces.* **Ron wants to eat $\frac{2}{3}$ of the pizza. How can you show $\frac{2}{3}$ of a pizza?** *Two $\frac{1}{3}$-sized pieces.* **How many pieces is that?** *two*
How might we write that? $\frac{2}{3}$

Once your student has written $\frac{2}{3}$, use that to write the following sentence on a whiteboard or notebook paper: $\frac{2}{3}$ is _____ out of _____ equal parts.

🗨 **Finish this sentence: Two-thirds is** *two out of three equal parts.* **How might we show the whole pizza?** *3 thirds* **How should we write that?** $\frac{3}{3}$ **Are you sure?** *Answers vary.*

If you have time, you can extend the concept to move toward a visual model that supports bar modeling later. Provide your student with Rectangular Paper Strips (TR26).

🗨 **What would happen if Ron's pizza were rectangular? Can he still eat $\frac{2}{3}$?** *yes* **Show me how.** *The thirds are a different shape, but each equal part is still one third, so two equal parts represent $\frac{2}{3}$.* **Can we divide any shape into thirds?** *Yes, if we can make three equal parts.*

Learn Together (Student Book, pages 72 to 74)

The purpose of this section is to solidify understanding regarding nonunit fractions. Provide your student with fraction circles and tiles, being careful to connect concrete learning to the pictorial stage of the concrete-pictorial-abstract learning progression.

Through questioning, lead your student to determine, write, and add fractions of wholes and learn the form of writing 1 whole in fractional form in **Learn Together**. As you go through the problems with your student, you may wish to ask the following questions:

🗨 **How do you find what fraction is colored? What do the numbers in this fraction mean? Write the whole that represents this model. What does the addition equation look like for this problem?**

After your student has explored the concepts in the **Lesson Opener**, **Learn**, and **Learn Together**, you may wish to ask these questions to encourage further reflection:

🗨 **How does your thinking compare to the book? Do you see anything in the book that helps you? What is the same? What is different? Do you need to change how you are reading or writing these fractions?**

You may wish to have your student summarize his/her learning in a math journal. Have your student explain everything he/she knows about using unit fractions to find the fraction of each figure that is colored.

- **QUESTION 1** requires your student to make a connection between a given fraction and the number of colored parts out of the total number of equal parts.
- Using the models on page 72 of the Student Book, your student will explore more ways to identify and write fractions within a whole. Have your student replicate the fraction shown for each figure using fraction circles and/or fraction tiles.

Learn Together Answers

(Student Book, pages 72 to 74)

1. **(a)** 5; 7
   (b) 3; 6

2. **(a)** $\frac{6}{8}$
   (b) 6; 8; $\frac{6}{8}$

3. $\frac{1}{3}$; $\frac{1}{3}$; 3; 3

4. $\frac{1}{4}$, $\frac{1}{4}$, $\frac{1}{4}$, $\frac{1}{4}$

5. $\frac{4}{5}$; 5; 5

- Point to Question I(a).
  - 💬 **What do you notice about this circle?** *There are 7 equal parts, 5 are colored.* **Knowing everything we have learned about fractions so far, fill in this sentence: _____ out of _____ equal parts are colored.** *five out of seven* **How might you write that?** $\frac{5}{7}$ **How do you read this?** *five-sevenths* **What do you notice about the fraction and the number of colored parts compared to the total number of equal parts?** *The top number of the fraction is the same as the number of colored parts. The bottom number is the same as the total number of equal parts.*
- Repeat the above line of building and questioning with each figure on the page until understanding is firm, varying your questions by what shape your student is asked to use.
- **QUESTION 2** requires your student to name the fraction given the number of equal colored parts.
- **QUESTION 3** requires your student to demonstrate an understanding that I whole is the sum of its fractional parts.
- Point to the first pizza, divided into thirds.
  - 💬 **How many equal pieces is the pizza divided into?** *three* **What fraction of the whole pizza is each slice?** $\frac{1}{3}$ *or one-third*
- Point to the second pizza.
  - 💬 **Ron wanted to eat $\frac{2}{3}$ of the pizza. How many $\frac{1}{3}$-sized pieces of pizza did he eat?** *Two one-thirds.* $\frac{2}{3}$ *is 2 out of 3 equal parts.*
- Write $\frac{2}{3} = \frac{1}{3} + \frac{1}{3}$ on the whiteboard.
  - 💬 **How many pieces are in the whole pizza?** *three* **How would you write a fraction to represent the whole pizza divided into three equal parts?** $\frac{3}{3}$ *or three-thirds*
- Write on the whiteboard: $\frac{3}{3}$ = I whole.
  - 💬 **Is this true?** *yes* **How do you know?** *If I have a pizza cut into 3 equal pieces, and I eat one piece at a time, 3 pieces of the pizza is the whole pizza.* **What do you notice about the fraction that represents the whole pizza and the parts Ron wanted to eat and did not eat?** $\frac{2}{3}$ *and* $\frac{1}{3}$ *make* $\frac{3}{3}$ *or one whole.* **What other ways can you think of to write one whole that look different from I?** $\frac{5}{5}$
- **QUESTION 4** reinforces your student's understanding of combining fractional parts (colored and not colored) to make I whole.
  - 💬 **What do you notice about the number of colored and uncolored parts of the shape compared to the total number of parts?** *There are 3 colored parts and I uncolored part. There are 4 parts altogether. 3 and I make 4.* **What fraction of the shape is colored?** $\frac{3}{4}$ **Not colored?** $\frac{1}{4}$ **What is the fraction for the whole shape?** *It is* $\frac{4}{4}$, *or 4 out of 4 equal parts.* **What can you say about the number of colored and uncolored parts compared to the total number of equal parts?** *The top number of the fraction is the same as the number of colored plus uncolored parts. The bottom number is the total number of equal parts.*
- **QUESTION 5** requires your student to recognize the colored ($\frac{1}{5}$) and uncolored ($\frac{4}{5}$) parts that make I whole ($\frac{5}{5}$). The part-whole model is also shown. This visual model will aid in your student's learning of addition and subtraction of like fractions.

👀 This is to solidify your student's understanding of the terms numerator and denominator, especially as they apply to nonunit fractions. Introduce the terms numerator and denominator. On the whiteboard, draw this model for reference:

Digging Deeper

In order to explore the concept of how we represent I whole with fractions more thoroughly, you may find that having the following discussion with your student can help deepen his/her understanding:

Show your student a whole fraction circle or tiles made of thirds. Point to where you wrote $\frac{3}{3}$ = I. $\frac{3}{3}$ does not look like I, but you have shown that it is I whole when you built it like this. It is 3 of 3 pieces, so the whole thing.

💬 **Is there anything you can think of that might be the same but does not look the same at first glance?** *Water can also be snow, ice, clouds, and steam. They all look different, but they are all forms of water.* **Can you think of anything that has different names but is the same thing?** *A mom is also a sister, friend, or daughter in different contexts, but remains the same person. You might have a nickname that is not your given name, but you are the same no matter what you are called.* **Sometimes the same things can have different names depending on the circumstance. The number I is an example. What are other ways you can name I?** $\frac{3}{3}$

For Additional Support

If your student struggles with the idea of adding fractions, allow him/her to build these problems with fraction circles or tiles, then draw the fractions. For Question 4, provide Paper Square (TR29) for your student to cut into fourths if needed. It is important to allow your student to move through the concrete-pictorial-abstract progression so that he/she can begin to use abstract symbols for fractions with understanding.

Invite your student to think about the model. Point to the vocabulary box on the student page.

🗨 **This fraction represents my drawing. How many pieces are colored?** *two* **How many pieces in all?** *3* **What can you say about the relationship between the picture and the numbers in the fraction?** *The colored parts match the top number; the total parts match the bottom number.* **The number on the top of the fraction is called the numerator. What does the numerator stand for?** *The number of parts out of the whole being referred to (for example: pizza eaten or not eaten; colored or uncolored parts; it answers the question, "How many?".* **The number on the bottom is called the denominator. What does the denominator stand for?** *The total number of equal parts in the whole. It answers the question, "What kind?".*

Activity! (Student Book, page 74)

In this activity, your student will investigate different ways to represent 1 whole using different fractional pieces.

Provide fraction circles and tiles to your student. Doing this activity alongside your student will give him/her an opportunity to compare models. Consider making a mistake with your labeling on purpose and asking your student to catch it.

You may wish to ask these questions:

🗨 **What fractions do our drawings represent? How are they the same? How are they different?** *Each has the same denominator; each has a different numerator.*

😊🗨 This provides your student an opportunity to talk through the process of making a whole from two different parts. Invite your student to share how he/she constructed the whole from two parts.

🗨 **How did you create your whole? What parts did you use? What helped you think about it so you could figure out how to make exactly one whole and no more?** *I know that 5 can be decomposed in to 2 and 3, so fifths can be decomposed into $\frac{2}{5}$ and $\frac{3}{5}$.* **Show me how you might write an addition equation to explain this. What makes it difficult? Why do you think so?**

Lesson Debrief

• Conclude the lesson and facilitate your student's reflection by asking him/her to answer the **Focus Question** and share his/her thinking.

• Extend the discussion by posing the following questions.

🗨 **How do the numerator and denominator help you understand fractions?** *The denominator tells me the total number of equal parts in the whole. The numerator tells me the number of parts out of the whole that are represented by the fraction.* **What are a few ways to describe the fraction for the colored parts of this picture?**

2 out of 5 equal parts; $\frac{2}{5}$; two-fifths; $\frac{1}{5}+\frac{1}{5}=\frac{2}{5}$. **How would you represent the uncolored parts of this picture?** *$\frac{3}{5}$; three-fifths.* **How would you represent the whole as a fraction?** *$\frac{5}{5}$*

Activity! Answers
(Student Book, page 74)

Answers vary. Example:

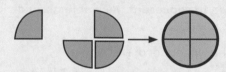

$\frac{1}{4}$ and $\frac{3}{4}$ make 1 whole.

- Allow time for your student to reflect on what he/she has learned and ask questions about what he/she may be unsure of.
- Encourage him/her to share anything that was confusing or difficult, and how thinking about it differently and perseverance helped the process of learning.
- Ask your student to answer a reflection question or draw a picture to show his/her reflection. You may offer these prompts:

  🗨 **How would you explain combining fractions to make a whole to a friend? What is your favorite problem from today? Draw a picture of it in your math journal and show me everything you know about it next to the picture.**

What to look for:
- ability to determine how many pieces of a whole are colored and how to write the fraction of the whole that the colored pieces represent
- ability to accurately model and add fractions
- ability to understand and define the terms numerator and denominator

Practice On Your Own (Student Book, pages 75 and 76)

- **QUESTION 1** assesses your student's ability to name fractions in different shapes.
- **QUESTION 2** assesses your student's understanding that fractions are the sum of unit fractions that are colored or uncolored parts and that the whole is made of both.
- If your student struggles with Question 2, provide fraction circles or tiles to help boost understanding, for example, in Question 2(a), $\frac{4}{6} = \frac{1}{6} + \frac{1}{6} + \frac{1}{6} + \frac{1}{6}$ and 2 more sixths are needed to make a whole.

  🗨 **Show me what fractions of the shapes are colored. How many more parts do you need to complete the whole?**
- **QUESTION 3** assesses your student's ability to identify and write the fractions that make 1 whole. The part-whole model is featured.
- **QUESTION 4** assesses your student's ability to find and match two fractions that make 1 whole. This is done without visual cues.

For Additional Support

Your student may have trouble keeping track when counting colored parts of each whole in Questions 1 to 3. Help him/her develop strategies to attend to precision, such as placing a dot in each part as it is counted.
Questions 2 and 3 are your student's first exposures to nonunit fraction + nonunit fraction. If your student has trouble with this leap, please refer to the **Do More at Home** and the next **For Additional Support**.

Practice On Your Own Answers

(Student Book, pages 75 and 76)

1. **(a)** $\frac{5}{6}$

   (b) $\frac{5}{8}$

2. **(a)** $\frac{1}{6}, \frac{1}{6}, \frac{1}{6}, \frac{1}{6}, \frac{2}{6}$

   (b) $\frac{1}{9}, \frac{1}{9}, \frac{1}{9}, \frac{1}{9}, \frac{1}{9}, \frac{4}{9}$

3. $\frac{5}{10}, \frac{5}{10}$

4.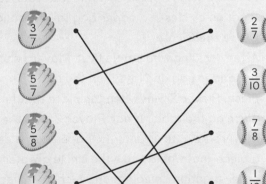

More Resources

- Refer to **Do More at Home** below and **Reteach 3, Exercise 7B** if your student needs additional support.
- When your student is ready, have him/her work on **Additional Practice 3B, Exercise 7B**.
- To provide your student with a challenge, have him/her work on **Extension 3, Exercise 7B**.
- You may also assign **Mastery and Beyond 3B, Chapter 7, Practices 2 and 3** to provide further support and development to sustain learning.

Do More at Home

If your student does not have a strong foundation in adding fractions and making wholes after today's lesson, extend the concept by providing practice building and adding fractions using manipulatives and drawings. Ideas for bridging the gap include:

- Use fraction circles and tiles to mix and match representations. You can use these for games of adding if you separate the fraction circles and tiles by like denominators.
- Make extra activities more fun by rolling a number cube to randomly generate numerators or denominators. This will keep the numbers small and give plenty of practice.
- Using Number Cards (TR03) will save your student from having to write and help him/her get more practice. Just make sure he/she builds the fractions in proper form. Draw a line on a whiteboard to separate numerator from denominator, or draw boxes to help guide your student to place the appropriate number cards in the correct spots.

It may help your student to hear you speak the problems out loud a few times using adjective-noun format as he/she builds or draws problems: "3 sevenths plus 2 sevenths is how many sevenths? 5 sevenths; yes. Good work!"

You may wish to play this game with your student using fourths and eighths fraction circles in a paper bag to help solidify understanding.

Close the Circle

After deciding who starts first, Player 1 chooses a piece of a fraction from the paper bag and lays it on the table. Then Player 2 chooses another piece. Player 2 wins when the piece that he/she takes make a whole with the piece on the table. If not, Player 2 puts the piece back into the paper bag. Players take turns until the paper bag is empty. Players may not lay down a piece that would make the circle greater than 1 whole. For variation, use other fraction combinations such as thirds and sixths or ninths. This game can be extended by inviting each player to write an addition equation for the fraction circles that make 1 whole.

For Additional Support

If your student has trouble adding two nonunit fractions, have him/her begin by adding nonunit fractions made with fraction circles or fraction tiles, then progress to visually representing the models before adding the nonunit fractions—even if it is a just matter of coloring in models you predraw. Be sure to require your student to write the addition equations represented by the manipulatives or drawing. You may wish to ask the following questions:

- 💬 **How is adding fractions like adding whole numbers?** *It is the same, only we are adding parts of wholes instead of whole numbers.* **What is important to know about adding nonunit fractions?** *Answers vary.*

7C Fractions Greater Than 1

Learning Objective(s)
- Read, write, and identify fractions greater than 1.

Material(s)
- 2 number cubes
- 1 set of fraction tiles
- 1 set of fraction circles
- 1 copy of Unit Fraction Cards (TR27)

FRACTIONS GREATER THAN 1 (Student Book, pages 77 to 82)

Lesson Opener

Task (Student Book, page 77)

Show your student the **Lesson Opener** and cover the rest of the page. Discuss the question with your student. Do not show your student how to do the task and allow him/her to explore and discover one or more possibilities to figure out how to represent fractions greater than 1.

Refer your student to **Learn** and **Learn Together** in the Student Book for reflection after your student has explored the concepts. Use questions to build understanding and direct instruction to refine understanding.

Lesson Development
Learn (Student Book, page 77)

After a period of productive struggle, with the Student Book closed and fraction circles in front of your student, pose the question about Ellen's two pies. You may wish to ask these questions:

🗨 **How could we use these tools to represent Ellen's two pies?** *Two whole fraction circles.* **Build those two pies. How will you represent dividing each pie into two equal pieces?**

- Allow your student to rebuild the pies with 4 halves.
  🗨 **What fraction represents this?**

- Give your student sufficient time to ponder before breaking it down this way:
  🗨 **What do you know about writing fractions?** *Answers vary.* **What fraction can you write to represent one piece of this pie?** $\frac{1}{2}$ **How many $\frac{1}{2}$-sized pieces are there in 1 whole pie?** *two* **How do you write that?** $\frac{2}{2}$

- Write: 1 whole $= \frac{2}{2}$ or _____ out of _____ equal pieces.
  🗨 **How will you fill in the blanks?** *2 out of 2 equal pieces.*

- Write $\frac{2}{2} = \frac{1}{2} + \frac{1}{2}$
  🗨 **Is this true?** *yes* **How do you know?** *If we have one half and add another, we have 2 out of 2 equal pieces.*

Focus Question

🗨 **How do you write a quantity greater than 1 whole as a fraction?**
Invite your student to ponder this question as you go through the lesson. Revisit this question when you reach the end of the lesson to check his/her understanding.

Teaching Tip

In this lesson, you will help your student learn to represent fractions greater than 1 as improper fractions. Your student will not need to name improper fractions on the **Chapter Review**, but it is important to use this chapter to solidify what the numerator and denominator of each fraction means, and that when the numerator is larger than the denominator, it means that the fraction is greater than 1 whole. You may wish to ask the following questions:

🗨 **What do you observe about fractions for numbers greater than 1? How are they different from fractions that show quantities less than 1?** *The numerator is larger than the denominator.* **How can we write fractions greater than 1?** *We form them just like fractions for quantities less than one: the number of colored pieces form the numerator and the total number of equal pieces in each whole form the denominator.* **What is true about fractions greater than 1?** *The number of colored pieces is greater than the total number of equal pieces in 1 whole.* **Why is the numerator greater than the denominator?** *There is a set number of equal pieces in a whole. When we have more than one whole, the number of pieces will be more than the total number of equal pieces in a whole.*

Learn Answer (Student Book, page 77)
$\frac{1}{2}$

- Point to both pies together.
  - 💬 **How many $\frac{1}{2}$-sized pieces are in the 2 pies?** *There are four $\frac{1}{2}$-sized pieces in 2 whole pies.* **How do you write a fraction to show 4 halves?** $\frac{4}{2}$
- Write $\frac{4}{2}$ on the board, then $\frac{4}{2} = \frac{1}{2} + \frac{1}{2} + \frac{1}{2} + \frac{1}{2}$.
  - 💬 **What do you notice about the numerator and denominator of the fraction $\frac{4}{2}$?** *The numerator tells the number of halves in 2 wholes. The denominator tells the number of halves or equal parts in 1 whole.* **Do you think this is always true?** *yes* **How do you know?** *We can prove it for other numbers.*
- Extend the task by asking the following questions:
  - 💬 **What if we had three wholes? What would our fraction be then?** $\frac{6}{2}$ *or 6 halves.* **What fraction would show the total number of equal pieces if Ellen cut the pies into three equal pieces? What about four equal pieces?**

Learn Together (Student Book, pages 78 and 79)

In this section, your student will solidify understanding that 1 can be written as a fraction, and that numbers greater than 1 can also be expressed as fractions. Provide your student with at least two different representations for building fractions, such as fraction circles and fraction tiles, in addition to a whiteboard for drawing them.

Through questioning, lead your student to solidify understanding about how to read, write, and model fractions greater than 1. As you go through the problems with your student, you may wish to ask the following questions:

- 💬 **What information does the numerator give us?** *It tells us the number of colored pieces.* **What information does the denominator give us?** *It tells us the total number of equal pieces in each whole.* **What is the relationship between the numerator and how many total pieces are there?** *As the number of colored pieces increases, the numerator also increases.* **When the numerator is greater than the denominator, what does that tell you?** *There is more than one whole.*

After your student has explored the concepts in the **Lesson Opener**, **Learn**, and **Learn Together**, **Question 1**, you may wish to ask these questions to encourage further reflection:

- 💬 **What do you notice about writing fractions greater than 1? What is important to know about the numerator and denominator? How does your thinking compare to the book? Do you see anything in the book that helps you understand fractions greater than 1 better?**

You may wish to have your student summarize his/her learning in a math journal. Have your student draw one of the problems and explain everything he/she knows about forming fractions greater than 1.

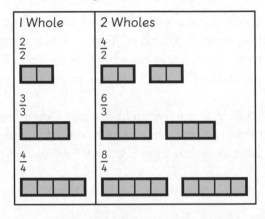
Learn Together Answers
(Student Book, pages 78 and 79)

1. (a) $\frac{1}{2}$; $\frac{1}{2}$
   (b) $\frac{5}{2}$
   (b) 10; $\frac{10}{4}$

- **QUESTION 1** requires your student to see a fraction greater than 1 as the sum of unit fractions.
  - 💬 In Question 1(a), how many equal parts does the whole circle have? *2 halves* How many halves are there in all? *3* What do you notice about the numerator and denominator of the fraction? *The numerator of the fraction names the number of colored parts. The denominator tells the number of equal parts in one whole.* How many $\frac{1}{2}$s are in $\frac{3}{2}$? *3;* $\frac{3}{2} = \frac{1}{2} + \frac{1}{2} + \frac{1}{2}$. Is there another way to represent this addition equation that would more accurately match the picture? $\frac{2}{2} + \frac{1}{2} = \frac{3}{2}$ In what way is Question 1(b) the same and different from Question 1(a)? *The shapes are still circles. Each circle is divided into 2 equal parts or halves, but there are 2 whole circles and one-half circle.* How many halves are there in all? *5 halves or* $\frac{5}{2}$. How would you write an addition equation to represent the picture? $\frac{2}{2} + \frac{2}{2} + \frac{1}{2} = \frac{5}{2}$ In what way is Question 1(c), how many equal parts are in 1 whole? *four or* $\frac{4}{4}$. How many parts are colored? *2 wholes and* $\frac{1}{2}$ *of a whole.* How many $\frac{1}{4}$ are there in all? *10 fourths or* $\frac{10}{4}$. What might the addition equation that matches the problem look like? $\frac{4}{4} + \frac{4}{4} + \frac{2}{4} = \frac{10}{4}$

Before proceeding with the remainder of **Learn Together**, check to see that your student is able to explain that the numerator is greater than the denominator because a fraction greater than 1 has all the pieces of a whole, plus more.

- **QUESTION 2** requires your student to demonstrate an understanding of fractions greater than 1 by coloring the number of parts needed to show the given fraction.
  - 💬 How many parts of each circle did you color? *7* Why? *Because the numerator is 7.* Is there another way you could have shown $\frac{7}{5}$? *Answers vary.* How do you know that the fraction you have colored is $\frac{7}{5}$? *Because I colored 7 one-fifths, or* $\frac{5}{5} + \frac{2}{5} = \frac{7}{5}$.
- **QUESTION 3** builds on your student's understanding of combining fractional parts to make more than 1 whole.
  - 💬 How did you show 2 wholes? *I colored all the sixths in the two wholes.* How many sixths are in 1 whole? $\frac{6}{6}$ How many sixths are in 2 wholes? $\frac{12}{6}$ If you had colored it a different way, could you still have colored two wholes? *Yes, but the pieces I colored would not be touching each other.*
- **QUESTION 4** requires your student to understand that a fraction is the sum of the unit fractions that make up the fraction.
  - 💬 How many $\frac{1}{3}$ are there? *5 thirds* How many wholes are there in $\frac{5}{3}$? *There is 1 whole* $\left(\frac{3}{3}\right)$ *and 2 more thirds* $\left(\frac{2}{3}\right)$. How could you write an addition equation to represent $\frac{5}{3}$? $\frac{3}{3} + \frac{1}{3} + \frac{1}{3} = \frac{5}{3}$ Draw a picture to represent $\frac{5}{3}$ that is different from the one in the Student Book.
- Your student might draw a square or other type of picture. Accept any response that clearly shows the whole divided into 3 equal parts.

2. Answers vary. Example:
(a)
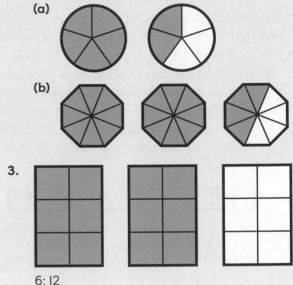
(b)

3.

6; 12

4. 5; $\frac{5}{3}$

Lesson Debrief

- Conclude the lesson and facilitate your student's reflection by asking him/her to answer the **Focus Question** and share his/her thinking.
- Extend the discussion by posing the following questions.

  💬 **What observations do you have about making fractions greater than 1? How do the numerator and denominator help you understand fractions greater than 1?** *The denominator tells me the total number of equal parts in 1 whole. The numerator tells me the total number of colored parts.* **What are some ways to describe the fraction for the colored parts of this picture?**

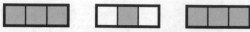

Seven thirds or $\frac{7}{3}$. **How could you write an addition equation to represent this fraction?** $\frac{7}{3} = \frac{1}{3} + \frac{1}{3} + \frac{1}{3} + \frac{1}{3} + \frac{1}{3} + \frac{1}{3} + \frac{1}{3}$ *or* $\frac{7}{3} = \frac{3}{3} + \frac{1}{3} + \frac{3}{3}$.

Reflect and Connect

- Allow time for your student to reflect on what he/she has learned and ask questions about what he/she may be unsure of.
- Encourage him/her to share anything that was confusing or difficult, and how thinking about it differently and perseverance helped the process of learning.
- Ask your student to answer a reflection question or draw a picture to show his/her reflection. You may offer these prompts:

  💬 **How would you explain fractions greater than 1 whole to a friend? What is your favorite problem from today? Draw a picture of it in your math journal, and show me everything you know about it next to the picture.**

What to look for:
- understand numerator and denominator
- ability to recognize and produce wholes and parts of wholes with equal parts
- ability to recognize, write, and construct (by building or drawing) fractions greater than 1

Practice On Your Own (Student Book, pages 80 to 82)

- **QUESTION 1** assesses your student's ability to name a fraction greater than 1 based on the number of parts shown.
- **QUESTION 2** assesses your student's ability to show a fraction greater than 1 by coloring the appropriate number of thirds and writing the fraction.
- **QUESTION 3** assesses your student's ability to identify and write the fraction for figures representing fractions greater than 1.
- **QUESTION 4** assesses your student's ability to color each figure to show the given fractional notation.

Think!

- **QUESTION 5** assesses your student's ability to reason why the statement is incorrect for the figure shown.
- 💬 **What might Lynn have been thinking when she made the denominator 2?** *Since there are 2 triangles, she probably thought that was the number of parts in her whole.* **What does the denominator tell us?** *The total number of equal parts in 1 whole.* **How many equal parts does each of the triangles have?** *9* **What should the denominator be? Why?** *Ninths, because each whole triangle has 9 equal parts.* **What is the correct fraction for this picture?** $\frac{18}{9}$ **What would the picture need to look like for Lynn to be correct? Draw it.** *5 triangles, all divided in half, with nine halves colored.*

Practice On Your Own Answers
(Student Book, pages 80 to 82)

1. 11; 11

2. Answers vary. Example:

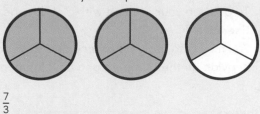

$\frac{7}{3}$

3. (a) $\frac{6}{2}$

   (b) $\frac{10}{6}$

4. Answers vary. Example:
   (a)

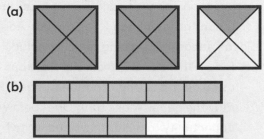

   (b)

Think! Answers

5. No, $\frac{9}{2}$ means 9 halves. The triangles are divided into ninths. Lynn colors 18 ninths or $\frac{18}{9}$.

More Resources

- Refer to **Do More at Home** below and **Reteach 3, Exercise 7C** if your student needs additional support.
- When your student is ready, have him/her work on **Additional Practice 3B, Exercise 7C**.
- To provide your student with a challenge, have him/her work on **Extension 3, Exercise 7C**.
- You may also assign **Mastery and Beyond 3B, Chapter 7, Practice 4** to provide further support and development to sustain learning.

Do More at Home

If your student does not have a strong foundation with fractions greater than I, extend the concept of by looking for ways to connect it to real-world understanding. This is an excellent opportunity to make cross-curricular connections, as there are many places in life and school where we see fractions greater than I. See the **For Additional Support** feature for a few ideas. Ideas for bridging the gap include:

- Play "Where Is It?" from the **Do More At Home** of Lesson 7A, this time using all of the Unit Fraction Cards (TR27).
- Play the game "More than One" below, to give your student an opportunity to build, draw, and write fractions greater than I.
- If you come across situations in daily life where fractions are greater than I whole, note it to your student.

More than One

Invite your student to roll two number cubes. This will keep the number of pieces in each whole to 6 or fewer. The larger number shown on the number cube is the numerator, and the smaller number shown on the other number cube is the denominator. If one of the number cubes is a I, reroll it. Encourage your student to write the fraction with the numbers shown. Then invite your student to build the fraction with fraction circles and tiles before drawing on the whiteboard. Encourage your student to explain his/her drawing. You may wish to ask the following questions:

💬 **Which part of the fraction tells you the number of pieces to shade?** *numerator* **Which part of the fraction tells you the total number of equal pieces in each whole?** *denominator* **Is there a way to know how many wholes there will be?** *yes* **How might you do that?** *We could add the total number of pieces in each whole until we got to our total.* *Example:* $\frac{13}{5} = \frac{5}{5} + \frac{5}{5} + \frac{3}{5}$. *Now, we know to make two wholes and three-fifths more.*

For more variation, use the smallest number for the denominator, then add the numbers on the two number cubes together to get the numerator. This will provide more opportunities for more than one whole.

For Additional Support

If your student has trouble understanding the idea of fractions greater than I, start a discussion about real-world examples. You may wish to ask the following questions:

💬 **What does it mean to have a fraction greater than I?** *The number is more than a whole.* **What are some examples of fractions greater than I?** $1\frac{1}{2}$ *candy bars;* $2\frac{1}{2}$ *cups of tea;* $3\frac{1}{2}$ *loads of laundry;* $8\frac{1}{2}$ *hours of sleep.* **What do these numbers mean?** *There is more than I.* **Can any number be written as a fraction?** *yes*

Digging Deeper

Consider these wholes. Whole numbers can be represented as fractions, too.

💬 **How might you represent the whole number shown below as a fraction?**

Allow your student sufficient time to think and come up with an idea. If he/she struggles, you may wish to ask the following questions:

💬 **What does a denominator tell us?** *The total number of equal pieces in the whole.* **What does a numerator tell us?** *The number of colored pieces.* **Think about how to show that as a fraction. Make a guess.**

Allow your student more time for productive struggle, then you may wish to ask the following questions:

💬 **How many pieces are in each whole?** *I* **So how many pieces should the denominator show that are?** *I* **And how many I-sized pieces do we have?** *5* **So what is the fraction?** $\frac{5}{1}$

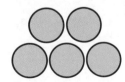

7D Compare and Order Fractions (1)

Learning Objective(s)
- Compare like and unit fractions.
- Compare fractions with the same numerators.

Material(s)
- 1 paper bag
- 1 set of fraction circles
- 1 copy of Number Cards (TR03)
- 1 number cube
- 1 set of fraction tiles

COMPARE TWO FRACTIONS (Student Book, pages 83 to 86)

Lesson Opener
Task (Student Book, page 83)

Show your student the **Lesson Opener** and cover the rest of the page. Discuss the question with your student. Do not show your student how to do the task and allow him/her to explore and discover one or more possibilities to determine which of the fractions is greater, and why. You may wish to provide fraction circles and tiles for discovery.

Refer your student to **Learn** and **Learn Together** in the Student Book for reflection after your student has explored the concepts. Use questions to build understanding and direct instruction to refine understanding.

Lesson Development
Learn (Student Book, page 83)

In this section, your student will begin to consider how to compare fractions using numerators. He/she should see the same fractions represented in two different ways: by fraction circles and in bar models, beginning to move toward a pictorial representational understanding of fractions.

On a whiteboard, draw the cakes from the **Lesson Opener** in the Student Book and pose the question. Have your student build the two fractions using fraction circles. Write the two fractions, $\frac{1}{4}$ and $\frac{3}{4}$. You may wish to ask these questions:

💬 **Which fraction is greater: $\frac{1}{4}$ or $\frac{3}{4}$? $\frac{3}{4}$ How do you know?** *3 parts is more than 1 part.* **What if we could not see a model? How could we prove that $\frac{3}{4}$ is greater than $\frac{1}{4}$?** $\frac{3}{4} = \frac{1}{4} + \frac{1}{4} + \frac{1}{4}$ *The numerator in $\frac{3}{4}$ tells us that there are 3 $\frac{1}{4}$-sized pieces compared to the numerator in $\frac{1}{4}$ that means there is only one-fourth.* **What do you notice about the fractions $\frac{1}{4}$ and $\frac{3}{4}$?** *The denominators are the same, but the numerators are different.* **How would you write a comparison sentence showing what you found?** $\frac{3}{4} > \frac{1}{4}$

© 2022 Marshall Cavendish Education Pte Ltd

💬 **How do you compare fractions?** Invite your student to ponder this question as you go through the lesson. Revisit this question when you reach the end of the lesson to check his/her understanding.

Teaching Tip

In today's lesson, you will help your student learn to compare fractions by numerator and by denominator. It is important to lead your student into self-discovery in this lesson. Your student should realize that if two fractions have the same number of colored pieces (same numerators), he/she can compare the sizes of the pieces to determine which fraction is greater. Likewise, if the size of the pieces is the same (same denominators), then he/she can compare how many pieces there are.

Comparing and ordering fractions also provides ample opportunities to help your student strengthen his/her ability with model drawing—comparison models. Practicing now will help later on.

A review of the symbols > and < may be necessary. The greater than symbol (>) always opens to the larger value, whereas the less than symbol (<) always points to the smaller value. You may wish to ask these questions:

💬 **What does the numerator tell us?** *The number of colored pieces.* **What does the denominator tell us?** *The total number of equal pieces in 1 whole.* **How can we compare these fractions using the numerators?** *If the denominators are same, we can compare the colored pieces.* **How can we compare these fractions using the denominators?** *If we have the same numerator, we can compare which fraction has larger pieces.* **When would you use each method?** *Answers vary.*

Invite your student to build the same scenario using fraction tiles, then draw two bar models to show the fraction tiles of $\frac{1}{4}$ and $\frac{3}{4}$ from the **Lesson Opener**. Use the visuals in the text as your guide.

💬 **How are these fractions different and how are they the same?** *Both show 4 equal parts, but one shows $\frac{1}{4}$ and the other shows $\frac{3}{4}$.* **Can we use either model to represent $\frac{1}{4}$ and $\frac{3}{4}$?** *yes* **Which do you find easier to draw?** *Answers vary.* **When we compare fractions using models, what is important?** *We must represent both fractions using the same model because we need to compare fractions from the same whole.* **We said $\frac{3}{4}$ is greater than $\frac{1}{4}$. You wrote that comparison in a math sentence as: $\frac{3}{4} > \frac{1}{4}$. Now, see if you can write your comparison another way.** $\frac{1}{4} < \frac{3}{4}$ **How would you say that?** *$\frac{1}{4}$ is less than $\frac{3}{4}$.* **How do you know that is true?** *One part is less than three parts.*

Activity! (Student Book, page 83)

In this activity, your student will solidify understanding about comparing fractions with the same denominators. Turn this activity into a game by placing several pieces of the same size fraction tiles into a paper bag. You and your student each take several tiles out of the paper bag. Find the greater fraction or the fraction that is less by comparing numerators. These are some variations to this activity:

- Roll number cubes to generate each numerator, or choose a Number Card from 7 to 10 (TR03) from a stack to generate the denominator.

  💬 **How do you know this fraction is the greater fraction?** *Accept any reasonable answer.*

- Extend this activity by placing fraction circles in the paper bag instead of fraction tiles. Have your student generate the matching bar models in a comparison model format.

  💬 **How can you use numerators to compare fractions?** *I check to see which fraction with the greater numerator has more equal parts colored, and that is the larger fraction.* **Why do we look at the numerator?** *To see which fraction has the greater number of parts colored.* **Why does the denominator have to stay the same to compare fractions this way?** *We need to know that we have the same total number of equal parts in order to compare how many parts are colored.* **What if we changed the denominator? How might we compare them?**

Activity! Answers

(Student Book, page 83)

Answers vary. Example:

$\frac{1}{3}$ is less than $\frac{2}{3}$.

$\frac{1}{3} < \frac{2}{3}$

Learn Together (Student Book, pages 84 and 85)

Provide your student with fraction tiles if you wish to have him/her build each of the fractions, and then compare them with the models in the Student Book.

Through questioning, lead your student to understand how to compare two fractions using numerators or denominators in **Learn Together**. As you go through the problems with your student, you may wish to ask the following questions:

🗨 **How do you know which fraction is greater? Which numbers will you use to compare, the numerators or the denominators? Why did you choose that? Prove to me why you think your answer is correct.**

After your student has explored the concepts in the **Lesson Opener**, **Learn**, and **Learn Together**, you may wish to ask these questions to encourage further reflection:

🗨 **How does your thinking compare to the book? Do you see anything in the book that helps you understand it better? What are some ways to compare fractions? How can you use numerators to compare fractions? How can you use denominators to compare fractions?**

You may wish to have your student summarize his/her learning in a math journal. Have your student explain everything he/she knows about using numerators or denominators to compare fractions.

- **QUESTION 1** requires your student to compare two fractions with the same denominators.
  🗨 **Which fraction is less, $\frac{3}{8}$ or $\frac{5}{8}$? Explain your thinking.** *$\frac{3}{8}$ because there are fewer number of colored pieces.*

😀😀 The intent is to provide an opportunity to reflect on what your student has learned, so he/she can prepare to apply it in a greater variety of ways. Invite your student to consider how he/she knows to compare the numerator given the same denominator. Look for reasoning that examines the numerator. Your student should be able to compare using numerators and justify his/her thinking.

🗨 **How do you know which fraction is greater?** *I can know which fraction is greater because there are more colored pieces.*

- **QUESTION 2** requires your student to determine which fraction is greater when comparing unit fractions.
  🗨 **What do you notice about these two fractions?** *They have different denominators but the same numerator.* **Which fraction is greater, $\frac{1}{2}$ or $\frac{1}{3}$?** *$\frac{1}{2}$* **What do you notice about the size of each piece as the denominator increases?** *As the denominator gets larger, the size of each piece gets smaller.* **Why is $\frac{1}{2}$ the greater fraction?** *There are fewer pieces in the whole, so each piece is larger.*

😀😀 This is for your student to consider how comparing denominators is different from comparing numerators. Invite your student to consider how to compare fractions using only the denominators. Look for reasoning that focuses on the size of each fractional piece. This will tell you if your student is capable of seeing the size of each piece in his/her mind's eye.

Learn Together Answers

(Student Book, pages 84 and 85)

1. $\frac{3}{8}, \frac{5}{8}$

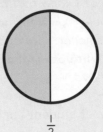
$\frac{1}{2}$

$\frac{1}{3}$

2. $\frac{1}{2}, \frac{1}{3}$

3. <

💬 **How do you know which fraction is greater?** *I know $\frac{1}{2}$ is greater than $\frac{1}{3}$ because there are fewer pieces in the whole, so each of those pieces is bigger.* **What would help you know how to compare these fractions if there were no picture?** *I know that the greater the denominator is, the more pieces the whole is divided into. That means if the denominator is larger, each piece is smaller. 1 out of 3 equal pieces is smaller than 1 out of 2 equal pieces.* **What other fractions could you compare using denominators?** *Answers vary.*

- **QUESTION 3** builds on your student's understanding of comparing fractions (other than unit fractions) where the numerators (number of parts) are the same, but the denominators (number of total equal parts) are different.
- You may wish to cover the picture in Question 3 and ask your student to produce a drawing or model on his/her own, since that will be required in the **Practice On Your Own**.

💬 **What do you notice about these two fractions? What is the same about them and what is different?** *They have the same numerators but different denominators.* **What can we say about comparing fractions when the numerators are the same, but the denominators are different?** *When the numerators are the same, compare fractions by looking at the denominator.* **Which denominator is smaller?** *4* **Which fraction is smaller?** *$\frac{3}{5}$* **What do you notice about the relationship between the denominators and size of the pieces?** *The smaller the denominator, the larger the size of the pieces. The greater the denominator, the smaller the size of the pieces.* **How could you compare these without looking at the picture?** *We can compare the denominators when the numerators are the same.* **Write a number sentence showing that $\frac{3}{5}$ is less than $\frac{3}{4}$.** *$\frac{3}{5} < \frac{3}{4}$* **Is it always true that if the denominators are the same, the fraction with the greater numerator is the greater number?** *In grade 3, yes.*

Lesson Debrief

- Conclude the lesson and facilitate your student's reflection by asking him/her to answer the **Focus Question** and share his/her thinking.
- Extend the discussion by posing the following questions.

💬 **How is comparing fractions like comparing whole numbers?** *We look to see which is greater and which is less. We use <, >, or =.* **What are some ways we learned to compare two fractions?** *See which one is larger or smaller by looking at the numerators and denominators and choosing whether to compare by numerators or compare by denominators.* **What are the different ways you can show comparing fractions?** *Build, model, or write the comparison sentence.*

- Allow time for your student to reflect on what he/she has learned and ask questions about what he/she may be unsure of.
- Encourage him/her to share anything that was confusing or difficult, and how thinking about it differently and perseverance helped the process of learning.
- Ask your student to answer a reflection question or draw a picture to show his/her reflection. You may offer these prompts:

  🗨 **How would you explain comparing fractions to a friend? What is important to know? What is your favorite comparison technique from today? If you have not already done so, draw a picture in your math journal showing everything you know about comparing fractions.**

What to look for:
- an example of comparing fractions by numerator and by denominator

Practice On Your Own (Student Book, pages 85 and 86)

- **QUESTION 1** assesses your student's ability to compare fractions and identify the greater fraction.
- **QUESTION 2** assesses your student's ability to compare fractions and identify the fraction that is less.
- **QUESTION 3** assesses your student's ability to compare fractions and use the > or < signs appropriately.

Think!

These two problems require your student to use mathematical reasoning to apply the concepts he/she learned in this lesson in unique situations never before encountered. In this case, your student must recognize that fractions can only be compared when the wholes are the same. See the **Digging Deeper** box to explore this concept further.

- **QUESTION 4** assesses your student's ability to reason whether $\frac{1}{2}$ is always greater than $\frac{1}{4}$ and explain why. This reinforces your student's understanding that for fractions to be compared, the wholes must be of the same size.
- **QUESTION 5** assesses your student's ability to reason whether $\frac{1}{9}$ of different shapes are the same size and explain why. The triangle is half the size of the square. The wholes are not the same size.

  🗨 **What do you know? What information is there for you to use? What do you need to find out? What does the question ask you to find? What problem-solving plan can you use? Can you make the problem simpler? Can you draw or build something? Put your plan into action and check your work when you are done.**

Practice On Your Own Answers

(Student Book, pages 85 and 86)

1. (a) Circle $\frac{3}{4}$

   (b) Circle $\frac{1}{4}$

   (c) Circle $\frac{3}{5}$

2. (a) Circle $\frac{4}{8}$

   (b) Circle $\frac{1}{5}$

   (c) Circle $\frac{4}{7}$

3. (a) >
   (b) <
   (c) >
   (d) >

Think! Answers

4. No. It is not correct when the 2 wholes are of different sizes.

   So $\frac{1}{2}$ of the rectangle is not greater than $\frac{1}{4}$ of the square.

5. No. $\frac{1}{9}$ of different shapes are not of the same size.

More Resources

- Refer to **Do More at Home** below and **Reteach 3, Exercise 7D (I)** if your student needs additional support.
- When your student is ready, have him/her work on **Additional Practice 3B, Exercise 7D (I)**.
- To provide your student with a challenge, have him/her work on **Extension 3, Exercise 7D (I)**.

Do More at Home

If your student does not have a strong foundation in comparing fractions, extend the concept to daily life by looking for situations in the real world and connecting them to the mathematical concept. Ideas for bridging the gap include:

- Practice comparing fractions in a game. For example, play "Which Would You Rather?" by asking questions such as "Which would you rather have? $\frac{1}{4}$ of a dollar or $\frac{3}{4}$ of a dollar? Why?"
- At the store, compare a half-pound of something dense, such as meat, to a half-pound of something less dense, such as artificial sweetener. Which looks bigger? How does this show that it is important to compare using the same wholes?
- Which is longer, $\frac{1}{4}$ of an hour or $\frac{1}{2}$ an hour? How do you know?

Digging Deeper

Although we can compare two fractions using different models such as circles and tiles, we cannot compare one fraction built with tiles against another built with circles. Your student must grasp this in order to be successful on the **Think!** questions in the **Practice On Your Own**.

In order to relate to real world, provide two similar objects of different sizes, such as a doll's T-shirt and an adult T-shirt. Ask your student which would be bigger—half of a doll's T-shirt or $\frac{1}{4}$ of an adult's T-shirt? You could also use food for this, such as a fun-size candy bar and a king-sized candy bar.

💬 **Does the whole make a difference?** *yes* **Why or why not?** *Answers vary.* **Is a fourth of a circle the same size as a fourth of a fraction bar?** *no* **Can we compare all fractions by looking at the numerators or denominators? Why or why not?** *Answers vary.* **What is important to know when you are comparing fractions?** *We must use with the same wholes to compare them, otherwise we are actually comparing different fractions.*

If your student has trouble making the leap from having the visuals supplied for each problem to not having any supporting visuals (as in **Practice On Your Own** Questions 1 to 3), encourage him/her to produce visual models for problems that are lack of them from this point forward. Encourage the use of the standard bar model format, since this model is used to represent algebraic thinking throughout elementary mathematics. You may need to allow use of two representations (concrete and pictorial) until understanding is solidified. If your student is able to solve the problems in the **Practice On Your Own** alone while using concrete fraction circles or tiles but is not able to solve the problems without manipulatives, he/she must draw the models until understanding is evident. It will take your student as many as three days of drawing to truly understand this concept. The very act of producing simple visual models will begin to map the concept to the brain. Be sure to keep a close watch on accuracy of the models he/she produces. You may wish to ask the following questions:

🗨 **Can you close your eyes and see the fraction bars in your mind's eye?** *Answers vary.*

Have your student draw these models until he/she can produce a visual picture without help of the manipulatives.

🗨 **How do both models help you compare fractions? Which is easier to draw: a fraction bar or circle? Why do you think so?**

After finishing today's lesson, you may wish to extend understanding by revisiting the **Activity** on page 83 of the Student Book, using fraction tiles with two different denominators, such as fourths and eighths. Make sure to use denominators your student can compare easily.

The following questioning sequence will give your student an opportunity to begin thinking about key ideas he/she will encounter in the next few days.

Offer your student fraction tiles in two different, but related, denominators, such as fourths and eighths. Invite him/her to build $\frac{3}{8}$ and $\frac{2}{4}$ to compare.

🗨 **Which is greater?** *The fraction with the smaller numerator,* $\frac{2}{4}$. **Can we compare all fractions by looking at the numerators? Why or why not? What do you notice about the relationship between (fourths) and (eighths)? What might be a way to compare fractions when both the denominators and the numerators are different, such as these?**

Your student will explore fractions with different denominators and learn about using equivalent fractions as this chapter unfolds, so there is no need to dwell on it at this point. Simply provide the opportunity to make observations and ask questions right now, so that your student might consider the ideas before formally encountering them.

7D Compare and Order Fractions (2)

Learning Objective(s)
- Compare and order like and unit fractions.
- Compare and order fractions with the same numerators.

Material(s)
- 1 number cube
- 1 set of fraction tiles
- 1 set of fraction circles
- 1 copy of Fraction Cards (TR30)

COMPARE AND ORDER FRACTIONS (Student Book, pages 87 to 90)

Lesson Opener

Task (Student Book, page 87)

Show your student the **Lesson Opener** and cover the rest of the page. Discuss the question with your student. Do not show your student how to do the task and allow him/her to explore and discover one or more possibilities to order fractions.

Refer your student to **Learn** and **Learn Together** in the Student Book for reflection after your student has explored the concepts. Use questions to build understanding and direct instruction to refine understanding.

Lesson Development
Learn (Student Book, page 87)

After a period of productive struggle, offer your student fraction tiles to build the **Lesson Opener**. You may wish to ask these questions:

💬 **How can you use these fraction tiles to find out who ate the least?**
Allow your student to build and/or draw the problem to figure out the answer.

💬 **Who ate the least?** *Ethan* **How do you know?** *3 pieces is fewer than 4 pieces.* **Is there another way we could find the answer without using fraction tiles?** *compare numerators* **Does that method always work?** *Yes, it should, as long as the denominators are the same.* **What do you notice about all three fraction bars?** *The units are all the same size. They are all made up of $\frac{1}{6}$-sized pieces.* **Which fraction shows the fewest sixths?** $\frac{3}{6}$ **Which fractions are greater than $\frac{3}{6}$?** $\frac{5}{6}$ and $\frac{4}{6}$ **Which fraction is greater, $\frac{5}{6}$ or $\frac{4}{6}$?** $\frac{5}{6}$ **How do you know?** *Because 5 is more than 4; $\frac{5}{6}$ has one more sixth than $\frac{4}{6}$.* **How can you order the fractions from least to greatest?** $\frac{3}{6}, \frac{4}{6}, \frac{5}{6}$

Write the fractions in order from least to greatest on a whiteboard.

💬 **Can you make a rule?** *When the denominators are all the same, we can put fractions in order by the comparing the numerators.*

Focus Question

💬 How does comparing fractions help you order them?

Invite your student to ponder this question as you go through the lesson. Revisit this question when you reach the end of the lesson to check his/her understanding.

Teaching Tip

This lesson extends the concepts your student learned yesterday to comparing, then ordering three fractions. Prompt the connection by asking the following questions:

💬 **What are some different ways we can compare fractions?** *We can compare the numerator or the denominator. We wrote the comparison in a number sentence using >, <, and =.*
What is different about these problems today? *We are comparing three fractions instead of just two.*
What is the same about this (these) problem(s)? *We are still comparing the numerators and denominators.*
What do you notice about the relationship between the fractions in this problem? *Answers vary through the lesson. In the first problem: the denominators are the same but the numerators are different; later on: the numerators are the same but the denominators are different.* **How will you order them?** *comparing the numerators*

Learn Answers

(Student Book, page 87)

$\frac{3}{6}, \frac{4}{6}, \frac{5}{6}$

Activity! (Student Book, page 88)

In this activity, your student will compare three different fractions with same denominator. Provide fraction circles or fraction tiles. Ask your student to justify his/her thinking with these questions:

💬 **Why did you put the fractions in the order that you did?** *Answers vary.* **What do you find is the best way to order fractions with the same denominators?** *compare numerators to order*

Learn Together (Student Book, pages 88 and 89)

In this section, your student will solidify understanding built in **Learn** and the **Activity** and extend it to ordering fractions with same numerators or a mix of fractions. You may wish to provide fraction circles to your student to help support this lesson. Alternately, in Question 3 the fraction tiles may be quickly and accurately sketched on a whiteboard to help support the pictorial stage of learning in the concrete–pictorial–abstract learning progression.

Through questioning, lead your student to understand how to compare and order fractions in **Learn Together**. As you go through the problems with your student, you may wish to ask the following questions:

💬 **What is the same about these fractions? What is different? What are two different ways you can tell which fraction is greatest or least?** *Look at the model and compare the numbers or look at the fractions to compare them.* **How does knowing how to compare help you order them?**

After your student has explored the concepts in the **Lesson Opener**, **Learn**, and **Learn Together**, you may wish to ask these questions to encourage further reflection:

💬 **How does your thinking compare to the book? Do you see anything in the book that helps you order fractions? How does knowing how to compare fractions help you order them?**

You may wish to have your student summarize his/her learning in a math journal. Have your student explain everything he/she knows about using numerators or denominators to compare and order fractions.

- **QUESTION 1** requires your student to order three fractions with like denominators from least to greatest.
- Provide fraction circles to show $\frac{3}{5}$, $\frac{4}{5}$, and $\frac{2}{5}$. Have your student build and/or draw representations for each before proceeding.
  💬 **What do you notice about the fractions?** *They have same denominators.* **How can you compare fractions with same denominators?** *by comparing the numerators* **What are all the ways you can think of to compare these fractions and order them from least to greatest?** *Build, draw, compare numerators, etc.*

Activity! Answers

(Student Book, page 88)

Answers vary. Example:

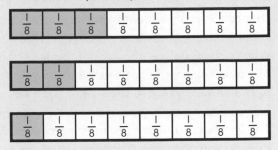

$\frac{3}{8}$, $\frac{2}{8}$, $\frac{1}{8}$

Learn Together Answers

(Student Book, pages 88 and 89)

1. $\frac{2}{5}$, $\frac{3}{5}$, $\frac{4}{5}$

2. $\frac{1}{6}$, $\frac{1}{5}$, $\frac{1}{7}$

   $\frac{1}{5}$, $\frac{1}{6}$, $\frac{1}{7}$

3. $\frac{5}{5}$, $\frac{3}{6}$, $\frac{3}{10}$

   $\frac{3}{10}$, $\frac{3}{6}$, $\frac{5}{5}$

- **QUESTION 2** requires your student to order three unit fractions from greatest to least.
- Your student will build understanding of comparing unit fractions and other fractions with same numerators by comparing the denominators. This is a chance for your student to solidify understanding that the greater the number in the denominator, the smaller the size of the pieces.

🗨 **What do you notice about the fractions?** *They are all unit fractions; they all have a numerator of one.* **What do you observe about the relationship of the denominator to the size of each equal part?** *The greater the digit in the denominator, the smaller the size of the piece.* **Why is that?** *The fractions with larger denominators are from wholes cut into more pieces.* **How do you compare fractions when the numerators are the same?** *I compare the denominators. The smaller the denominator the larger the fraction; the larger the denominator the smaller the fraction.*

- **QUESTION 3** requires your student to order three fractions from least to greatest.
- Two of the fractions have same numerators but different denominators, one is a fractional representation of 1 using a completely unrelated denominator.

🗨 **How does answering Question 2 help you answer Question 3?** *In both questions, at least some of the numerators of the fractions being compared are the same, so you compare the denominators. The smaller the denominator, the larger the fraction.* **How can you think about $\frac{5}{5}$?** *It is 1.* **How does thinking of $\frac{5}{5}$ as 1 help you compare these fractions?** *Answers vary.*

Lesson Debrief

- Conclude the lesson and facilitate your student's reflection by asking him/her to answer the **Focus Question** and share his/her thinking.
- Extend the discussion by posing the following questions.

🗨 **Why do we need to know how to compare so we can order fractions?** *When we know which one is greater, we can know which comes first or last.* **What are the different ways we can compare and order fractions?** *If the denominators are the same, we can use the numerators to compare and order the fractions. If the numerators are the same, we can use the denominators to help us compare and order the fractions.*

🗨 **How is using the numerators to compare and order fractions different from using the denominator to compare and order fractions?** *The numerator tells us the number of colored pieces in the fraction. It is only helpful if the pieces are all the same size or have the same denominator. The denominator tells us the size of the pieces in the fraction. We can use it to compare and order fractions when we have the same numerators.*

- Allow time for your student to reflect on what he/she has learned and ask questions about what he/she may be unsure of.
- Encourage him/her to share anything that was confusing or difficult, and how thinking about it differently and perseverance helped the process of learning.
- Ask your student to answer a reflection question or draw a picture to show his/her reflection. You may offer these prompts:
  - 💬 How would you explain ordering fractions to a friend? What is the most complicated problem you solved today? Draw a picture of it in your math journal and show me everything you know about it next to the picture.

What to look for:
- ability to order three fractions with like denominators
- an example, with a picture and comparison sentence of how to compare and order fractions using numerators and denominators
- ability to order three fractions after comparing them by numerators or by denominators
- ability to take two fractions that are related by either numerator or denominator and one fraction that is 1, then compare and order all three fractions

Repeat the **Activity** on page 88 of the Student Book, inviting your student to use three different fractions with the same numerator but three different denominators. If your student struggles with this **Activity**, please refer to the **For Additional Support** box in the **Do More at Home** section.

Continue to move your student through the concrete-pictorial-abstract learning progression by requiring him/her to produce simple bar model diagrams of the fractions in **Learn Together** Questions 1 and 2, and in the **Practice On Your Own**. In doing so, you support the development from real-world understanding (the concrete) to the ability to work efficiently in the abstract with understanding.

Practice On Your Own (Student Book, page 90)

- **QUESTION 1** assesses your student's ability to compare three fractions and order them from greatest to least.
- **QUESTION 2** assesses your student's ability to compare three fractions and order them from least to greatest, and to recognize their relationship with 0 and 1.
  - 💬 How do you know that is true? *Answers vary.* What do you know about 0? What do you know about 1? How are these fractions related to 0 or 1? *All of the fractions are between 0 and 1. They are not whole numbers.*

Think!

- **QUESTION 3** assesses your student's ability to make a connection between comparing three fractions to determine the greatest fraction in a real-world context.
  - 💬 What do you know? What information is there for you to use? What do you need to find out? What does the question ask you to find? What problem-solving plan can you use? Can you make the problem simpler? Can you draw or build something? Put your plan into action and check your work when you are done.

Practice On Your Own Answers

(Student Book, page 90)

1. (a) $\frac{7}{9}; \frac{5}{9}; \frac{3}{9}$

   (b) $\frac{1}{2}; \frac{1}{4}; \frac{1}{10}$

   (c) $\frac{5}{6}; \frac{5}{7}; \frac{5}{8}$

2. (a) $0; \frac{1}{9}; \frac{1}{6}$

   (b) $\frac{4}{7}; \frac{4}{5}; 1$

   (c) $\frac{1}{7}; \frac{3}{7}; \frac{11}{7}$

Think! Answers

3. Wednesday, because 3 out of 4 is greater than 3 out of 5 and 3 out of 9.

Your student may order all fractions from greatest to least or from least to greatest without reading the instructions carefully. This is an excellent opportunity to call attention to an important mathematical practice: attention to precision.

More Resources

- Refer to **Do More at Home** below and **Reteach 3, Exercise 7D (2)** if your student needs additional support.
- When your student is ready, have him/her work on **Additional Practice 3B, Exercise 7D (2)**.
- To provide your student with a challenge, have him/her work on **Extension 3, Exercise 7D (2)**.
- You may assign **Mastery and Beyond 3B, Chapter 7, Practice 5** to provide further support and development to sustain learning.

Do More at Home

If your student does not have a strong foundation in ordering fractions extend the concept by building your student's ability to compare visually and numerically. Ideas for bridging the gap include:

- Use a quick memory game to match Fraction Cards (TR30) to fraction tiles or circles, then have your student order all the pairs (no writing or drawing required!). Narrow the possibilities by selecting in advance groups of fractions with either same denominators or same numerators. Mix easier and more difficult pairs.
- Practice comparing and ordering a variety of items to check if there is a more general conceptual gap with the idea of comparison: Is this object lighter/heavier/taller/shorter than that object?
- Make sure your student is able to visualize the fractions in order to compare them (see further suggestions in the **For Additional Support** box.)
- Play the suggested game below in order to help your student learn to see fractions using circles or tiles, and compare them without having to write.

Which is Greater?

Invite your student to play this game by arranging fraction cards by pairs of same denominators or same numerators. Place fraction tiles in the center of the table and fraction cards in a stack. You and your student will each choose a card. The person who correctly points to the greater fraction first gets a point. Both of you will build your fractions with the fraction tiles, then compare the built fractions to double-check which fraction is greater. The person with the most points wins.

If your student has trouble ordering fractions, have him/her practice drawing models to match given fractions, then compare them by choosing three fractions from Fraction Cards (TR30). Start with same denominators, as they are easier to model, then move to same numerators, and finally a mix. Here are three suggested fraction groups, Group I: $\frac{3}{6}, \frac{5}{6}, \frac{4}{6}$; Group 2: $\frac{2}{5}, \frac{2}{7}, \frac{2}{4}$; Group 3: $\frac{2}{5}, \frac{4}{5}, \frac{4}{8}$. Invite your student to draw the models, then color to show the fractions on the models. If your student has trouble at this step, have him/her build the fractions concretely with fraction tiles before doing so pictorially. Next, have your student compare the fractions and order them. You may wish to ask the following questions:

🗩 **How do you know if you drew the models correctly?** *I can check the number of units for the denominators and count how many units I colored for the numerators.* **How do the models help you compare fractions?** *They help us see the fractions.* **What is another way to compare them?** *We can compare by numerators or denominators.* **How can you compare these fractions just by looking at the numbers?** *compare the numerators or the denominators*

Here are some ideas to extend your student's understanding of comparing and ordering fractions. Please note that comparing equivalent fractions such as eighths and fourths as in the first fraction set suggested below may be too difficult for your student because it previews the next lesson, Lesson 7E. If that is the case for your student, alter the activity as needed so that it is more accessible. This is intended to stretch your student, but not to frustrate him/her. If your student loves a challenge and thrives on discovering unknown principles, enjoy the process and see what he/she does with the new possibility as written below.

Instructions: Choose sets of three Fractions Cards (TR30) for your student to compare. Choose two of the fractions that have the same denominators and two that have the same numerators, such as $\frac{5}{8}, \frac{3}{8}$, and $\frac{3}{4}$ or $\frac{5}{7}, \frac{5}{8}$, and $\frac{1}{7}$. Have your student order the fractions and explain his/her strategy. (For example, your student might first compare the fractions with the same denominators, then compare those with the same numerators.)

On a few sets, use a fractional form of I that is not related by numerator or denominator to either number, for example, as in **Learn Together** Question 3: $\frac{3}{10}; \frac{3}{6}; \frac{5}{5}$.

You may wish to ask the following questions:

🗩 **How do you decide which to compare first?** *Answers vary.* **Why compare one way first and then the other?** *It helps us be orderly with our thinking. Mathematicians attend to precision.* **What do you think about ordering fractions when they are not the same?** *We need to find something common and that helps us solve the problem.* **What is another strategy?** *Finding I or thinking about how close a fraction is to I.*

7E Equivalent Fractions

Learning Objective(s)
- Identify equivalent fractions.
- Find equivalent fractions.

Vocabulary
- equivalent fractions

Material(s)
- 1 piece of graph paper
- 1 set of fraction circles
- 2 copies of Rectangular Paper Strips (TR26)
- 2 copies of Fraction Bars (TR31)
- 1 set of colored pencils
- 1 set of fraction tiles
- 1 copy of Fraction Cards (TR30)

EQUIVALENT FRACTIONS (Student Book, pages 91 to 94)

Lesson Opener

Task (Student Book, page 91)

Show your student the **Lesson Opener** and cover the rest of the page. Discuss the question with your student. Do not show your student how to do the task and allow him/her to explore and discover one or more possibilities to find equal parts.

Refer your student to **Learn** and **Learn Together** in the Student Book for reflection after your student has explored the concepts. Use questions to build understanding and direct instruction to refine understanding.

Lesson Development
Learn (Student Book, page 91)

Provide your student with Rectangular Paper Strips (TR26) as in the **Lesson Opener**. Have your student do the activity as described. You may wish to lightly mark the sections of each strip with a pencil, so your student can see the parts more easily. As your student answers your questions, on a whiteboard draw a model of each new fold under the next, along with the fraction each new fold creates. Invite your student to fold the strip of paper in half and color one half. Lightly mark the line in the middle.

- 🗨 **How many is colored?** *half* **How many pieces are in the whole?** *2* **What fraction of the strip is colored?** $\frac{1}{2}$

Fold the strip of paper in half again. Mark the lines that the new fold makes.

- 🗨 **How many is colored?** *half* **How many pieces are in the whole?** *4* **What fraction of the strip is colored?** $\frac{2}{4}$

Focus Question

🗨 How do you know if two or more fractions are equivalent?

Invite your student to ponder this question as you go through the lesson. Revisit this question when you reach the end of the lesson to check his/her understanding.

Teaching Tip

In this lesson, you will help your student learn to identify equivalent fractions. You have thoroughly explored the concepts from **Learn** through page 91 of the Student Book with your student. Keep this as hands-on as possible until your student can prove understanding.

As you teach, keep in mind that we say fractions are equivalent, or equal, if they name the same part of the same-sized whole. It may help your student when you encounter the symbol = for "equal," you occasionally say "is the same as." $\frac{1}{3}$ is the same as $\frac{2}{6}$. The part named is identical.

You may wish to ask the following questions:

🗨 **What does it mean to say that these fractions are equivalent?** *They show the same part of the same-sized whole.* **How can we show that this fraction is the same as that one? Why are the numerators and denominators different when the fractions are the same?** *Answers vary.*

Fold the strip of paper in half again. Mark the lines that the new fold makes.

- 🗨 **How many is colored?** *half* **How many pieces are in the whole?** *8* **What fraction of the strip is colored?** $\frac{4}{8}$

Point to the models you drew and each fraction.

- 🗨 **What do you notice about the amount of the strip that is colored in each case?** *It is always half.* **How can that be?** *The numbers are different.* **What is going on?** *As the number of pieces in the whole rises, the fraction changes but the amount that is colored remains the same.* **The fractions look different, but the colored part is the same. Why do you think this is so?** *The fractions name the same part even though the numbers are different.* **What is the relationship between the 1 and the 2 in $\frac{1}{2}$?** *One is half of 2.* **What is the relationship between the 2 and the 4 in $\frac{2}{4}$?** *2 is half of 4.* **What is the relationship between the 4 and the 8 in $\frac{4}{8}$?** *4 is half of 8.* **Is $\frac{2}{4}$ the same as $\frac{1}{2}$? Is $\frac{4}{8}$ the same as $\frac{1}{2}$?** *Yes to both.* **Is there another way to check to make sure the fractions are the same?** *Lay the pieces on top of each other. If they are a perfect match, they are the same.* **What do we call fractions that are a perfect match?** *equivalent fractions*

Write $\frac{1}{2} = \frac{2}{4} = \frac{4}{8}$ on the whiteboard.

- 🗨 **Is this true?** *yes* **How do you know?** *They do not look the same to me.* *Answers vary.*

Digging Deeper

Focus on the mathematical relationships between the numbers in each of the equivalent fractions, as questioned in **Learn**. You may wish to ask the following questions:

- 🗨 **Is there a way to know if fractions are equivalent besides looking at them or building them? What is the relationship between the numbers in these two fractions? What is the relationship of the numerator to the denominator in each fraction? Is there a pattern? What is it? Can you make a rule for making equivalent fractions just by looking at the numbers?**

This line of questioning will be thoroughly addressed in Grade 4, so if your student does not see it, just ask a few questions and move on, letting your student continue to think about it at leisure and draw his/her own conclusions.

For Additional Support

To help your student gain certainty in this concept, you may wish to repeat the **Lesson Opener** with a strip of paper folded into thirds. You may wish to ask the following question:

- 🗨 **How could we make equivalent fractions from thirds?**

Allow your student to explore, leading them to shade $\frac{1}{3}$, then fold the strip again to discover how many parts are in the whole now, and how many of those are colored. $\frac{1}{3}$ is the same as $\frac{2}{6}$.

Teaching Tip

After your student realizes there are a few ways to name the same piece, you may wish to ask the following questions:

- 🗨 **What do you notice about the whole in each case?** *It is the same size.* **Does that matter? Can we change the size of the whole and have the fraction represent the same thing?** *Answers vary.* **If I give you half a million dollars, is that the same as half of ten dollars?** *no* **Why not?** *Answers vary.* **For a fraction to be equivalent, what must be true of the whole?** *The wholes must be the same size.*

Learn Together (Student Book, pages 92 and 93)

In this section, your student will extend conceptual understanding to other equivalent fractions. Here again, use concrete and pictorial models in conjunction with each other to help solidify thinking.

Through questioning, lead your student to understand how to identify and find equivalent fractions in **Learn Together**. As you go through the problems with your student, you may wish to ask the following questions:

🗨 **What are your observations about these fractions? How are these fractions the same? How are they different? How can you know for sure that this fraction is the same as that fraction?**

After your student has explored the concepts in the **Lesson Opener**, **Learn**, and **Learn Together**, you may wish to ask these questions to encourage further reflection:

🗨 **How does your thinking compare to the book? Do you see anything in the book that helps you understand the concept better? What is the same? What is different?**

You may wish to have your student summarize his/her learning in a math journal. Have your student draw a few equivalent fractions and explain everything he/she knows about the concept.

- **QUESTION 1** requires your student to use a model of fraction bars to find fractions equivalent to $\frac{3}{4}$.

Provide actual fraction bars for this problem, along with a copy of Fraction Bars (TR31).

🗨 **What do you notice about this picture?** *Some fractions line up, some do not.* **What else do you see?** *Answers vary.* **Is there a way to tell if fractions are equivalent by using this visual model?** *If we look to see which lines end at the same places, that would tell us which fractions are the same, or equivalent.* **What do you notice about $\frac{3}{4}$?** *It shares a line with $\frac{6}{8}$ and $\frac{9}{12}$.* **So what can we say about them?** *They are equivalent.*

Activity! (Student Book, page 92)

In this activity, your student will generate two other fractions that are equivalent to $\frac{2}{4}$. Encourage your student to prove thinking for each fraction he/she discovers. Using fraction bars, have your student find at least two fractions that are equivalent to $\frac{2}{4}$ (or a different fraction you choose, if you explored $\frac{2}{4}$ carefully in the **Lesson Opener**). Facilitate a discussion by asking the following questions:

🗨 **Why did you choose the fractions you did?** *Answers vary.* **How do you know the fractions are equivalent?** *Answers vary.* **What is another way to prove your thinking?**

Look for visual, concrete, or mathematical responses. Encourage your student to repeat and extend the above activity by choosing another fraction to find equivalent fractions.

Learn Together Answers
(Student Book, pages 92 and 93)

1. $\frac{6}{8}$; $\frac{9}{12}$

2.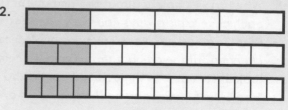

2; 4

3. 2; 3; $\frac{4}{4}$

Activity! Answers
(Student Book, page 92)

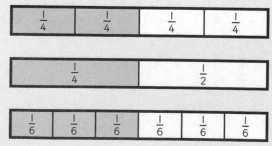

$\frac{1}{2} = \frac{3}{6}$

- **QUESTION 2** requires your student to model three equivalent fractions by coloring the appropriate amounts on fraction strips to represent $\frac{1}{4}$, $\frac{2}{8}$, and $\frac{4}{16}$.

  - 💬 **What do you notice about these three fractions?** *They all represent the same amounts, but the colored parts are subdivided differently.* **Look at the denominators written below the models. What can you say about them?** *They name the number of units in each model.* **How will you finish the fractions?** *Write the numerators, which I can find by counting the colored pieces in each bar.* **What do we call fractions that occupy the same space but are named with different numbers?** *equivalent fractions*

- **QUESTION 3** requires your student to understand that a whole can be represented as a fraction in different ways.

  - 💬 **What do you notice about each of the fractions equivalent to one whole?** *The numerator and denominator are the same in each fraction.* **Why are they all different?** *The wholes divided into different numbers of equal parts.* **What are they all equivalent to?** *1*

Lesson Debrief

- Conclude the lesson and facilitate your student's reflection by asking him/her to answer the **Focus Question** and share his/her thinking.
- Extend the discussion by posing the following questions.

  - 💬 **What are all the ways you know to tell equivalent fractions?** *Build or draw it and see if the parts occupy the same space; see if the numbers have the same relationships to each other.* **Given one fraction, what are some ways you can create an equivalent fraction?** *Build something exactly the same with the same-sized whole but different total number of equal parts and color the same number of parts. Alternately, we can make the numbers all have the same relationships to each other. $\frac{1}{3}$ is one out of three equal parts. $\frac{3}{9}$ is 3 out of 9 equal parts, but 3 + 3 + 3 make 9, so that is actually one of three parts too! They are equivalent.*

- Allow time for your student to reflect on what he/she has learned and ask questions about what he/she may be unsure of.
- Encourage him/her to share anything that was confusing or difficult, and how thinking about it differently and perseverance helped the process of learning.
- Ask your student to answer a reflection question or draw a picture to show his/her reflection. You may offer these prompts:
  - 🗨 **How would you explain equivalent fractions to a friend? What is your favorite equivalent fraction from today? Draw a picture of it in your math journal, and show me everything you know about it next to the picture.**

What to look for:
- ability to identify equivalent fractions by looking for the fractions that are exactly the same lengths
- ability to recognize and build equivalent fractions that are exact matches

Practice On Your Own (Student Book, pages 93 and 94)

- **QUESTION 1** assesses your student's ability show given fractions then determine which fractions are equivalent to $\frac{1}{2}$.
- **QUESTION 2** assesses your student's ability to show $\frac{2}{3}$ of a whole then show the correct number of sixths and twelfths to make equivalent fractions.
- **QUESTION 3** assesses your student's ability to find equivalent fractions by dividing a given pictorial representation of $\frac{2}{5}$ to show the equivalent fractions, then writing the equivalent fractions.
  - 🗨 **What do you notice about these three fractions?** *They all represent the same amount.* **Do you think there are other fractions equivalent to these three fractions?** *yes* **How would you draw lines to show what they might be?** *I could use the marks provided, then split the box in 2.*
- **QUESTION 4** assesses your student's ability to divide a hexagon into equal parts to show fractions that are equivalent to I whole, then write the equivalent fractions.
- Your student will demonstrate understanding of fractional pieces in a whole: the parts of the whole are equal (the same size), and the fraction must show a numerator identical to the denominator—that is, as many pieces as the size of the piece to make a whole, for example, 2 out of 2 equal pieces.

Practice On Your Own Answers

(Student Book, pages 93 and 94)

1.
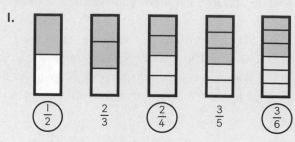

2.
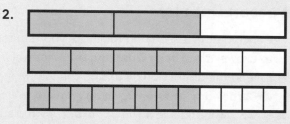

4; 8

3. Answers vary. Example:
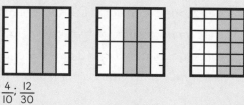

$\frac{4}{10}, \frac{12}{30}$

4. Answers vary. Example:

$\frac{2}{2}, \frac{3}{3}$

Caution

Your student may not subdivide figures equally. Remind your student that he/she needs to start with the same-sized whole and end up with the same-sized parts. Question 3 is an interesting problem that can help your student see that the number of parts within the colored area multiplies as the number of pieces in the whole increases. Your student may get confused by that as he/she is counting.

More Resources

- Refer to **Do More at Home** below and **Reteach 3, Exercise 7E** if your student needs additional support.
- When your student is ready, have him/her work on **Additional Practice 3B, Exercise 7E**.
- To provide your student with a challenge, have him/her work on **Extension 3, Exercise 7E**.
- You may also assign **Mastery and Beyond 3B, Chapter 7, Practice 6** to provide further support and development to sustain learning.

Do More at Home

If your student does not have a strong foundation in equivalent fractions, extend the concept by doing the following activity. You may wish to play this game to help solidify understanding:

Match It

You and your student are the participants of this activity. According to his/her ability, provide your student with several equivalent fractions from the Fraction Cards (TR30). Place the equivalent fractions from the fraction cards face down and mix them up. You may want to arrange them in a rectangle. Player 1 turns over two cards and determine if they are equivalent. Your student may build them with fraction tiles or use Fraction Bars (TR31) to check. If the cards are equivalent, take them and put them in your pile. If they are not equivalent, turn them back over. Player 2 repeats the steps.

Continue to play until all cards are matched. The person with the most cards at the end wins!

If your student still struggles with the concept of equivalent fractions, he/she will need to work through the concrete-pictorial-abstract progression, drawing the models as well as producing them.

Using Rectangular Paper Strips (TR26) and beginning with halves, follow the steps in the **Chapter Opener** to help your student gain a deeper understanding of equivalent fractions.

Repeat the sequence in the **Chapter Opener** using thirds to sixths to twelfths.

Allow your student to prove, then draw the models he/she built using fraction strips.

After refreshing the **Chapter Opener**, have your student draw several different equivalent fractions using thirds with sixths, fourths with eighths, and halves with fourths, sixths, and eighths. Below is an example of what your student should be able to produce. Be sure to have him/her write the equivalent fraction with it.

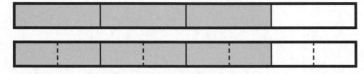

$\frac{3}{4} = \frac{6}{8}$

If your student needs extra support to achieve this, draw and lightly shade the initial model of halves, thirds or fourths on a whiteboard in one color marker. Have your student identify and record the fraction you drew. Then have your student subdivide the same model in a different color and write the equivalent fraction as below:

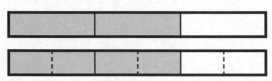

$\frac{2}{3} = \frac{4}{6}$

If your student has trouble grasping the idea that the same-sized fraction can be named using different numbers, you may want to ask him/her what else your student can think of that is the same but has different names under different circumstances. For example, the person your student calls "Mom" may also have a different name used by the neighbor or doctor or the child's father. Or, snow, ice, clouds, and water are all forms of water, but they look different in different circumstances. There are many such instances in life. How many can your student name?

Digging Deeper Answers

1.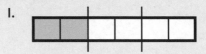

(a) $\frac{1}{6} + \frac{1}{6} = \frac{2}{6} = \frac{1}{3}$

(b) $\frac{1}{9} + \frac{1}{9} + \frac{1}{9} = \frac{3}{9} = \frac{1}{3}$

(c) $\frac{1}{12} + \frac{1}{12} + \frac{1}{12} + \frac{1}{12} = \frac{4}{12} = \frac{1}{3}$

(d) $\frac{1}{18} + \frac{1}{18} + \frac{1}{18} + \frac{1}{18} + \frac{1}{18} + \frac{1}{18} = \frac{6}{18} = \frac{1}{3}$

Use the following problems to challenge your student to extend and deepen his/her thinking about equivalent fractions.

1. You may wish to have your student use graph paper for this entire problem. For all sections, have your student draw and write as shown:

   (a) Using sixths, build or draw and color $\frac{1}{3}$.

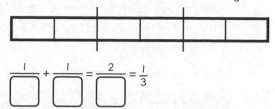

   (b) Using ninths, build or draw and color $\frac{1}{3}$.
   (c) Using twelfths, build or draw and color $\frac{1}{3}$.
   (d) Using eighteenths, build or draw and color $\frac{1}{3}$.
   (e) With graph paper, draw a bar model over 36 boxes. Using different colors for each:
   - Use two boxes to show eighteenths,
   - Use three boxes to show twelfths,
   - Use four boxes to show ninths,
   - Use six boxes to show sixths,
   - Use twelve boxes to mark thirds.

   Note: the number of groups of boxes to get to 36 is the size of the fraction. It represents the equal groups of the denominator. 12 boxes is $\frac{1}{3}$ of the whole. Your drawing may look like this:

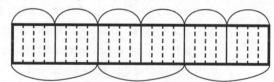

   (f) 🗨 **Now, place all the fractions you found in items (a) to (d) in the same equation. What do you notice?**

   $$\frac{1}{3} = \frac{\square}{6} = \frac{\square}{9} = \frac{\square}{12} = \frac{\square}{18}$$

   (g) 🗨 **Consider this statement with equivalent fractions:**

   $$\frac{1}{3} = \frac{2}{6} = \frac{4}{12}$$

   What pattern can you see in the numbers?

   (h) 🗨 **Consider this statement with equivalent fractions:**

   $$\frac{1}{3} = \frac{3}{9} = \frac{6}{18}$$

   What pattern can you see in the numbers?
   I wonder if that pattern works for all equivalent fractions, or only some? What do you think?

   (i) 🗨 **Is it true or false that $\frac{2}{6} = \frac{6}{18}$? How do you know? How might you prove it? How is this pattern different?**

   (j) 🗨 **Is there any relationship between multiplication and fractions? If so, what?**

(e) This is an intricate activity, but it may help your student see equivalent fractions more clearly, as well as the relationship between fractions and multiplication. 36 is used here because it is the least common denominator of all the given fractions in this problem.

(f) $\frac{1}{3} = \frac{2}{6} = \frac{3}{9} = \frac{4}{12} = \frac{6}{18}$

(g) and (h)
Answers vary. Both numerators and denominators are doubling or being multiplied by 2 in each set of fractions. Do not explain the algorithm for making equivalent fractions to your student if he/she does not spontaneously recognize it. It will be taught explicitly in Grade 4.

(i) True. Your student may prove it visually, build it, or prove it mathematically if he/she has generated the procedure.

(j) Yes. Multiplication can be used to explain or generate equivalent fractions. Just move on if your student has not identified the relationship or answers "No" to this question.

Your student may figure out the mathematical pattern for equivalent fractions, then get stumped by $\frac{2}{6} = \frac{3}{9}$ or $\frac{4}{12} = \frac{6}{18}$. In these pairs of fractions, the numerators and denominators are related by 1.5. Since your student does not yet know how to multiply decimals, he/she may want to prove it concretely. Using the equation $\frac{2}{6} = \frac{3}{9}$, have your student first build $\frac{2}{6}$ with fraction tiles, then $\frac{3}{9}$. Help your student observe as he/she places the ninths that "two plus half a two make three" (one-and-a-half twos) and "six plus half a six make nine" (one-and-a-half sixes).
🗨 **Is this also true for $\frac{4}{12} = \frac{6}{18}$?** yes
What might that tell you? Answers vary. We can multiply by parts of numbers (i.e., by fractions).
$$\frac{1}{3} = \frac{2}{6} = \frac{3}{9}$$

7F Fractions on a Number Line

Learning Objective(s)
- Show fractions as numbers on a number line.

Material(s)
- 1 set of fraction tiles
- 1 copy of Fraction Cards (TR30)
- 3 copies of Number Line Template (TR33)
- 1 copy of Rectangular Paper Strips (TR26)
- 1 copy of Fraction Strips (TR32)

FRACTIONS ON A NUMBER LINE (Student Book, pages 95 to 100)

Lesson Opener

Task (Student Book, page 95)

Show your student the **Lesson Opener** and cover the rest of the page. Discuss the question with your student. Do not show your student how to do the task and allow him/her to explore and discover one or more possibilities to create a rudimentary number line that represents the problem.

Refer your student to **Learn** and **Learn Together** in the Student Book for reflection after your student has explored the concepts. Use questions to build understanding and direct instruction to refine understanding.

Lesson Development
Learn (Student Book, page 95)

In this section, your student will work to discover how to use a number line to represent fractions. After a period of productive struggle, give your student a Rectangular Paper Strip (TR26) and invite him/her to build the track, then represent where Ava and Ben are on it. Do not use fraction tiles for this section. Use a Rectangular Paper Strip (TR26) so your student can determine the fraction he/she is finding. Allow your student to look at the **Lesson Opener**, with the track and the two children, if needed. Encourage your student to draw the same number line on a whiteboard to represent the track. Invite your student to fold the Rectangular Paper Strip (TR26) into four equal parts. You may wish to ask these questions:

🗨 **If we were to show the track with just one strip, where would Point A be located on the paper strip? Where is Point B on your paper strip? What is the starting point on this track?** *0* **What is the end point?** *1* **How many equal parts does the track have?** *4* **How might we name 1 part of the track?** *Your student may not be able to make the leap to naming $\frac{1}{4}$ yet.* **Are points A and B whole numbers?** *no* **Why not?** *They are only part of the track and are less than 1.* **What kind of numbers are they?** *Fractions; parts of a whole.* **How do you know?** *The track is broken into 4 equal parts.*

Focus Question

🗨 How does a fraction help you to represent intervals smaller than one on a number line?

Invite your student to ponder this question as you go through the lesson. Revisit this question when you reach the end of the lesson to check his/her understanding.

Teaching Tip

In this lesson, your student will learn to locate fractions on a number line. Your student will extend their understanding of using number lines to represent whole numbers to fractions and their relationships to whole numbers and other fractions on the number line. Number lines are important mathematical visual tools that will eventually help your student learn about positive and negative integers in addition to what he/she is learning in this lesson. Since number lines are abstract visual tools, it is important to check for understanding and deepen it through the questions you ask. Using concrete-pictorial-abstract progression, have your student build the **Lesson Opener** and **Learn** with Rectangular Paper Strips (TR26), then invite him/her to represent that with a number line. This will provide support for difficult questions later in the lesson. After the **Activity** on page 96 of the Student Book, you will direct your student toward more abstract understanding. You may wish to ask the following questions:

🗨 What is another way to think of 1 in this problem? Is this fraction closer to 0 or to 1? How do you know? Where is $\frac{1}{2}$ on this number line? How are these fractions related to 0, 1, or $\frac{1}{2}$? How is a number line like a bar model? How is it different? Why use a number line? How does it help you?

Continue to generate discussion using the following questions:

💬 **How is the track like a number line?** *it is straight; it has a starting point and an ending point; it is divided into equal parts* **How can knowing the number of equal parts the track is divided into help you label points A and B?** *Point B comes at the end of 2 out of the 4 equal parts, so Point B is $\frac{2}{4}$; Point A is at the end of 1 out of 4 equal parts so it is $\frac{1}{4}$.*

Write on the whiteboard: I whole $= \frac{1}{4} + \frac{1}{4} + \frac{1}{4} + \frac{1}{4} = \frac{4}{4}$; draw four jumps on the number line to represent the four equal parts of the track. Show a picture of Ava on the track.

💬 **What is the distance from 0 to Point A?** *Point A is 1 jump or $\frac{1}{4}$ of the distance from 0 to 1.* **What fraction names 1 out of 4 equal parts?** $\frac{1}{4}$ **Show the picture of Ben on the track. What is the distance from 0 to Point B?** *Point B is 2 jumps or $\frac{2}{4}$ of the distance from 0 to 1.* **What fraction names 2 out of 4 equal parts?** $\frac{2}{4}$ **Which fractions are represented at Point A and B?** $\frac{1}{4}$ *and* $\frac{2}{4}$

Encourage your student to label the points on the number line $\frac{1}{4}, \frac{2}{4}, \frac{3}{4}, \frac{4}{4}$. Emphasize that fractions can be represented by points on a number line.

💬 **Do fractions have a place on the number line?** *yes* **How do you know?** *They are real numbers.* **How might we represent them on a number line?** *more than 0 and less than 1*

Activity! (Student Book, page 96)

In this activity, your student will solidify his/her understanding of locating thirds on a number line and extend it to fourths. He/She will use fraction tiles or Fraction Strips (TR32) to find the fractions on the number line.

💬 **How many $\frac{1}{3}$ strips are in 1 whole?** *3* **Use a Fraction Strip (TR32) to draw a number line showing $\frac{1}{3}, \frac{2}{3}$, and I.**

Invite your student to do the following on the backdrop of a whiteboard: Your student may benefit from drawing the model on a whiteboard in addition to building it as presented in the **Activity**. You may wish to ask the following questions:

💬 **What number does the number line begin with?** *0* **What other number should you put on it to start?** *1* **Which fraction is closest to 0?** $\frac{1}{3}$ **Why?** *Our strips are $\frac{1}{3}$-sized pieces, so $\frac{1}{3}$ comes after 0.* **Which fraction is less than $\frac{2}{3}$?** $\frac{1}{3}$ **Which fraction is further from 0 than $\frac{2}{3}$?** $\frac{3}{3}$ **What fraction is greater than $\frac{2}{3}$?** $\frac{3}{3}$

Activity! Answers
(Student Book, page 96)

(a)
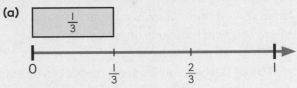

(b)
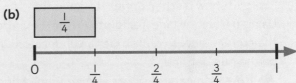

Learn Together (Student Book, pages 96 to 98)

In this section, your student will apply the concepts just learned to locate a variety of fractions on number lines. You may wish to provide your student with Fraction Strips (TR32) to use as a guide to create matching number lines on a whiteboard to help support the concrete-pictorial-abstract learning progression.

Through questioning, lead your student to understand how to represent fractions on a number line in **Learn Together**. As you go through the problems with your student, you may wish to ask the following questions:

🗨 How many equal parts are in the whole for this problem? How do you know that? What can you understand about the problem just by looking at the numbers they have given you? What are the equivalent fractions you can see or locate on this number line? What is true about where you put equivalent fractions on a number line? *Equivalent fractions are located in the same place.*

After your student has explored the concepts in the **Lesson Opener, Learn,** and **Learn Together**, you may wish to ask these questions to encourage further reflection:

🗨 What is easy about this lesson? What is difficult about this lesson? What do you know about fractions on a number line? What do you still wonder about fractions on a number line? How does your thinking compare to the book? Do you see anything in the book that helps you understand better?

You may wish to have your student summarize his/her learning in a math journal. Have your student draw a number line and explain everything he/she knows about locating fractions on a number line.

- **QUESTION 1** requires your student to fill in the missing fractions on a number line and show his/her understanding that $1 = \frac{5}{5}$.
- Using a Number Line Template (TR33) representing 1 whole divided into fifths, the picture builds your student's understanding of the equal parts/intervals on the number line.
  - 🗨 How many equal parts is the number line divided into? *5* What fraction of the whole is each part? $\frac{1}{5}$ What does 1 jump on the number line represent? $\frac{1}{5}$ What do 2 jumps represent? $\frac{2}{5}$ How do we know what the missing fractions are on the number line? *Each jump is $\frac{1}{5}$, so the fractions are $\frac{1}{5}, \frac{2}{5}, \frac{3}{5}, \frac{4}{5}, \frac{5}{5} = 1$.*
- **QUESTION 2** requires your student to label fractions on a number line and compare unit fractions.
- Have your student do the second part of the problem first, comparing the unit fractions. Using that information, your student can begin placing the fractions on the Number Line Template (TR33).
- For $\frac{2}{3}$ and $\frac{3}{4}$, this is your student's first encounter with comparisons between fractions of different numerators and denominators. Moreover, the answer is difficult to see with so many different fractions on the same number line.

Learn Together Answers
(Student Book, pages 96 to 98)

1.

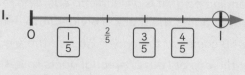

$1 = \boxed{\dfrac{5}{5}}$

2.

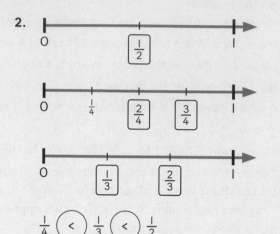

$\frac{1}{4}$ (<) $\frac{1}{3}$ (<) $\frac{1}{2}$

3.

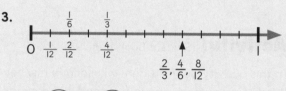

$\frac{2}{3}$ (=) $\frac{4}{6}$ (=) $\frac{8}{12}$

4. (a)

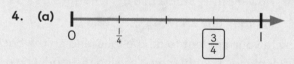

(b)

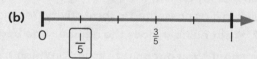

(c)

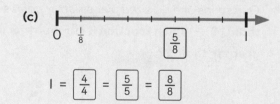

$1 = \boxed{\dfrac{4}{4}} = \boxed{\dfrac{5}{5}} = \boxed{\dfrac{8}{8}}$

5. (a)

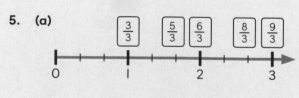

(b)

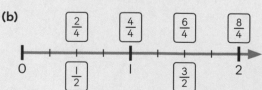

- Help your student begin to make sense of the problem by asking the following questions:
  - 💬 **How many equal parts of the whole are there for this ($\frac{2}{3}$; $\frac{3}{4}$) fraction?** *three; four.* **How might you make this problem easier for yourself? What are some things you can do to help yourself when a problem is confusing?** *Start with what you know and what you can do, change the visual, think about it logically, make the numbers easier, etc.* **What do you know?** *I know that thirds are three equal parts to a whole and fourths are four equal parts to a whole.* **What can you do with what you know?** *I can mark thirds and fourths on a number line.* **What equivalent fractions do you see on these number lines?** $\frac{1}{2}$ *and* $\frac{2}{4}$

- **QUESTION 3** requires your student to label fractions with different numerators and denominators on a number line and compare equivalent fractions.
- Follow the general line of questioning outlined for Question 2. Start by marking thirds, then sixths, then twelfths. For each, prompt your student to observe the relationship between the larger fraction and the next one, promoting visual understanding that sixths are half the size of thirds, and twelfths are half the size of sixths. You may want to use a different color for each denominator.
- For the second part of this question, your student will need to place the fractions correctly on the number line before being able to compare them.
  - 💬 **How can you locate equivalent fractions on a number line?** *Equivalent fractions go in the same spot on a number line.*
- **QUESTION 4** requires your student to fill in the missing numbers on a number line and to understand that 1 whole can be written as a fraction where the numerator and denominator are the same.
  - 💬 **How will you determine the missing fraction? What clues do you have to help you unravel the problem?** *I can look at the other fractions on the number line.* **How can you write the number I divided into 4 equal parts as a fraction?** $\frac{4}{4}$ **How would you complete the equation?**
- **QUESTION 5** requires your student to write missing numerators for fractions given on a number line.
  - 💬 **How can we write whole numbers as fractions?** $\frac{4}{4}$, $\frac{5}{5}$, *etc.* **What do you notice about the whole numbers when they are written as fractions? Do you see any patterns?** *The numerator and the denominator are the same.* **What can you tell me about the equivalent fractions on this number line?** *Answers vary.* **What kind of numbers can we put on a number line?** *Answers vary.*

After all the fractions are marked for **Learn Together** Question 3, the result might be visually confusing to your student. Your student will see the relationships better from three separate number lines. Using a different color for each denominator can also help. You may wish to ask the following questions if your student has trouble finding a starting point in **Learn Together** Question 3:

🗨 **Can you separate the number line into two different number lines to help you see where these fractions should go?** *yes* **Are there any mathematical tools we have that can help you?** *fraction tiles or fraction strips; drawing bar models*

Allow your student to build each of the fraction bars with fraction tiles or strips for halves, thirds, and fourths or draw corresponding bar models. Then have your student compare and mark his/her Number Line Template (TR33), and transfer that to the book.

Lesson Debrief

- Conclude the lesson and facilitate your student's reflection by asking him/her to answer the **Focus Question** and share his/her thinking.
- Extend the discussion by posing the following questions.
  - 🗨 **What are some things that are the same about locating fraction and whole number on a number line?** *Both progress from 0 up.* **How can we show equivalent fractions on a number line?** *They are located in the same spot if they are equivalent.*

- Allow time for your student to reflect on what he/she has learned and ask questions about what he/she may be unsure of.
- Encourage him/her to share anything that was confusing or difficult, and how thinking about it differently and perseverance helped the process of learning.
- Ask your student to answer a reflection question or draw a picture to show his/her reflection. You may offer these prompts:
  - 🗨 **How would you explain fractions on a number line to a friend? What is the most difficult problem you encountered today? Draw a picture of it in your math journal, and show me everything you know about it next to the picture.**

What to look for:
- ability to locate missing fractions on the number line
- ability to begin number lines at 0
- ability to count intervals or jumps on a number line
- show understanding of where fractions should fall when constructing a number line
- ability to explain why equivalent fractions fall in the same place on a number line

You may wish to ask following questions to probe understanding once your student notices in **Learn Together** Question 5 that some of the given fractions are equivalent:

🗨 **What do you notice about the relationship between these fractions? Is there a relationship? Is there a pattern? Is there a way to just know if a fraction is equivalent?** *Answers vary.*

You may wish to ask the following questions if your student begins to note the mathematical pattern:

🗨 **Is this enough evidence to make a rule? I wonder if all equivalent fractions have such a relationship, or only some? What do you think?**

Do not force your student to come to a conclusion that leads to the standard algorithm. Your student will learn how to generate equivalent fractions in Grade 4. For now, just present the idea and see how far your student takes it.

Practice On Your Own (Student Book, pages 99 and 100)

- **QUESTION 1** assesses your student's ability to fill in the missing fractions on a number line and recognize that 1 whole can be written as $\frac{10}{10}$.
- **QUESTION 2** assesses your student's ability to correctly label two fractions with the same numerator on number lines and then compare them.
- **QUESTIONS 3** and **4** assess your student's ability to label fractions with different denominators on the same number line. In Question 3, your student compares two fractions with different numerators and denominators using the number line. In Question 4, your student writes pairs of equivalent fractions by observing the fractions on the number line.

  🗨 **In Question 3, what is different about this problem? What have you done before that might help you solve it? What do you know about thirds and sixths that might help you? In Question 4, what do you notice about this problem? How will you know where to label the fractions on the number line? Why?** *The problem itself gives us a clue.* **What strategy might you use to help you fill in the missing fractions?** *We could imagine it as two number lines, the top with eighths and the bottom with fourths, since that is how they are marked.*

- **QUESTION 5** assesses your student's ability to identify and label fractions greater than 1 on a number line. Your student is required to understand that each interval on a number line increases by $\frac{1}{b}$, where b refers to the number of equal parts in 1 whole.

  🗨 **What do you know about fractions greater than 1 that can help you solve this problem?**

Think!

- **QUESTION 6** assesses your student's ability to reason which pair of fractions would not be marked at the same point on a number line and explain his/her reasoning. You may wish to ask the following questions:

  🗨 **What do you know? What information is there for you to use? What do you need to find out? What does the question ask you to find? What problem-solving plan can you use? Can you make the problem simpler? Can you draw or build something? Put your plan into action and check your work when you are done.**

Practice On Your Own Answers
(Student Book, pages 99 and 100)

1.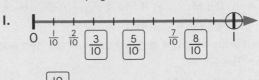

$$1 = \boxed{\frac{10}{10}}$$

2.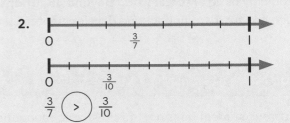

$$\frac{3}{7} \; \textcircled{>} \; \frac{3}{10}$$

3.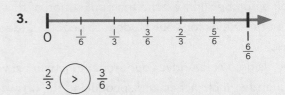

$$\frac{2}{3} \; \textcircled{>} \; \frac{3}{6}$$

4.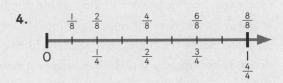

$$\boxed{\frac{1}{4}} = \boxed{\frac{2}{8}}$$

$$\boxed{\frac{2}{4}} = \boxed{\frac{4}{8}}$$

$$\boxed{\frac{3}{4}} = \boxed{\frac{6}{8}}$$

$$\boxed{\frac{4}{4}} = \boxed{\frac{8}{8}}$$

5. (a)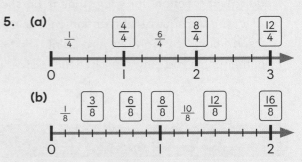

   (b)

Think! Answers

6. $\frac{2}{5}$ and $\frac{4}{10}$ $\frac{2}{4}$ and $\frac{1}{2}$ $\boxed{\frac{2}{4} \text{ and } \frac{4}{6}}$

   $\frac{2}{4}$ is equivalent to $\frac{1}{2}$ and $\frac{4}{6}$ is not.

More Resources

- Refer to **Do More at Home** below and **Reteach 3, Exercise 7F** if your student needs additional support.
- When your student is ready, have him/her work on **Additional Practice 3B, Exercise 7F**.
- To provide your student with a challenge, have him/her work on **Extension 3, Exercise 7F**.
- You may assign **Mastery and Beyond 3B, Chapter 7, Practices 7 and 8** to provide further support and development to sustain learning.

Do More at Home

If your student does not have a strong foundation in locating fractions on a number line, extend the application of this concept by creating opportunities for your student to practice. Ideas for bridging the gap include:

- Using a ruler, have your student measure a variety of items in $\frac{1}{2}$-, $\frac{1}{3}$-, $\frac{1}{4}$-, and $\frac{1}{8}$-inch increments, producing the answer as a fraction. This will also provide practice for writing whole numbers as fractions.
- Make life-sized number lines for thirds, fourths, fifths, sixths, or eighths (use whichever fractions your student finds difficult). Have your student draw a Fraction Card (TR30) (preselect them for difficulty), then jump to the correct fraction.

Line Up!

Invite your student to play the game of Line Up! You and your student each choose a Fraction Card (TR30) from the stack and each of you draw a number line for that fraction. Choose for each other either "whole number" or "equivalent fraction." For example, if you choose "whole number" for your student, he/she must take your number line and locate any whole number on it using the same denominator. If you choose "equivalent fraction" for your student, he/she must take your number line and locate the equivalent fraction on it using a different denominator. The person who gets it right earns a point. The first person to 5 points wins. Tip: the faster you play, the more fun it is!

For Additional Support

If your student has trouble with this concept, have him/her build then draw bar models for the problems that are difficult in this lesson. Finally, invite him/her to draw the number lines for himself/herself. Use Fraction Cards (TR30) for locating specific fractions, as there is most likely enough of writing from the process of drawing the models and the lines. You may wish to ask the following questions:

- 💬 **How do you know that this line represents the correct intervals for these fractions? How can you check your work?** *use manipulatives to prove it* **How do you locate more than one type of fraction on the same line? What makes the number lines difficult to interpret? How can you simplify the problem for yourself so you can do it?**

Digging Deeper

Here is a problem you may wish to use to extend your student's understanding of fractions and their relationships to whole numbers and other benchmarks (such as $\frac{1}{2}$) on a number line.

After finishing the question and getting it correct, your student may observe a pattern of diagonal stripes in the answer. Using the chart below, have your student follow these instructions:

- Color the fractions less than $\frac{1}{2}$, yellow.
- Color the fractions greater than $\frac{1}{2}$, blue.
- Put a check mark on the fractions that are equal to 1.
- Place an X on the fractions that are greater than 1.
- Circle the fractions that are equal to $\frac{1}{2}$. For extra challenge, explain how you know that they are the same as $\frac{1}{2}$.
- Finally, place fractions marked with an X or a check mark on a number line, along with one circled fraction.

$\frac{3}{10}$	$\frac{6}{7}$	$\frac{4}{12}$
$\frac{5}{10}$	$\frac{1}{4}$	$\frac{4}{4}$
$\frac{2}{5}$	$\frac{6}{12}$	$\frac{1}{9}$
$\frac{11}{10}$	$\frac{2}{8}$	$\frac{4}{8}$

Answers for **Digging Deeper**:

From left to right by rows: fractions less than $\frac{1}{2}$: $\frac{3}{10}$; $\frac{4}{12}$; $\frac{1}{4}$; $\frac{2}{5}$; $\frac{1}{9}$; $\frac{2}{8}$. Fractions greater than $\frac{1}{2}$: $\frac{6}{7}$; $\frac{4}{4}$; $\frac{11}{10}$. Fractions equal to 1: $\frac{4}{4}$. Fractions greater than 1: $\frac{11}{10}$. Fractions equivalent to $\frac{1}{2}$: $\frac{5}{10}$; $\frac{6}{12}$; $\frac{4}{8}$.

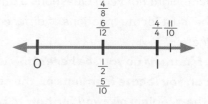

7G Fractions of a Set

Learning Objective(s)
- Identify fractions of a set.

Material(s)
- 1 paper plate
- 15 colored cubes (6 red, 3 yellow, 3 green, and 3 blue)
- 1 set of counters
- 1 pack of construction paper
- 1 set of connecting cubes

FRACTIONS OF A SET (Student Book, pages 101 to 106)

Lesson Opener

Task (Student Book, page 101)

Show your student the **Lesson Opener** and cover the rest of the page. Discuss the question with your student. Do not show your student how to do the task and allow him/her to explore and discover how to find the fraction of buttons that are red.

Refer your student to **Learn** and **Learn Together** in the Student Book for reflection after your student has explored the concepts. Use questions to build understanding and direct instruction to refine understanding.

Lesson Development
Learn (Student Book, page 101)

Use counters or connecting cubes to replicate the picture in the **Lesson Opener** and give your student time to think about it. You may wish to ask these questions:

💬 **What is the same or different about all of the items in the picture?** *They are all buttons, but they are in different colors.* **How many buttons are there altogether?** *5* **How many are red?** *2* **What fraction could we write to show that 2 out of 5 buttons are red?** $\frac{2}{5}$ **How is 2 out of 5 buttons like (draw a rectangle on the board with 2 out of 5 equal parts colored)?** *Answers vary.*

Extend the discussion using the following questions.

💬 **What if I added one more blue button? Would the fraction of red buttons change?** *Yes, there would be 2 out of 6 buttons that are red, so the fraction would be* $\frac{2}{6}$. **What if I exchanged one of the differently colored buttons for another red one so that now there are three red buttons? What fraction of the buttons would be red then?** $\frac{3}{6}$, *because now there are 3 red buttons out of 6 total buttons.*

Draw or build the set of buttons from the **Lesson Opener** again but this time with the two red buttons first as in the first picture of **Learn**. Remind your student that the group of buttons makes up a set. Use connecting cubes to represent the buttons.

Focus Question

💬 **How can you find fractions of a set?** Invite your student to ponder this question as you go through the lesson. Revisit this question when you reach the end of the lesson to check his/her understanding.

Teaching Tip

In this lesson, your student will learn to find fractions of a set. Move seamlessly from the **Lesson Opener**, through the **Learn** and into the **Activity** as one task, using colored cubes or counters or even squares of construction paper if needed, so your student can see how fractions of a set are directly related to equivalent fractions. It is important to build understanding that $\frac{2}{5}$ and $\frac{6}{15}$ represent the same relationship.

Allow your student ample processing time throughout this lesson to ensure understanding, since it will form the conceptual foundation needed for fluently manipulating equivalent fractions, multiplying fractions, and understanding ratios in later grades. You may wish to ask the following questions:

💬 **What is the relationship between this set and that set? What is another way to express this fraction? How do you know that? How can you determine the fraction of a set for any set?**

Learn Answer
(Student Book, page 101)

$\frac{2}{5}$

🗨 How many buttons are there in the set? *5* How many are red? *2* How do we write 2 out of 5 as a fraction? $\frac{2}{5}$

Write on the whiteboard: 2 out of 5 buttons are red; $\frac{2}{5}$ of the buttons are red.

🗨 What if we added another set just like the first one? What is the fraction that are red now? $\frac{4}{10}$

Use the following ideas to highlight with your student that we can divide sets of objects into equal groups or subsets.

🗨 What if we divided these two sets into 5 equal groups by color? How many would you put in each group so that each group had the same color? *2*

Draw a circle around each of the 5 groups of 2.

🗨 How many equal groups of buttons are there? *5* How many groups are red? *2 out of 5 groups are red* What fraction of the groups of buttons are red? $\frac{2}{5}$ When we name the fraction of a set, what does the denominator tell us? *the total number of equal groups in the set* What does the numerator tell us? *The number of groups we are considering. In this set, $\frac{2}{5}$ means we have 2 red groups out of 5 total groups.*

Activity! (Student Book, page 102)

In this activity, your student will extend his/her understanding of finding fraction of a set to finding a set of objects divided into equal subsets. Provide a mixed set of 6 red cubes, 3 yellow, 3 green, and 3 blue cubes to your student. Invite your student to arrange the cubes and determine what fraction of the cubes are red.

🗨 How many cubes are there? *15* How many are red? *6* What fraction of the total number of cubes are red? $\frac{6}{15}$ What if we divided these into 5 equal groups by color? How many cubes would you put in each group so that each group has the same color? *3* How do you know that? *Answers vary.* Look at your groups and tell me what fraction of groups of cubes are red? *2 out of 5 groups are red, so $\frac{2}{5}$.* And how many groups of the total groups of cubes are red? $\frac{2}{5}$ When the red cubes are 2 out of 5 total cubes, what is the fraction? $\frac{2}{5}$ When the red cubes are 4 out of 10 total cubes, what is the fraction? $\frac{4}{10}$ And how many groups of the total groups of cubes are red? $\frac{2}{5}$ When the red cubes are 6 out of 15 total cubes, what is the fraction? $\frac{6}{15}$ And how many groups of the total groups of cubes are red? $\frac{2}{5}$ What can you say about the relationship among the fractions $\frac{2}{5}$, $\frac{4}{10}$, and $\frac{6}{15}$? *They are all equivalent.* How could you prove it? *We could build or draw a bar model, or look at the numerical relationships between the fractions.*

😊 Invite your student to consider the relationships between $\frac{2}{5}$ and $\frac{6}{15}$ in a deeper way. You may wish to ask the following questions:

🗨 How do you know that $\frac{6}{15}$ and $\frac{2}{5}$ are equivalent? *They represent the same number or amount.* Did you add or take away any cubes when you named each fraction of a set? *no* What did change? *How they were grouped.*

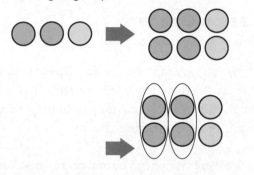
Activity! Answers

(Student Book, page 102)

(a) There are 15 cubes and 6 of the cubes are red; $\frac{6}{15}$

(b) There are 5 groups and 2 of the groups are red; $\frac{2}{5}$

(c) They are equivalent.

Draw two bar models on the whiteboard to represent fifteenths.

On one, shade in $\frac{6}{15}$ of the bar, in red if possible.

On the other, show the 15 cubes in 5 groups of 3 each, arranged by colors.

Label the model this way:

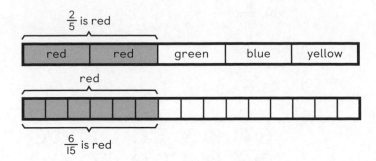

$\frac{2}{5}$ is red

| red | red | green | blue | yellow |

red

$\frac{6}{15}$ is red

💬 **What do you notice about the fractions $\frac{6}{15}$ and $\frac{2}{5}$?** *The fractions are equivalent.*

Digging Deeper

The **Learn** and **Activity** provide another opportunity for your student to think about the patterns that emerge when he/she plays with fractions. You may wish to ask the following questions:

💬 **How is finding the fraction of a set similar and different to finding a fraction of a whole? What patterns do you see in the numbers as you add sets? As the number of buttons increases, what remains true about the number of groups in the set?** *The number of groups remains the same.* **Why is that so?** *Answers vary.* **How might you prove your thinking? Look again at your groups and tell me what fraction of groups of buttons are red?** *2 out of 5 groups are red, so $\frac{2}{5}$.* **And what was the fraction of red buttons to the total number of buttons?** $\frac{4}{10}$ **So are you saying that the fraction of red buttons in the set is $\frac{4}{10}$, but the fraction of red groups to all the groups is $\frac{2}{5}$?** *Yes. Allow your student some processing time.* **Why are there two different fractions?** *One is by total number of items and the other is by groups of items.* **What, if anything, does this remind you of?** *equivalent fractions* **What is the relationship between the fraction for the total number of pieces and the fraction of a set?** *They are related by a multiple; the fraction of the whole has a denominator that is larger than the fraction of the set; fractions of a whole and fractions of a set made from the same whole are equivalent.*

Learn Together (Student Book, pages 103 and 104)

Provide your student with connecting cubes or counters on paper plates or squares of paper to represent each of the groups within a set. Have him/her replicate the fraction shown for each example using the counters or cubes, then fill in the blanks for each item. Bar modeling the problem should help cement understanding if it is slow to come.

Through questioning, lead your student to understand how to identify fractions of a set in **Learn Together**. As you go through the problems with your student, you may wish to ask the following questions:

🗨 **What are the groups in this set? How do you know how many are in a group? What fraction of the set is each group? How can you think about it to make it easier to determine how many are in each equal part?**

After your student has explored the concepts in the **Lesson Opener, Learn**, and **Learn Together** of the Student Book, you may wish to ask these questions to encourage further reflection:

🗨 **What is important to know about making fractions of a set? Does your thinking compare to the book? Do you see anything in the book that helps you better understand this concept?**

You may wish to have your student summarize his/her learning in a math journal. Have your student draw the problems and explain everything he/she knows about the fraction of a set.

- **QUESTION I** requires your student to determine the fraction of a set of figures that is colored.
  - 🗨 **How many hearts (objects) are there altogether?** 4 **How many are colored?** 2 **What fraction of the hearts (objects) are colored?** 2 out of 4 or $\frac{2}{4}$. **How many equal groups are the hearts divided into?** 2 **How many of the equal groups are colored?** I **What fraction of the set of hearts is colored?** $\frac{1}{2}$ **How many triangles (objects) are there altogether?** 12 **How many are colored?** 8 **What fraction of the triangles (objects) are colored?** 8 out of 12 or $\frac{8}{12}$. **How many equal groups are the triangles divided into?** 3 **How many of the equal groups are colored?** 2 **What fraction of the set of triangles is colored?** $\frac{2}{3}$

- **QUESTION 2** requires your student to apply the part-whole relationship to items in a set.
  - 🗨 **How many comic books are there?** 3 **How many storybooks are there?** 4 **How many comic books and storybooks are there in all?** 7 **What fraction could you write to represent the number of books that are storybooks? How do you know?** 4 out of 7 books are storybooks, so $\frac{4}{7}$.

- Draw a bar model representing the problem. Help your student see that in this problem, we are looking for the part-whole relationship. 3 comic books + 4 storybooks = 7 books in all

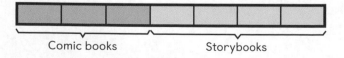

Comic books   Storybooks

Learn Together Answers
(Student Book, pages 103 and 104)

I. (a) $\frac{2}{4}$ or $\frac{1}{2}$

   (b) $\frac{8}{12}$ or $\frac{2}{3}$

2. 7; 4; 7; $\frac{4}{7}$

3. 2; 4; $\frac{2}{4}$ or $\frac{1}{2}$

4.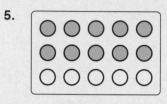

12; 12

5.

5; 10

6.

Caution

Your student may confuse finding the fraction of a whole and finding the fraction of items in a set. A whole is one item, for example, one circle, or one rectangle. A fraction of a whole refers to a whole that has been divided into equal parts (halves, thirds, fourths, etc.) A set is a group of items (for example, hearts, triangles, books). A group of items can be further divided into subgroups or subsets.

Questions I(a) and (b) are pictures of sets that are divided into subsets. In Question I(a), the fraction $\frac{2}{4}$ tells us that 2 items out of 4 total items are colored. The fraction $\frac{1}{2}$ tells us I out of 2 subsets are colored.

- **QUESTION 3** requires your student to identify a fraction of the total number of items in a set.
  - 💬 **How many stickers are there in all?** *8* **How many are squares?** *4 out of 8 are squares.* **What fraction of the stickers are squares?** $\frac{4}{8}$ **How many groups of stickers are there?** *4* **How many of the groups have squares?** *2* **What fraction of the set is squares?** $\frac{2}{4}$

- **QUESTION 4** requires your student to find the number of items in a fraction of a set.
  - 💬 **How many groups of circles are there?** *5* **How many circles are in a group?** *4* **How many groups of circles do you need to color to show** $\frac{3}{5}$ **of the circles?** *3* **If there are 4 circles in each group, how many circles are colored?** *12* **How do you know?** *3 groups of 4 is 12*

- **QUESTION 5** requires your student to find a fraction of a set by dividing the set into equal groups.
  - 💬 **How many circles are in the whole set?** *15* **How many groups are in the set?** *3* **How do you know?** *The denominator tells me that I need 3 equal groups because it is a 3.* **How many circles are in one group?** *5* **So what is** $\frac{1}{3}$ **of 15?** *5* **How many circles are there in** $\frac{2}{3}$ **of 15?** *10* **How do you know?** *2 groups of 5 is equal to 10.* **What is the robot saying? Do you agree or disagree with his thinking?**

- **QUESTION 6** requires your student to show that a fraction of a set is true by dividing the set into equal groups and color to show the number of items.
  - 💬 **How can you make it true? What do you know? What information is there for you to use? What can you tell about the number of groups you should have?**

Lesson Debrief

- Conclude the lesson and facilitate your student's reflection by asking him/her to answer the **Focus Question** and share his/her thinking.
- Extend the discussion by posing the following questions.
  - 💬 **What is a fraction of a set?** *A fraction of a group of objects or a fraction of groups of objects.* **How can you find the fraction of a set?** *Determine how many objects or groups there are and then find what fraction of those objects or groups is the part you are looking for.* **Which is easier to find, the fraction of a set or the set that represents a certain fraction?**

- Allow time for your student to reflect on what he/she has learned and ask questions about what he/she may be unsure of.
- Encourage him/her to share anything that was confusing or difficult, and how thinking about it differently and perseverance helped the process of learning.
- Ask your student to answer a reflection question or draw a picture to show his/her reflection. You may offer these prompts:

  🗨 **How would you explain fractions of a set to a friend? What is important to know? What is your favorite problem from today? Draw a set in your math journal and show me everything you know about finding a fraction of a set or the set represented by a fraction next to the picture.**

What to look for:
- ability to determine the fraction of the whole, the fraction of the set, and see that the fractions are equivalent
- ability to represent fractions of a set by making equal groups
- ability to determine a set based on a fraction

Practice On Your Own (Student Book, pages 105 and 106)

- **QUESTION 1** assesses your student's ability to find the fraction of objects in a set, where the objects are arranged randomly, by applying his/her understanding of the part-whole relationship.
- **QUESTION 2** assesses your student's ability to recognize that a set can be divided into equal groups, color a fraction of the set, then find the total number of items colored.
- **QUESTION 3** assesses your student's ability to write the fraction of a set in two ways, as individual items out of a total number of items, and as groups of items out of a total number of groups.
- **QUESTION 4** assesses your student's ability to write the fraction of a set by identifying the group with the stated characteristics.

Think!

- **QUESTION 5** assesses your student's ability to reason and justify which of the examples given represent $\frac{1}{6}$ of a set.

  🗨 **What do you know? What information is there for you to use? What do you need to find out? What does the question ask you to find? What problem-solving plan can you use? Can you make the problem simpler? Can you draw or build something? Put your plan into action and check your work when you are done. Which of these represents $\frac{1}{6}$ of a set? Why or why not?**

Practice On Your Own Answers

(Student Book, pages 105 and 106)

1. $\frac{3}{7}$

2. (a)
2; 2

   (b)
3; 3

3. $\frac{1}{4} = \frac{4}{16}$

4. (a) 3
   (b) 4
   (c) 2

Think! Answers

5. (a) and (b). In (a), 1 out of 6 circles is colored. In (b), 1 out of 6 groups of triangles are colored. In (c), the groups are not equal, and 3 out of 19 shapes are colored. 3 out of 19 is not equivalent to 1 out of 6.

Caution

In Question 4, your student may count the total number of objects instead of noticing the groups.

🗨 **What clues does the problem give you to help you know how to think about it?**

More Resources

- Refer to **Do More at Home** below and **Reteach 3, Exercise 7G** if your student needs additional support.
- When your student is ready, have him/her work on **Additional Practice 3B, Exercise 7G**.
- To provide your student with a challenge, have him/her work on **Extension 3, Exercise 7G**.
- You may also assign **Mastery and Beyond 3B, Chapter 7, Practices 9** and **10** to provide further support and development to sustain learning.

Do More at Home

If your student does not have a strong foundation in finding the fraction of a set, extend the concept by doing some of the following activities as you go about your day. Ideas for bridging the gap include:

- Practice breaking sets into equal groups. For example, allow your student to play with his/her food, arranging crackers, fruit snacks, or trail mix, etc., into equal groups to find the fraction of the set.
- Look for anything you can subdivide into equal groups to find the fraction of a set. Many toys have small parts that can be subdivided. Invite your student to share with you or a sibling and tell you what fraction of the set each person gets.
- Do a "Model of the Day". Draw a bar model and have your student shade a certain fraction of units, then subdivide it differently to produce a different fraction of a set.

If your student has trouble finding fractions of a set or determining the differences between a fraction of a set and a fraction of a total, the remedy is to provide both a hands-on and pictorial, logical progression. Have your student:

1. build the total,
2. determine the fraction of the total,
3. take the set and subdivide the total into reasonable groups
4. circle the groups,
5. find the fraction of the set,
6. produce both fractions,
7. model if needed, according to the example provided for the Activity

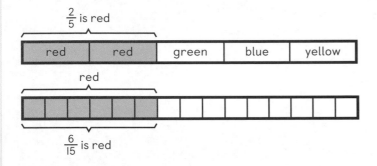

You may wish to ask the following questions:

💬 **How are the fractions related?** *They are equivalent fractions.* **How do you know these are equivalent fractions?** *The two fractions occupy the same space.* **What is a good strategy for helping you make groups from a set?** *Look for equal numbers to make equal groups; use what you know about multiplication and division.* **Why do we find the groups in the set?** *It shows us how to break the number down.*

If your student demonstrates understanding and has little trouble with this concept, refer back to the problem in the **Activity**. You may wish to rewrite it, or another equivalent fraction from this lesson, on the whiteboard. For example, $\frac{6}{15} = \frac{2}{5}$.

You may wish to ask following questions:

💬 **What do you notice about the relationship between these fractions? Is there a relationship? Is there a pattern? How do you know? Is there a way to prove that for sure?**

Allow your student to prove his/her thinking. You may wish to ask the following questions if your student begins to see how to generate equivalent fractions mathematically with the standard algorithm (in this above case, divide the numerator and denominator by 1 in the form of $\frac{3}{3}$):

💬 **Is this enough evidence to make a rule? I wonder if all equivalent fractions have such a relationship, or only some? What do you think?**

Do not force your student to come to this conclusion. Your student will learn how to generate equivalent fractions in Grade 4. For now, just present the idea and see how far your student takes it.

Chapter Wrap Up

Before your student works on **Performance Task**, help him/her recap the key learning objectives and develop a concept map to reflect the concepts and skills of the chapter. Use the following key terms to start constructing the concept map:

- Fractions
- Part/Whole
- Equivalent fractions
- Comparing

Encourage your student to complete the **Chapter Self-Reflection** on page 122 as a form of self-reflection.

Performance Task (Student Book, pages 107 to 110)

Refer your student to the **Performance Task** to consolidate and deepen his/her understanding of the chapter through tasks that require him/her to show, explain, and/or apply thinking. You may use the rubric on page 119 to encourage your student to set his/her own goals.

QUESTION 1 requires your student to draw models to show how he/she divided a whole into equal parts and reason how he/she arrived at his/her answers.
💬 **How can you carry out the task? What should you find first? What strategies can you apply? How do you know that your answers are correct?**

QUESTION 2 requires your student to draw models to show and reason about the sizes of two fractions to compare them.
💬 **How can you carry out the task? What should you find first? What strategies can you apply?**

QUESTION 3 requires your student to draw models to show and reason about the sizes of the three fractions to compare them.
💬 **What methods can you use to explain your answer? Does your reasoning make sense in this situation? What helps you justify your reasoning? When comparing fractions, what are two ways you can compare? When does it make sense to use each method?**

> ### Teaching Tip
>
> For Question 3, look for your student to be able to justify his/her response with the techniques of comparing numerators or comparing denominators. A sample response may sound like this: When we have the same number of colored pieces, such as $\frac{2}{6}$ and $\frac{2}{3}$, we can compare denominators to see which pieces are larger. When we have the same size fraction, such as $\frac{5}{12}$ and $\frac{6}{12}$, we can compare number of colored pieces to see which is greater.

QUESTION 4 requires your student to divide a whole into equal parts and find the fraction left after removing some parts from the whole. Your student is also required to compare two fractions and reason who has more chocolate.
💬 **How can you carry out the task? What should you find first? What strategies can you apply? How do you know that your answers are correct?**

Performance Task Answers
(Student Book, pages 107 to 110)

1. (a)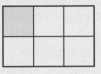
   $\frac{1}{6}$

   (b)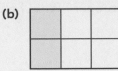
   $\frac{2}{6}$ or $\frac{1}{3}$;
   $\frac{1}{6} + \frac{1}{6} = \frac{2}{6}$

2. (a)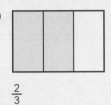
   $\frac{2}{3}$

   (b) David.
   Explanations vary. Example:
   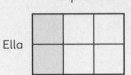
   Ella   David
   $\frac{2}{3}$ is greater than $\frac{2}{6}$

3. David.
   Explanations vary. Example:
   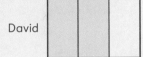
   Ella
   David
   Jack
   $\frac{2}{3}$ is the greatest fraction.

4. (a) Accept any of the following answers:
   $\frac{6}{12}$, $\frac{3}{6}$, $\frac{2}{4}$, or $\frac{1}{2}$

   (b) Kerry, because $\frac{6}{12}$ is greater than $\frac{5}{12}$.

5.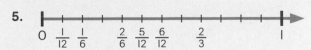
   0   $\frac{1}{12}$ $\frac{1}{6}$ $\frac{2}{6}$ $\frac{5}{12}$ $\frac{6}{12}$ $\frac{2}{3}$ 1

6. (a) 2; 12
   (b) 6; 6

QUESTION 5 requires your student to write fractions of different denominators on the same number line.

💬 **How can you carry out the task? What should you find first? What strategies can you apply?**

QUESTION 6 requires your student to use the number line in Question 5 to locate equivalent fractions.

💬 **What methods can you use to explain your answer? Does your reasoning make sense in this situation? What helps you justify your reasoning?**

Rubric (Student Book, page 110)

Use the scoring guide to help you give feedback on your student's work. Use the comments section to provide information about what was done well and what could be improved. Write words of encouragement to let your student know what he/she has done well.

Scoring Rubric

	Description	Point(s)
1(a)	Your student: • gives the correct answer. ($\frac{1}{6}$)	0.5
(b)	Your student: • gives the correct answer. ($\frac{2}{6}$ or $\frac{1}{3}$) • correctly explains that Ella took an extra piece, resulting in the fraction of chocolate she received to be $\frac{2}{6}$ or $\frac{1}{3}$. ($\frac{1}{6} + \frac{1}{6} = \frac{2}{6}$)	0.5 0.5
2(a)	Your student: • gives the correct answer. ($\frac{2}{3}$)	0.5
(b)	Your student: • gives the correct answer. (David) • correctly draws a model to show $\frac{2}{3}$ and $\frac{2}{6}$. • correctly explains that since both fractions have the same numerator, the lesser denominator is the greater fraction.	0.5 0.5 0.5
3	Your student: • gives the correct answer. (David) • draws a model to show and explain the answer.	0.5 1
4(a)	Your student: • gives the correct answer. ($\frac{6}{12}$) Extra credit can be given if your student gave $\frac{1}{2}$.	0.5
(b)	Your student: • gives the correct answer and correctly explains thinking. (Kerry)	0.5
5	Your student: • correctly labels the fractions on a number line. ($\frac{2}{6}, \frac{5}{12}, \frac{6}{12}, \frac{2}{3}$) Extra credit can be given if your student gave $\frac{1}{2}$ instead of $\frac{6}{12}$.	1
6(a)	Your student: • correctly uses the number line in Question 5 to identify equivalent fractions to $\frac{1}{3}$, ($\frac{2}{6}, \frac{4}{12}$).	0.5
(b)	Your student: • correctly uses the number line in Question 5 to identify equivalent fractions to $\frac{1}{2}$, ($\frac{3}{6}, \frac{6}{12}$).	0.5
	Total	**8**

Use this table as a guide to help you relate your student's scores to his/her performance levels.

Level	Score
	7–8
	2.5–6.5
	0–2

 **STEAM** **Project Work** (Student Book, Chapter 6, page 52)

- Your student is given an opportunity to make connections between engineering and mathematics as he/she designs a playroom.
- At the end of **Chapter 7**, your student should be able to complete **Parts 2** to **4**.
- **Part 2** requires your student to reconsider his/her drawing from Part 1 to see if it meets the two given conditions. Encourage your student to explain how he/she can check that $\frac{1}{2}$ of the area of his/her playroom is taken up by the reading corner and the study desk. Have your student show how he/she ensures his/her play area is $\frac{1}{4}$ the area of the playroom.
- **Part 3** requires your student to add other features to his/her plan.
- **Part 4** requires your student to create a presentation about his/her design and the total floor area of his/her design elements.

Chapter Practice (Student Book, pages 111 to 114)

- Have your student work on **Chapter Practice** in the Student Book independently to help him/her consolidate and extend understanding of the chapter.
- You may find a summary of the chapter learning objectives and the difficulty level of the questions.
- Teaching prompts are provided for Levels 2 and 3 questions.
- When your student is ready, have him/her work on **Additional Practice 3B, Chapter Practice**.

Chapter Practice Answers
(Student Book, pages 111 to 114)

1. Option B

2. Answers vary. Example:

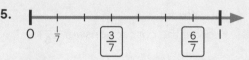

3. $\frac{4}{9}$; $\frac{5}{9}$

4. (a) $\frac{5}{7}$

   (b) $\frac{11}{12}$

5.

6. (a) <

   (b) <

   (c) >

   (d) >

7. $\frac{1}{9}$; $\frac{1}{6}$; $\frac{1}{5}$

8. $\frac{3}{7}$; $\frac{1}{7}$; $\frac{1}{12}$

Question	Level	Chapter 7 Learning Objectives	Section(s)	Day(s)
1	1	Read, write, and identify unit fractions as part of a whole.	7A	2
2, 3, 4	1	Read, write, and identify fractions within 1 whole as part of a whole.	7B	3
5	1	Show fractions as numbers on a number line.	7F	8
6	1	Compare like and unit fractions. Compare fractions with the same numerator.	7D	5
7, 8	1	Compare and order unit fractions.	7D	6
9	1	Read, write, and identify fractions within 1 whole as part of a whole. Identify and find equivalent fractions.	7B, 7E	3, 7
10	2	Identify and find equivalent fractions. Show fractions as numbers on a number line.	7E, 7F	7, 8
11	2	Compare and order fractions. Show fractions as numbers on a number line.	7D, 7F	6, 8
12, 13, 14	1	Identify fractions of a set.	7G	9
15	2	Identify and find equivalent fractions.	7E	7
16	3	Read, write, and identify fractions within 1 whole as part of a whole.	7B	3

QUESTION 10 requires your student to locate fractions on a number line and reason which fractions are equivalent to $\frac{3}{4}$.

💬 What do you know about writing equivalent fractions on a number line that can help you? What do you notice about the denominators of the numbers you are given? Does the answer make sense? Why or why not?

QUESTION 11 requires your student to locate fractions with different denominators on a number line and order them.

💬 What is this question asking you to do? How do you know? What do you know that can help you solve it? How can you carry out the task? What should you find first? What strategies can you apply?

QUESTION 15 requires your student to study the circles given and identify and reason which two circles show equivalent fractions.

💬 What do you know about comparing fractions that can help you here? What do you observe about these wholes? What methods can you use to explain your answer? Does your reasoning make sense in this situation? How do you know that your explanation is correct?

QUESTION 16 requires your student to identify the fraction of the rectangle that is colored.

💬 What similar problems have you done that can help you here? What strategies will you use to help you get started? How can the picture itself help you? Is there a different way to look at it? How will you check your work?

Days 14–17 of 17

Chapter Test

- Assign **Chapter Test 7** in **Assessment Guide Teacher Edition** to assess your student's understanding of the chapter.
- Assign **Cumulative Assessment 3** in **Assessment Guide Teacher Edition** to allow your student to consolidate his/her learning and assess his/her understanding of Chapters 6 and 7.

9. Answers vary. Example:

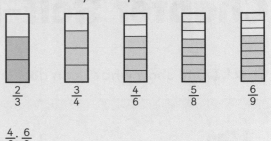

$\frac{2}{3}$ $\frac{3}{4}$ $\frac{4}{6}$ $\frac{5}{8}$ $\frac{6}{9}$

$\frac{4}{6}, \frac{6}{9}$

10. (a)

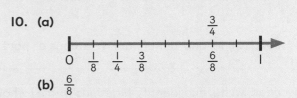

(b) $\frac{6}{8}$

11.

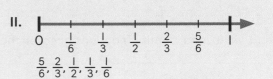

$\frac{5}{6}, \frac{2}{3}, \frac{1}{2}, \frac{1}{3}, \frac{1}{6}$

12. $\frac{3}{4}$

13. $\frac{5}{15}$ or $\frac{1}{3}$

14. 18; 6;
$\frac{6}{18}, \frac{2}{6}$ or $\frac{1}{3}$

15. A and C. They are same-sized wholes, $\frac{2}{5} = \frac{4}{10}$. B is not the same because the whole is smaller. D is not the same because there are only 9 parts.

16. $\frac{15}{24}$

Chapter Self-Reflection

Check (✓) to show what I can do.

I Can	Yes	Not Sure	No
read, write, and identify unit fractions as part of a whole.			
read, write, and identify fractions within 1 whole as part of a whole.			
read, write, and identify fractions greater than 1.			
compare like and unit fractions.			
compare fractions with the same numerators.			
compare and order like and unit fractions.			
compare and order fractions with the same numerators.			
identify equivalent fractions.			
find equivalent fractions.			
show fractions as numbers on a number line.			
identify fractions of a set.			

MY JOURNAL

I can show...

I still wonder...

Chapter 8

MASS AND LIQUID VOLUME

Chapter Overview

In this chapter, your student's knowledge of measuring length with metric and standard measures from Grade 2 will be extended to understanding the measurement of mass and volume using kilograms, grams, and liters. Your student will:

• learn to read different types of scales.

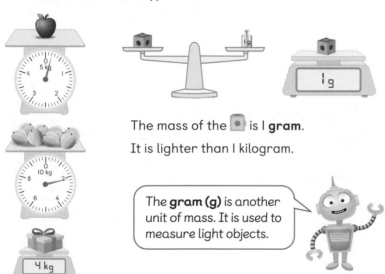

The mass of the is **1 gram**.
It is lighter than 1 kilogram.

> The **gram (g)** is another unit of mass. It is used to measure light objects.

• use different types of scales with different faces to measure the mass of items in kilograms and grams.

(a)

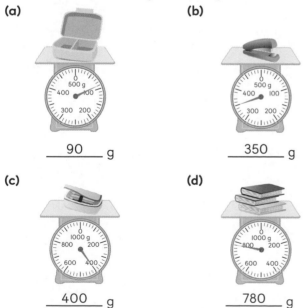

_____90_____ g

(b)

_____350_____ g

(c)

_____400_____ g

(d)

_____780_____ g

Order the objects from heaviest to lightest.

Object X   Object Y   Object Z

297g   432g   425g

• measure and estimate volume and capacity using liters.

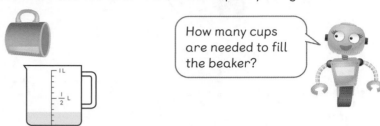

> How many cups are needed to fill the beaker?

The cup holds _____less_____ than 1 liter of water.

• solve one-step word problems involving mass and volume.

A box of 100 paperclips weighs 164 grams.
The empty box weighs 64 grams.

(a) What is the mass of 100 paperclips?
$164 - 64 = 100$
The mass of 100 paperclips is _____100_____ grams.

(b) Estimate the mass of 1 paperclip.
The mass of 1 paperclip is about _____1_____ gram.

Key Ideas

• We can read, measure, estimate, and compare masses in kilograms using a weighing scale and a digital scale.

What is the mass of the pineapple in kilograms?

The mass of the pineapple is _____2_____ kilograms.

• We can read, measure, estimate, and compare masses in grams using a weighing scale and a digital scale.

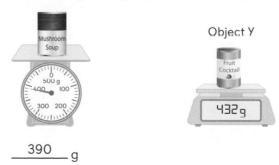

Object Y

_____390_____ g   432g

- We can measure and estimate volume of liquid to the benchmark of I liter.

  Circle the container that holds more than I liter of liquid.

- We can solve one-step word problems involving mass and volume.

  There are 9 liters of water and oil in a container.
  How many liters of oil are there?

  9 - 4 = 5

  There are ____5____ liters of oil.

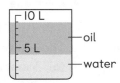

Materials You Will Need

- I I-cm cube
- 4 paper bags
- 2 paper cups
- 2 pencils
- 2 pieces of string
- I pot with a capacity of 7 measuring cups
- 2 recycled jars
- I set of index cards
- I set of paper strips
- I syringe plunger (optional)
- I wire coat hanger
- I I-liter measuring cup
- I balance scale with metric weights
- I set of I-cm connecting cubes (three colors)
- I weighing scale (500 g, 1,000 g, 5 kg, 10 kg)
- Number Cards from 0 to I0 (TR03)
- Blank Scale Faces (TR34)

Chapter at a Glance

	Day	Learning Objective(s)	Vocabulary	Resource(s)	Material(s)
Chapter Opener / Recall Student Book, pp. 115–118	1 of 12				• 1 set of index cards
Section 8A *Measure Mass in Kilograms* Student Book, pp. 119–124	2 of 12	• Measure and estimate the mass of objects to the nearest kilogram.	• mass • kilogram (kg)	• **Additional Practice 3B,** Exercise 8A • **Reteach 3,** Exercise 8A • **Extension 3,** Exercise 8A • **Mastery and Beyond 3B,** Chapter 8, Practice 1	• 2 paper cups • 2 pieces of string • 1 wire coat hanger • 1 balance scale with metric weights • 1 weighing scale (5 kg and 10 kg)
Section 8B *Measure Mass in Grams* Student Book, pp. 125–130	3 of 12	• Measure and estimate the mass of objects to the nearest gram.	• gram (g)	• **Additional Practice 3B,** Exercise 8B • **Reteach 3,** Exercise 8B • **Extension 3,** Exercise 8B • **Mastery and Beyond 3B,** Chapter 8, Practice 2	• 2 pencils • 1 balance scale • 1 set of 1-cm connecting cubes • 1 weighing scale (500 g and 1,000 g) • 2 copies of Number Cards from 0 to 10 (TR03) • 2 copies of Blank Scale Faces (TR34)
Section 8C *Measure Volume in Liters* Student Book, pp. 131–134	4 of 12	• Measure and estimate liquid volumes to the nearest liter. • Compare capacities to the benchmark of 1 liter.	• capacity • liter (L)	• **Additional Practice 3B,** Exercise 8C • **Reteach 3,** Exercise 8C • **Extension 3,** Exercise 8C • **Mastery and Beyond 3B,** Chapter 8, Practice 3	• 1 syringe plunger (optional) • 1 1-cm cube • 1 1-liter measuring cup
Section 8D *Word Problems* Student Book, pp. 135–138	5 of 12	• Solve word problems involving mass. • Solve word problems involving liquid volume.		• **Additional Practice 3B,** Exercise 8D • **Reteach 3,** Exercise 8D • **Extension 3,** Exercise 8D • **Mastery and Beyond 3B,** Chapter 8, Practice 4	• 4 paper bags • 1 set of paper strips • 1 set of connecting cubes

	Day	Learning Objective(s)	Vocabulary	Resource(s)	Material(s)
Chapter Wrap Up / Performance Task Student Book, pp. 139–141	6 of 12				
STEAM Project Work Student Book, p. 142	7 of 12				
Chapter Practice Student Book, pp. 143–146	8–9 of 12			• **Additional Practice 3B,** Chapter Practice	• 1 set of connecting cubes (two colors)
Chapter Test	10–11 of 12			• **Assessment Guide Teacher Edition,** Chapter Test 8	
Solve! Heuristics Student Book, pp. 147–148	12 of 12				• 2 recycled jars • 1 pot with capacity of 7 measuring cups • 1 measuring cup • 1 set of connecting cubes (three colors)

Chapter Opener (Student Book, page 115)

Consider the picture and the questions on the page. Discuss them with your student. Prompt him/her to consider the information given in the picture and what is being asked. You may wish to ask the following questions:

🗨 **What do you notice about the picture? What are the children doing? How do you know? What is everything you know from the picture?** *The children are going to bake a cake. They have 2 kg of flour, 450 g of butter, and 1 liter of milk.* **How do you find that information?** *It is on the packages.* **Why do you think they have to follow the recipe?** *so that they have the right amounts of everything They would not want to use so much butter that the cake is all greasy, for instance.* **What do you think g and kg mean?** *Your student may not know these abbreviations stand for gram and kilogram.*

For Additional Support

To connect this to real life, you may wish to cook a simple recipe with your student using metric measures. This will help your student gain a sense of metric measures in everyday terms. See **Teaching Tip** for more about this.

Digging Deeper

🗨 **How do you measure mass?** *I weigh it.* **Why do you think some cooks prefer to weigh ingredients like flour instead of using a measuring cup?** *A measuring cup will have more or less depending how tightly it is packed. Mass is the same no matter what.*

Recall (Student Book, pages 116 to 118)

Material(s)
- 1 set of index cards

Before moving on to the problems on pages 116 to 118 of the Student Book, first practice comparing masses and quantities of items in a real-world way.

Toss your student two objects, such as a feather and a soft toy.
🗨 **Which is heavier?**
Show your student a jug of water and a juice box.
🗨 **Which contains less?**

Teaching Tip

If your student is new to Singapore Math in Grade 3, this chapter provides a wonderful opportunity to explore numbers in a way that is nonthreatening and enjoyable.

Start things right by finding a recipe on the internet that features metric measures. Bake or cook together with your student using the metric measures and explore what they mean before you get started with a discussion of the opening picture. In this way, your student will have experienced it concretely before you begin.

As you work through the chapter, keep real metric measures handy and take care to use them whenever your student needs a boost of real-world understanding. Most digital kitchen scales allow you to switch between metric and customary measures, and many measuring cups feature both. Also consider asking your student to compare standard measures with which he/she is familiar to metric measures. A kilogram is 2.2 pounds, so half a kilogram is 1.1 pounds. When a recipe calls for 500 g of meat, for example, a pound is a reasonable substitution.

🗨 **About how much is a liter? Can you picture it in your mind's eye? What does a kilogram feel like? How much is a pound in kilograms? How can you make it easier to switch between measures in practical situations?** *Find something you can relate the measure to and think about that as a benchmark. For example, a pound is a little less than a half a kilogram.*

Recall Answers

(Student Book, pages 116 to 118)

1. (a) heavier
   (b) lighter

2. (a) toy car; teddy bear
   (b) teddy bear; toy car

As you work, make sure your student encounters the vocabulary more/less and lighter/heavier and can compare objects. After your student shows some proficiency, play a game to see if he/she can make the same accurate comparisons using pictures instead of actual objects.

Make it a Game!

Invite your student to look through old magazines to cut out pictures of things that match, such as two animals or two pieces of furniture. You and your student are participants of this game.

Paste each picture on a separate blank index card. Turn all the index cards upside down on a table and mix them up. Players take turns trying to make a match. For each pair, one should be a picture of something that is heavier than the other. When a player finds a match, he/she must state which of the pair is heavier or lighter than the other. If correct, the player gets to keep the match. The player with the most matches wins the game!

After this review, your student should be able to complete the tasks on pages 116 to 118 of the Student Book independently.

- **QUESTION 1** assesses your student's ability to compare the masses of two animals using "lighter" or "heavier".
- **QUESTION 2** assesses your student's ability to compare the masses of two objects using a balance.
- **QUESTION 3** assesses your student's understanding that mass is not related to size.
- **QUESTION 4** assesses your student's ability to reason about glasses that are of the same size with the same amount of water.
- **QUESTION 5** assesses your student's ability to reason about jugs that are of the same size but have different amounts of juice.
- **QUESTION 6** assesses your student's ability to reason about bottles that are of different sizes with different amounts of water.

3. (a)

(b)

(c)

4. Option C

5. Option A

6. F; E

8A Measure Mass in Kilograms

Learning Objective(s)
- Measure and estimate the mass of objects to the nearest kilogram.

Vocabulary
- mass
- kilogram (kg)

Material(s)
- 2 paper cups
- 2 pieces of string
- 1 wire coat hanger
- 1 balance scale with metric weights
- 1 weighing scale (5 kg and 10 kg)

MEASURE MASS IN KILOGRAMS (Student Book, pages 119 to 124)

Lesson Opener

Task (Student Book, page 119)

Show your student the **Lesson Opener** and cover the rest of the page. Discuss the question with your student. Do not show your student how to do the task and allow him/her to explore the concept of measuring and estimating the mass of objects to the nearest kilogram.

Refer your student to **Learn** and **Learn Together** in the Student Book for reflection after your student has explored the concepts. Use questions to build understanding and direct instruction to refine understanding.

Lesson Development
Learn (Student Book, page 119)

Provide your student with a 1-liter bottle. Fill it with water. Do not use other liquids.

🗨 **How much does it weigh?** *1 kg*

Encourage your student to weigh the liter of water on a scale.

🗨 **What do you notice?** *1 liter of water weighs 1 kilogram.*

Uncover the **Learn** on page 119 in the Student Book and read it with your student to discuss it together. You may wish to ask these questions:

🗨 **What is the mascot telling us?** *Kilogram is abbreviated kg.* **What is a kilogram?** *It is a unit used to measure mass.* **What is mass?** *It is the amount of matter in an object.* **Tell me about these scales. What differences do you observe?** *The balance scale shows the mass of an object is equal to a specific unit of measure, such as a kilogram weight, by balancing. A scale has a face that we can read to measure the mass of an object.* **How will we read the mass of the water on the scale?** *If we look at the markings on the face of the scale, we can see that the scale measures 4 kg and 1 liter is a quarter of that, or 1 kg.*

Focus Question

🗨 How can you use a balance and a scale to measure and estimate the mass of objects in kilograms?

Invite your student to ponder this question as you go through the lesson. Revisit this question when you reach the end of the lesson to check his/her understanding.

Teaching Tip

Your student will find working with metric measurements easier than customary measures because metric measures are grounded in base ten. Take advantage of this "brain break" to work on mental math as it relates to base ten. Numerical flexibility within 10 leads to confident arithmetic at any place value. Ask your student the following types of questions to deepen his/her thinking about place value while enjoying the seemingly unrelated topic of measurement.

🗨 Is there a way to predict what the answer will be? What if you use the first digit in each number to predict what the answer is? What is a related multiplication fact that you could use to know whether or not your answer is reasonable? Is your answer reasonable? What are some ways to prove if it is close?

Digging Deeper

Deepen your student's interaction with this material by making it real. Offer 4 to 5 real objects to compare to the weight of a liter of water, and see if your student can order them by mass using the kilogram as the benchmark. Then have your student measure all the objects on a scale to determine if he/she was correct. After exploring the idea concretely, your student will more readily grasp the content of this lesson.

Learn Together (Student Book, pages 120 and 121)

In this section, your student will measure objects that have a mass more or less than a kilogram using a balance scale and measure the mass of objects using different weighing scales. Invite your student to observe each picture before proceeding with the problems in **Learn Together**.

Through questioning, lead your student to compare the mass of different objects and measure them in kilograms in **Learn Together**. As you go through the problems with your student, you may wish to ask the following questions:

💬 **How is a balance scale different from a weighing scale? What is the capacity of this scale? How do you know? How is the capacity of this scale different than that scale?**

After your student has explored the concepts in the **Lesson Opener**, **Learn**, and **Learn Together**, you may wish to ask these questions to encourage further reflection:

💬 **What do you notice about your estimates and your measurements? Were you accurate? What unit of mass have you used today? How do different scales show mass?**

You may wish to have your student summarize his/her learning in a math journal. Invite your student to write his/her own question along with an explanation of how to measure the mass of objects using kilograms and different types of scales.

- **QUESTION 1** requires your student to interpret the mass of an object using a balance and describe the mass of the lighter object.
- **QUESTION 2** requires your student to interpret the mass of an object using a balance and describe the mass of the heavier object.
  - 💬 **Is the tennis ball lighter or heavier than the papaya?** *lighter* **How do you know?** *I can feel that it is, and when I put it on the balance scale, it goes up.* **Is its mass more or less than a kilogram?** *less; it is lighter.* **Is the mass of the papaya more or less than a kilogram?** *more; it is heavier.* **How do you know?** *I can feel that it is, and when I put it on the balance scale, it goes down.* **How does the balance scale behave for lighter or heavier objects?** *The balance scale goes up for lighter objects and down for heavier objects.* **Why does the scale do that?** *The heavier the object, the more it will push down on the scale.*

Activity! (Student Book, page 120)

Invite your student to estimate the mass of three objects in relationship to a kilogram, then measure their masses to see how accurate his/her estimate was. Your student can measure any three items in your home.

- 💬 **What might you think about when deciding if the object is more than a kilogram, less than a kilogram, or about a kilogram?** *I can think about the mass of the 1-liter water bottle I measured earlier.*

- **QUESTION 3** requires your student to read the mass of an object using two different weighing scales.
  - 💬 **What do we call these scales?** *weighing scales, one is digital.* **What does it mean that there is a zero at the same place it says 5 kg?** *The scales start at zero and end at the highest measurable mass.*
- **QUESTION 4** requires your student to read the analog scales and determine whether the mass of each object is more or less than the stated mass.
  - 💬 **Do all scales measure up to the same mass?** *no* **How many kilograms do the scales measure?** *Some on the page measure up to 5 kg and some up to 10 kg.* **How do you know?** *We can tell by looking at the highest number*

Learn Together Answers
(Student Book, pages 120 and 121)

1. less

2. more

3. 2

4. (a) More
   (b) Less

For Additional Support

Make sure your student actually measures mass using balance scales and weighing scales. If you have trouble finding these for use in your home school, arrange a field trip to the grocery store. There, you will find a variety of scales to use in the produce department, the deli, and the meat department. Workers are usually very happy to demonstrate and even let your student measure mass using them.

Teaching Tip

Please note that the scale faces in Questions 3 and 4 on page 121, and later in the **Practice On Your Own** pages 122 and 123 of the Student Book, alternate between 5 kg and 10 kg.

Part of learning to read a scale face is observing the highest mass the scale can measure.

💬 **What must you look for on the scale to be able to read it correctly?** *I must look for the highest mass the scale can measure by reading the number under the zero.*

Activity! Answers
(Student Book, page 120)

Answers vary.

on the face of the scale. **What numbers do you see marked? What does it mean when there is a thick line that does not have a number?** *For 5 kg scales, all kilograms are marked and the unnumbered thick lines stand for half a kilogram. For 10 kg scales, the even numbered kilograms are marked and the unmarked thick lines are the odd numbered kilograms.*

👀 This Math Talk supposes that your student will be able to imagine adding the pineapple from Question 3 to the scale in Question 4a. If this is not the case, provide your student with a weighing scale and recreate a similar scenario to force the scale to measure to its full capacity and then move past zero. If you do not have a weighing scale that measures kilograms, using one in pounds will work just as well. Follow this teaching sequence with your scale, then move back to the Student Book and proceed with the lesson.

Your student must understand that when a mass more than the capacity of the scale is placed on it, the scale will register past zero until the scale can no longer handle the mass of the object and comes to rest. The best way to show this is with a weighing scale that has a smaller capacity for measuring mass. Have your student add mass to the scale until the needle moves past zero.

You may wish to provide an actual object with a mass slightly more than the capacity of the scale, as well as an object much lighter, both of which should register a mass at about the same spot on the scale face. Have your student compare to see which object is heavier, and consider why the needle on a weighing scale moves past zero when measuring the mass of an object more than its capacity.

🗨 **Is the mass of this object heavy or light?** *heavy* **Why does the needle show just over zero?** *It actually shows the full capacity of the scale plus the amount of mass over zero.* **How can that help you measure mass? What must you observe when using a weighing scale?** *the capacity of the scale* **How do you determine the capacity of an analog weighing scale?** *Look at the number under the zero.*

Lesson Debrief

- Conclude the lesson and facilitate your student's reflection by asking him/her to answer the **Focus Question** and share his/her thinking.
- Extend the discussion by posing the following questions.
  🗨 **How do you use different scales to measure the mass of objects? What is important to observe before measuring mass on a weighing scale?** *The highest weight of the scale.* **How can you estimate mass of objects?** *Use something you know, like the mass of a 1-liter bottle of water that is 1 kg.*

- Allow time for your student to reflect on what he/she has learned and ask questions about what he/she may be unsure of.
- Encourage him/her to share anything that was confusing or difficult, and how thinking about it differently and perseverance helped the process of learning.
- Ask your student to answer a reflection question or draw a picture to show his/her reflection. You may offer these prompts:

  🧠 **What have you learned about measuring mass? What would you tell someone who does not know how to use a balance scale? What is important to know? What would you tell someone who does not know how to use a weighing scale? What is important to know?**

What to look for:

- an explanation that shows your student understands how to measure mass and how scales show mass
- the ability to read each scale correctly and answer the problems

Practice On Your Own (Student Book, pages 122 to 124)

- **QUESTION 1** assesses your student's ability to read the mass of each object on a weighing scale and match it to the appropriate description.
- **QUESTION 2** assesses your student's ability to read the mass of each object on an analog weighing scale.
- **QUESTION 3** assesses your student's ability to determine whether the mass of each object is more or less than the stated mass.

Question 3 is tricky because your student will use the terms more and less in relation to a certain number of kilograms, but not in relation to each other. The lighter object is more than 5 kg, while the heavier object is less than 7 kg.

Practice On Your Own Answers

(Student Book, pages 122 to 124)

1.

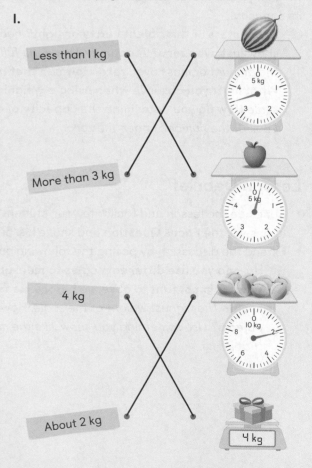

2. **(a)** 3
   (b) 5

3. **(a)** More
   (b) Less

- Invite your student to think about what the pointer on a scale indicates.
  - 💬 **Where will the pointer be if there are only potatoes on the scale? Draw a mark outside the scale to show that. After you add 4 kilograms of carrots to the scale, where will the pointer point?** *move past 0* **How do you know?** *Because 6 + 4 makes 10. Since the potatoes weigh slightly more than 6 kg, the pointer will move past 0.* **Draw it now.**

Think!

- **QUESTION 4** assesses your student's ability to reason through the way a balance changes when objects are removed and deduce the mass of an object indirectly.
  - 💬 **What do you know? What do you need to find? What clues can you find in the picture? What strategies can you use to solve this problem?** *Act it out would be an excellent strategy for this problem!* **What can you tell about the mass of the flour on both sides of Balance A?** *It is the same.* **What does that tell you about the mass of the melon?** *The melon is 3 kg.*

More Resources

- Refer to **Do More at Home** below and **Reteach 3, Exercise 8A** if your student needs additional support.
- When your student is ready, have him/her work on **Additional Practice 3B, Exercise 8A**.
- To provide your student with a challenge, have him/her work on **Extension 3, Exercise 8A**.
- You may also assign **Mastery and Beyond 3B, Chapter 8, Practice 1** to provide further support and development to sustain learning.

Do More at Home

Have your student build a simple balance scale using common household items including 1 wire coat hanger, 2 paper cups, and 2 pieces of string. Invite your student to tie one string to each cup by putting it through each of two holes in exactly the same manner on the rim of each cup. Then hang each paper cup from the notches at the shoulders of the coat hanger, one on each side. Suspend the hanger from a doorknob or a spot where it can freely move. Lastly, use your balance scale to compare the masses of different items. Heavier items will sink lower, while lighter items will be higher.

Think! Answers

4. (a) It remains balanced. The same mass is removed from each side of the balance.
   (b) After removing the packs of flour from each side of Balance A, I know that the melon has a mass of 3 kg. From Balance B, I could then tell that the mass of the pack of flour is 3 + 1 = 4 kg.
   4

Teaching Tip

You may wish to use the three-step problem-solving method found in Lesson 8D to help your student solve Question 4 after a period of productive struggle. Experience thinking through two-step problems like this one will help your student solve the last two problems of the **Chapter Practice**.

8B Measure Mass in Grams

Learning Objective(s)
* Measure and estimate the mass of objects to the nearest gram.

Vocabulary
* gram (g)

Material(s)
* 2 pencils
* 1 set of 1-cm connecting cubes
* 1 weighing scale (500 g and 1,000 g)
* 2 copies of Number Cards from 0 to 10 (TR03)
* 2 copies of Blank Scale Faces (TR34)
* 1 balance scale

MEASURE MASS IN GRAMS (Student Book, pages 125 to 130)

Lesson Opener

Task (Student Book, page 125)

Show your student the **Lesson Opener** and cover the rest of the page. Discuss the question with your student. Do not show your student how to do the task and allow him/her to explore the concept of measuring the mass of objects in grams.

Refer your student to **Learn** and **Learn Together** in the Student Book for reflection after your student has explored the concepts. Use questions to build understanding and direct instruction to refine understanding.

Lesson Development
Learn (Student Book, page 125)

After a period of productive struggle, uncover the **Learn** in the Student Book and read it with your student to discuss it together. You may wish to ask these questions:

💬 **How heavy do you think a connecting cube is?** *Answers vary.* **How would you know this for sure?** *We could weigh it on a scale.* **What types of scales can you describe for me?** *Balance scales; weighing scales, either analog or digital.* **How do you read each one?** *Answers vary; Your student should have an opportunity to use a variety of different scales and measure weights with masses on a balance scale if possible.* **How can a connecting cube be used as a mass?** *If we know it has a mass of 1 gram, we can use it to weigh other items on a balance scale.* **How do we determine mass from a balance scale?** *We put a known quantity on one side, such as a 1-gram weight, and see if it balances with an object on the other side.* **How do we determine mass from a digital weighing scale?** *We place the object on the scale and read the measure.* **How do we determine mass from an analog weighing scale?** *We read the mass from the face of the weighing scale by taking note of the markings.* **How will you use different types of scales to determine the mass of a connecting cube?** *We can measure its mass on any scale as long as we have the right tools such as accurate weights, and as long as we know how to read the scales.* **What is the mascot telling us?** *Gram is abbreviated as g. We use it to measure lighter objects.* **What is a gram?** *It is a unit used to measure mass.* **What is the difference between a kilogram and a gram?** *A kilogram is 1,000 g, so it is much heavier than a gram.*

Activity! (Student Book, page 126)

Invite your student to begin to internalize what a gram is. Your student will measure various small, common objects by using 1-g connecting cubes as weights. You may wish to use the balance scale your student made for **Do More at Home** in Lesson 8A if you do not have a real balance scale.

🗨 **About how many 1-g connecting cubes do you think you will need in order to measure the mass of this pencil/these quarters?** *Answers vary.*

Allow your student to estimate and then measure to check his/her thinking and find out how accurate he/she was.

Learn Together (Student Book, pages 127 to 128)

In this section, your student will gain a lot more practice reading a scale face. Invite your student to look closely at each picture and tell you everything he/she knows about it before beginning to solve the problem.

Through questioning, lead your student to measure objects that have mass in grams and compare the mass of different objects in **Learn Together**.
As you go through the problems with your student, you may wish to ask the following questions:

🗨 **What is the capacity of this scale? How many grams does each line mark? How do you know? What is different about this scale compared to the other scale?**

After your student has explored the concepts in the **Lesson Opener**, **Learn**, and **Learn Together**, you may wish to ask these questions to encourage further reflection:

🗨 **What can you say about measuring in grams? What do you find easy? What do you find difficult? How can you read the mass of an object when the needle does not fall on a numbered line? What do you need to look at on each different scale to correctly measure mass in grams?**

You may wish to have your student summarize his/her learning in a math journal. Invite your student to write his/her own question along with an explanation of how you can measure the mass of objects using grams.

• **QUESTION 1** requires your student to interpret the markings on each scale and tell the mass in grams.

🗨 **How much can scales a and c measure?** *500 g* **How do you know? Which lines are marked?** *0, 100, 200, 300, 400, and 500 grams* **What is the value of each line?** *10 g* **Why do you say that?** *There are 10 lines in each 100 g. 100 divided by 10 is 10.* **How much can scales b and d measure?** *1,000 g* **How do you know? Which lines are marked?** *0, 200, 400, 600, 800, and 1,000 grams* **What is the value of each line?** *20 g* **Why do you say that?** *There are 5 lines in each 100 g. 100 divided by 5 is 20.* **What is the value of each thick line that falls between the numbers?** *They are all in counts of 100 g.* **Why do you say that?** *There are 5 lines in each 100 g. 100 divided by 5 is 20.* **What is important to know about these scales?** *Scales a and c measure 500 g and scales b and d measure 1,000 g.* **Where do the pointers point? How do you know?** *Quite near to the whole number; they both point to the line just before or after the whole number.* **How will you determine the weight of the object?** *I can figure out the value of each line and count back from the nearest whole number, or I can measure from the last whole number and skip count up, etc.*

Activity! Answers

(a) 11; 11

(b) Answers vary. 10; 10

Learn Together Answers

(Student Book, pages 127 and 128)

1. **(a)** 80
   (b) 260
   (c) 390
   (d) 640

2. Box C; Box A; Box B

3. orange; banana; apple

4.
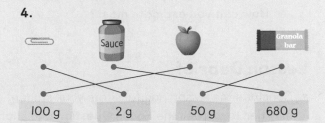

Teaching Tip

The beauty of mathematics is that it is flexible; we get to be the number boss if we play within the rules, and we can use base ten to help us figure out answers quickly and accurately. Have your student attempt to use both methods for determining the mass of grams: Go to the nearest 100 and count on/add or count back/subtract as appropriate.

🗨 **Which is most efficient? When would you use one method or the other?**

For Additional Support

Your student who struggles with this absolutely need to be supported with real-world experience using real scales. However, it is also effective to draw the concept, as that will help map ideas to long-term memory. Use Blank Scale Faces (TR34). Give your student a few different masses in grams and have him/her draw in the scale pointer on 500-gram and 1,000-gram scale faces.

👀 Invite your student to think about what each small marking stands for on this scale.

💬 **Are the small markings the same on every scale?** *no* **How can you tell what each stands for?** *Observe the capacity of the scale, then determine how many grams each line represents.* **How are the smaller markings different on a 1,000-gram scale than on a 500-gram scale?** *On a 500-gram scale, each mark stands for 10 grams. On a 1,000-gram scale, each mark stands for 20 grams.*

- **QUESTION 2** requires your student to read the masses on a digital scale and order the masses from lightest to heaviest.
- **QUESTION 3** requires your student to read the masses on an analog scale and order the masses from heaviest to lightest.
- **QUESTION 4** requires your student to estimate the mass of each object and match it to an appropriate mass.
  - 💬 **What is different about these scales in Question 2?** *They are digital scales and can measure to the 1 g. The other scales we used can measure to 10 g.* **How can you tell which is lightest/heaviest? Why do you think so? How can you estimate mass?**

Lesson Debrief

- Conclude the lesson and facilitate your student's reflection by asking him/her to answer the **Focus Question** and share his/her thinking.
- Extend the discussion by posing the following questions.
  - 💬 **How is measuring in grams different from measuring in kilograms?** *We need to be careful to check the value of each line, as well as the scale face.* **How do we determine the value of each line on a scale face?** *Look at how it is marked and divide the number of grams on the first marked number by the number of lines in that section.*

Reflect and Connect

- Allow time for your student to reflect on what he/she has learned and ask questions about what he/she may be unsure of.
- Encourage him/her to share anything that was confusing or difficult, and how thinking about it differently and perseverance helped the process of learning.
- Ask your student to answer a reflection question or draw a picture to show his/her reflection. You may offer these prompts:
  - 💬 **What have you learned about measuring mass in grams? What would you tell someone who does not know how to measure mass in grams? What is important to know?**

What to look for:
- an explanation that shows your student understands how to measure mass on different scales. Your student should observe that to make an accurate measurement, he/she must know the value of each line, which can be determined from the face of the scale. Additionally, he/she can use the benchmark numbers to count on/add or count back/subtract as appropriate
- ability to read each scale correctly and answer the problems

Practice On Your Own (Student Book, pages 129 and 130)

- **QUESTION 1** assesses your student's ability to read different gram scales and find the mass of each object.
- **QUESTION 2** assesses your student's ability to read the masses on a digital scale and order the masses from heaviest to lightest.
- **QUESTION 3** assesses your student's ability to read the masses on an analog scale and identify the object that meets the given requirements.

Caution

For Question 1b, your student might skip count by 100 g and read the unmarked line as 400 g. Have your student recognize that the unmarked line is exactly halfway between 300 g and 400 g.

More Resources

- Refer to **Do More at Home** below and **Reteach 3, Exercise 8B** if your student needs additional support.
- When your student is ready, have him/her work on **Additional Practice 3B, Exercise 8B**.
- To provide your student with a challenge, have him/her work on **Extension 3, Exercise 8B**.
- You may also assign **Mastery and Beyond 3B, Chapter 8, Practice 2** to provide further support and development to sustain learning.

Do More at Home

Use Blank Scale Faces (TR34), 2 stacks of Number Cards from 0 to 10 (TR03), and 2 pencils as pointers for each scale. Enjoy this activity with your student to practice making your own analog scale faces and recording mass on them.

Invite your student to turn over 2 cards to form the hundreds and tens of a 3-digit number. The ones will always be zero. If your student chooses an even tens digit, instruct him/her to draw a 1,000-g scale. If your student chooses an odd tens digit, instruct him/her to draw the 500-g scale. Encourage your student to place the pointer to show the 3-digit number. Prompt your student to check to see if he/she got it right. Celebrate well drawn scales with high fives.

Practice On Your Own Answers
(Student Book, pages 129 and 130)

1. (a) 90
    (b) 350
    (c) 400
    (d) 780

2. Object Y; Object Z; Object X

3. box of crayons
    I identify the two objects that are heavier than the playdough — the box of crayons and the pair of running shoes, by comparing their masses.

8C Measure Volume in Liters

Learning Objective(s)
- Measure and estimate liquid volumes to the nearest liter.
- Compare capacities to the benchmark of I liter.

Vocabulary
- capacity
- liter (L)

Material(s)
- I syringe plunger (optional)
- I 1-cm cube
- I 1-liter measuring cup

MEASURE VOLUME IN LITERS (Student Book, pages 131 to 134)

Lesson Opener

Task (Student Book, page 131)

Show your student the **Lesson Opener** and cover the rest of the page. Discuss the question with your student. Do not show your student how to do the task and allow him/her to explore the concept of measuring and estimating the capacity of a container or volume of a liquid in liters.

Refer your student to **Learn** and **Learn Together** in the Student Book for reflection after your student has explored the concepts. Use questions to build understanding and direct instruction to refine understanding.

Lesson Development
Learn (Student Book, page 131)

Uncover the **Learn** in the Student Book and read it with your student to discuss it together. You may wish to ask these questions:

💬 **What is the mascot telling us?** *The mascot is defining capacity: the amount of liquid a container can hold.* **Which bucket has the smaller capacity?** *the blue one* **Which bucket has the greater capacity?** *the red one* **Name something you know with a small capacity to hold liquid and something with a large capacity.** *a teacup and a fish tank; a water bottle and a swimming pool*

Focus Question

💬 **How can you measure liquid volume?** Invite your student to ponder this question as you go through the lesson. Revisit this question when you reach the end of the lesson to check his/her understanding.

Teaching Tip

Your student will apply the concepts learned while comparing, ordering, and measuring mass to problems involving measuring volume. As much as possible, try to introduce your student to real objects before having him/her work with pictures on the page. The best learning progression is always concrete (3-dimensional, real life) to pictorial to abstract.

Learn Answer

(Student Book, page 131)

Peter

Learn Together (Student Book, pages 132 and 133)

In this section, your student will begin to explore liquid measures, specifically liters. Invite your student to observe each picture before proceeding with the problems in **Learn Together**. Cover the mascot's speech bubble to give your student time to discover the concept on his/her own.

Through questioning, lead your student to use liters to measure and estimate capacities and volumes in **Learn Together**. As you go through the problems with your student, you may wish to ask the following questions:

🗨 **How do you measure water? Can you just pour it on a scale? When we cook or bake, what do we use to measure liquid?** *measuring cup* **How can you tell how much liquid there is?** *Pour it into the measuring cup and see how high the liquid goes.* **What are all the measurements about?** *liters* **What standard unit of measure is close to a liter?** *a quart*

After your student has explored the concepts in the **Lesson Opener**, **Learn**, and **Learn Together**, you may wish to ask these questions to encourage further reflection:

🗨 **What can you say about measuring in liters? What do you find easy? What do you find difficult? What is the difference between volume and capacity? What do you need to look at to correctly measure volume?**

You may wish to have your student summarize his/her learning in a math journal. Invite your student to think about measuring the volume of something smaller than a liter that he/she enjoys drinking, like a cup of tea. Put a picture of it along with an explanation of how you would measure its volume and indicate the capacity of the mug. Do not forget to show the abbreviation for liter.

- **QUESTION 1** requires your student to establish the volume of 1 liter of liquid.
  - 🗨 **What does the measuring line show you?** *It says 1 liter.* **What is the capacity of the measuring cup?** *The capacity of the cup is 1 liter.* **What do you think volume is?** *Volume is a unit of liquid measure.* **What is the difference between volume and capacity?** *We use volume as a unit of measure for liquid. Capacity tells us the amount of liquid a container can hold.*
- **QUESTION 2** requires your student to identify a container that would possibly hold more than 1 liter of liquid.
  - 🗨 **What can you do to help you find the container that holds more than 1 liter?** *Order the containers from least capacity to greatest capacity.* **What is the volume of liquid that will fit in this 1-liter bottle?** *1 liter* **Which of these containers fit a volume of liquid that is less than 1 liter?** *the soda can and the mug* **How do you know?**

Learn Together Answers

(Student Book, pages 132 and 133)

1. 1; 1

2.

3. less

4.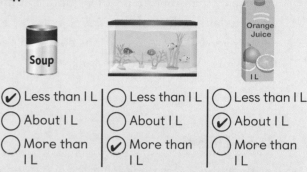

✓ Less than 1 L	○ Less than 1 L	○ Less than 1 L
○ About 1 L	○ About 1 L	✓ About 1 L
○ More than 1 L	✓ More than 1 L	○ More than 1 L

For Additional Support

Allow your student to act it out by pouring water from the 1-liter measure into each container.

If he/she has trouble figuring out which containers have a capacity more than, less than, or exactly one liter, extend the activity. Have an extra empty container and call attention to the fact that the entire liter did not fit into the new container.

🗨 **You know that you started with one liter of water. What can you say about the capacity of the container if the 1 liter of water cannot be all poured into the new container?** *Its capacity is less than one liter.* **What can you say if the 1 liter of water can be poured into the new container completely and with room to spare?** *The container has a capacity of more than one liter.* **Which has the greatest capacity? Which has the least capacity?**

- **QUESTION 3** requires your student to understand that there are containers with capacities that are less than 1 liter.
- **QUESTION 4** requires your student to estimate the capacities of different containers and determine whether the containers can hold less than, about, or more than 1 liter of water.
  - 💬 **What clues do the pictures give you regarding their capacities?** *The 1-liter carton of orange juice that can be used to estimate the capacities of the other two containers.* **Which has a greater or lesser capacity than 1 liter?**

Caution

Since the 1-liter bottle is taller than the fish tank, your student might mistakenly think it has a greater capacity than the fish tank. Encourage your student to think about real objects, try to picture them in his/her mind's eye, and draw conclusions based on personal experience with a 1-liter water bottle and a fish tank.

Lesson Debrief

- Conclude the lesson and facilitate your student's reflection by asking him/her to answer the **Focus Question** and share his/her thinking.
- Extend the discussion by posing the following questions.
  - 💬 **What do you know about a liter of water?** *It has a mass of 1 kg.* **How do we measure liquids?** *Answers vary.* **What do you think a liter has to do with measuring liquids?** *Answers vary.* **Why are capacity and volume important to know?** *If you know how much of a liquid you need, you can measure the volume and put it in a container of the proper capacity.*

Digging Deeper

Your student may find it interesting to investigate the relationships between and among the various metric measurements. He/she explored the mass of a liter in the previous lesson, but may not have internalized how the two units of measure are compatible. Please note that you must use water for this activity, as other liquids have different densities.

💬 **Are metric measures related to each other? How can we prove if they are or are not? Pour 1 liter of water in a measuring container and weigh it in grams and in kilograms. What do you notice?** *The mass of 1 liter of water is about 1,000 g or 1 kg.* **Why do you think that is so? Is it accidental?** *No!* **How are metric measures more helpful to a scientist than standard measures?** *They are consistent, related to each other mathematically, and interchangeable on some level.*

If your student has some real-world familiarity with milliliters, which are not covered in the scope of Grade 3, you may wish to extend this idea even further to strengthen the point. Measure the mass of 1 g of water. Put it in a 1-cm cube or syringe plunger marked with cubic centimeters.

Syringe plungers are sold inexpensively at most drugstores, and you can request larger plungers without needles.

💬 **What do you notice?** *1 cubic centimeter of water has a mass of about 1 g.* **What is a cubic centimeter?** *1 cm length × 1 cm width × 1 cm depth.* **Pour 100 g of water into a measure. What do you notice?** *It is 100 mL.* **How many milliliters is 1 g of water?** *about 1 mL* **How are metric measures related to each other?** *1 cubic cm = 1 g = 1 mL. Mass, volume, and length are directly related. Units of distance arranged 3 dimensionally can be converted into units of volume and mass. 1,000 cubic centimeters = 1 kg = 1,000 mL* **What is 1,000 cubic cm?** *10 × 10 × 10 = 1,000. It is 1,000 g/1 kg, or 1,000 mL/1 L.*

Practice On Your Own (Student Book, page 134)

- **QUESTION 1** assesses your student's ability to read the amount of liquid in a beaker.
- **QUESTION 2** assesses your student's ability to identify the containers with a capacity of more than or less than 1 liter.
- **QUESTION 3** assesses your student's ability to estimate and identify a possible capacity of the given containers.

Caution

Question 3 requires your student to recognize that two of the containers hold significantly more than a liter, something they have not yet encountered. You may wish to ask the following questions:

💬 **What choices do you have under each container? What choice makes the most sense? Why? Think about these containers in real life. Can you imagine a liter of water in them? What would that look like?**

Practice On Your Own Answers

(Student Book, page 134)

1. 1

2. (a) less
   (b) more
   (c) more

3. (a)

   $\frac{1}{2}$ liter
   (10 liters)

   (b)

   ($\frac{1}{4}$ liter)
   10 liters

   (c)

   1 liter
   (100 liters)

More Resources

- Refer to **Do More at Home** below and **Reteach 3, Exercise 8C** if your student needs additional support.
- When your student is ready, have him/her work on **Additional Practice 3B, Exercise 8C**.
- To provide your student with a challenge, have him/her work on **Extension 3, Exercise 8C**.
- You may also assign **Mastery and Beyond 3B, Chapter 8, Practice 3** to provide further support and development to sustain learning.

Do More at Home

In order to build a better sense of volume in liters, try this activity with your student.

Gather several empty containers with capacities of more or less than a liter, water, a measuring cup marked with a liter, and a shallow plastic bin to catch spills (or use the kitchen sink).

Invite your student to close his/her eyes while you choose a container to set in front of him/her. Then have your student to open his/her eyes, look at the container, guess if the capacity of the container is more than, less than, or about a liter. Next, fill the container with water over the sink or plastic bin. Encourage your student to carefully pour the water from the container into the measuring cup. Together, measure the water. Celebrate every good guess! Take turns until you both have a few chances and begin to make good guesses.

8D Word Problems

Learning Objective(s)
- Solve word problems involving mass.
- Solve word problems involving liquid volume.

Material(s)
- 4 paper bags
- 1 set of paper strips
- 1 set of connecting cubes

Focus Question

💬 **How do you solve word problems involving mass and liquid volume?**
Invite your student to ponder this question as you go through the lesson. Revisit this question when you reach the end of the lesson to check his/her understanding.

WORD PROBLEMS (Student Book, pages 135 to 138)

Lesson Opener

Task (Student Book, page 135)

Show your student the **Lesson Opener** and cover the rest of the page. Discuss the question with your student. Do not show your student how to do the task and allow him/her to explore the concept of solving word problems involving mass.

Refer your student to **Learn** and **Learn Together** in the Student Book for reflection after your student has explored the concepts. Use questions to build understanding and direct instruction to refine understanding.

Lesson Development

Learn (Student Book, pages 135 and 136)

Walk through the three-step problem-solving method to solve word problems.
1. Understand the problem.
2. Solve the problem.
3. Check the answer.

See the **Teaching Tip** box for questions your student can ask himself/herself at each of the three steps.

Encourage your student to think about what is happening in the word problem and what operation is needed to solve it by drawing a model. In addition to the questions in the **Teaching Tip**, you may wish to ask these questions:

💬 **What do you know about the problem?** *The mass of the basket + oranges is 970 g.* **What do you need to find out? Write a sentence with a blank where the answer will go.** *The empty basket has a mass of _____ g.* **What is a strategy you could use to solve it?** *I could take the oranges away from the basket and weigh it; I could model it.* **What is the mass of the oranges, according to the scale?** *800 g* **How will you check your work?** *I can add back to see if my subtraction was correct: 800 + 170 = 970. The mass of the empty basket is, indeed, 170 g.* **What is another way to check your work?** *I can estimate to see If my answer is close. 970 is around 950. 950 – 800 is 150. My answer is close to 150, so I am probably correct.* **What do you notice about your estimates? Were you accurate?** *yes*

Teaching Tip

Your student will use what he/she learned about measuring mass and volume to solve one- and two-step word problems with the four operations: addition, subtraction, multiplication, and division. Think about how to extend a few of the problems in this lesson, so your student can have some exposure to solving more difficult two-step problems. Each of the three problem-solving steps taught in this lesson can be used to help your student learn to break apart tough problems in order to solve them. Encourage your child to use these steps to unravel any problem, along with one or more of the suggested questions at each step.

Step 1: Understand the Problem

Ask yourself: **What do I know from the problem? What do I need to find? Is there any missing information? How can I find the missing information?**

Step 2: Solve it (using a plan!)

Ask yourself: **Can I estimate to predict an answer? How can I think logically about it to determine a reasonable possible answer? Have I solved any similar problems that will help me solve this one? How can I use simpler numbers to make solving it with more complicated numbers possible?**

What was your strategy? *make a model* What else did you need to know to solve this? *how to measure mass* What are the mascots thinking? *They say what I need to do to understand and solve it, and how to check my answer.* Is there anything you want to change in your thinking? *Answers vary.*

Learn Together (Student Book, pages 136 and 137)

In this section, your student will solve word problems using the remaining operations. Invite your student to observe each picture before proceeding with the problems in **Learn Together**. Encourage your student to use bar modeling as a problem-solving tool.

Through questioning, lead your student to solve word problems involving grams and kilograms in **Learn Together**. As you go through the problems with your student, you may wish to ask the following questions:

🗩 **What do you notice about this picture? What do you know? What is this asking you to find? Underline it. What kind of problem is this? What strategy would you like to use to solve it? Write your number sentence. What is the next step? What is your solution? Where will you write it? How will you check your work to know if you are correct? What methods could you use?**

After your student has explored the concepts in the **Lesson Opener**, **Learn**, and **Learn Together**, you may wish to ask these questions to encourage further reflection.

🗩 **What are the three steps we use when we solve problems? What are some ways to help understanding a problem? What are some ways you have to check your work?**

You may wish to have your student summarize his/her learning in a math journal by making up his/her own word problem and showing how to use the three problem-solving steps, along with a few good questions to ask himself/herself when problem-solving.

- **QUESTION 1** requires your student to find the total mass of two of the same object.
- **QUESTION 2** requires your student to multiply the mass of a given object to find the mass of 7 of the objects.
- **QUESTION 3** requires your student to divide the given mass into 3 equal groups.

Lesson Debrief

- Conclude the lesson and facilitate your student's reflection by asking him/her to answer the **Focus Question** and share his/her thinking.
- Extend the discussion by posing the following questions.
  🗩 **What are some types of problems you solved using measurements for mass and volume?** *We solved addition, subtraction, multiplication, and division problems.* **What question did you find most helpful to ask yourself when solving word problems?** *What do I know?; what do I need to find?; can I estimate to predict the answer?*

Step 3: Check my work
Ask yourself: **Can I solve it a different way that will prove if my answer is correct? How can I prove my thinking? Can I solve it backwards or use reverse operations?**

For Additional Support

Model drawings are excellent to help your student to see the math in their mind's eye. If your student is not quite comfortable with them yet, offer concrete help in the form of paper strips (for addition and subtraction problems) or connecting cubes (for multiplication and division problems), building and then drawing what he/she built, until your student masters the drawings themselves.

Learn Answers

(Student Book, pages 135 and 136)

800; 170; 170; 170

Learn Together Answers

(Student Book, pages 136 and 137)

1. 453 + 453; 906; 906

2. 2 × 7; 14; 14

3. 21 ÷ 3; 7; 7

- Allow time for your student to reflect on what he/she has learned and ask questions about what he/she may be unsure of.
- Encourage him/her to share anything that was confusing or difficult, and how thinking about it differently and perseverance helped the process of learning.
- Ask your student to answer a reflection question or draw a picture to show his/her reflection. You may offer these prompts:

🗨 **Tell me what you have learned about using what you know about measuring mass and volume to solve problems? What would you tell someone who does not know how to solve problems? What is important to know?**

What to look for:

- an explanation that shows your student understands how to use the operations to solve word problems involving mass and volume with the three-step model.

Practice On Your Own (Student Book, pages 137 and 138)

- **QUESTION 1** assesses your student's ability to read a scale on a measuring pitcher and find the volume of one liquid using subtraction.
- **QUESTION 2** assesses your student's ability to find the mass of two objects using addition.
- **QUESTION 3** assesses your student's ability to find the mass of one object using division.
- **QUESTION 4** assesses your student's ability to find the total volume using multiplication.
- **QUESTION 5** assesses your student's ability to reason through a problem and estimate the mass of one object given the mass of multiples of the same object.

Practice On Your Own Answers

(Student Book, pages 137 and 138)

1. $9 - 4 = 5; 5$

2. $94 + 138 = 232; 232$

3. $9 \div 3 = 3; 3$

4. $2 \times 12 = 24; 24$

5. **(a)** $164 - 64 = 100; 100$
    (b) 1

More Resources

- Refer to **Do More at Home** below and **Reteach 3, Exercise 8D** if your student needs additional support.
- When your student is ready, have him/her work on **Additional Practice 3B, Exercise 8D**.
- To provide your student with a challenge, have him/her work on **Extension 3, Exercise 8D**.
- You may also assign **Mastery and Beyond 3B, Chapter 8, Practice 4** to provide further support and development to sustain learning.

Do More at Home

Build a Problem

Prepare 4 paper bags: 1 paper bag containing slips of paper with the four operations: +, −, ×, and ÷; 1 paper bag containing slips of paper with a measurement in L, g, or kg; 1 paper bag containing slips of paper with a favorite object written on them; 1 paper bag containing slips of paper with friends' names.

Take turns drawing a slip of paper from each bag and making word problems from them, then checking each other's work.

Chapter Wrap Up

Before your student works on the **Performance Task**, help him/her recap the key learning objectives and develop a concept map to reflect the concepts and skills of the chapter. Use the following key terms to start constructing the concept map:

- Mass
- Kilograms
- Grams
- Capacity
- Volume
- Liters

Encourage your student to complete the **Chapter Self-Reflection** on page 151 as a form of self-reflection.

Digging Deeper

After your student completes Question 3, ask him/her to use that answer to solve this extended problem below, in order to practice solving more complicated problems:

Ms. Jones has 27 kg of pumpkins in all, each having the same mass as in Question 3. She wants to decorate each of the four columns on her front porch with more than one pumpkin. The maximum mass she can place around any single column is 12 kg. She wants the same number of pumpkins for each column.

💬 **Can she decorate all her columns with pumpkins?** *yes* **How many pumpkins will she place around each column?** *2* **Will she use all of the pumpkins she has?** *no* **What is the total mass of the pumpkins she will use on each column?** *6 kg* **What is the total mass of all the pumpkins she will use for decorating all of her columns?** *24 kg* **How many leftover pumpkins will Ms. Jones have?** *one* **What do you think Ms. Jones should do with the leftover pumpkin?** *Answers vary.*

Performance Task (Student Book, pages 139 to 141)

Refer your student to the **Performance Task** to consolidate and deepen his/her understanding of the chapter through tasks that require him/her to show, explain, and/or apply thinking. You may use the rubric on page 148 to encourage your student to set his/her own goals.

QUESTION 1 requires your student to read a scale to find the masses of three watermelons, then add to find their total mass.

🗨 **How can you tell the mass on each scale?** *These scales show whole kilograms, but only the even kilograms are marked with numerals. Each thick line is 1 kg and each thin line stands for 200 g.* **How might someone get confused?** *Someone might think that the lines that do not have numerals are half kilograms, when they are not. They are the odd kilograms.*

QUESTION 2 requires your student to find the total mass of apples and oranges given the number of bags, then compare to find which fruit has a greater mass.

🗨 **What do you know?** *The mass of each bag of oranges or apples; the number of bags that each fruit has.* **What do you need to find out?** *Which fruit has the greater mass.* **What plan might you make to help you solve this?** *I could draw or build a model, make a list, or solve it in parts.*

QUESTION 3 requires your student to reason the volume of orange juice and apple juice needed to fill different containers given their capacities, and then decide which is more.

🗨 **How might you calculate this problem?** *use fractions*

QUESTION 4 requires your student to find out if Jack can make 1 liter of cranberry juice given that each pack of cranberries can make 2 cups of cranberry juice.

🗨 **What information must you gather from the chart in order to solve this?** *I need to find out how many packs of cranberries Jack has.* **What other information have you learned in this problem that can help you here? What do you know about the capacity of Jack's cups in relation to a liter, as stated in Question 3?** *4 of Jack's cups make a liter.*

Performance Task Answers
(Student Book, pages 139 to 141)

1. $6 + 7 + 5 = 18$
   The total mass of the three watermelons is 18 kg.

2. Mass of oranges = $2 \times 5 = 10$ kg
   The total mass of the oranges is 10 kg.
   Mass of apples = $3 \times 4 = 12$ kg
   The total mass of the apples is 12 kg.
   So, the apples have a greater mass.

3. Answers vary. Example:
   5 glasses have a capacity of 1 liter, so 3 glasses have a capacity of $\frac{3}{5}$ of 1 liter.
   4 cups have a capacity of 1 liter, so 3 cups have a capacity of $\frac{3}{4}$ of 1 liter.
   Since $\frac{3}{4} > \frac{3}{5}$, I know that Jack prepares more apple juice.

4. 4 of Jack's cups equal 1 liter, so Jack has enough cranberry to make 1 liter of cranberry juice.

> **Teaching Tip**
>
> Invite your student to think practically about the information presented here in the chart and given in the problems. Note that the cups mentioned here are not standard cup measures. 4 standard cups equal 0.946 liters, but Question 3 tells us that 4 of Jack's cups make 1 liter. Therefore, Jack's cups are not standard cup measures.

Rubric (Student Book, page 141)

Use the scoring guide to help you give feedback on your student's work.
Use the comments section to provide information about what was done well and what could be improved. Write words of encouragement to let your student know what he/she has done well.

Scoring Rubric		
	Description	**Point(s)**
1	Your student: • correctly reads the mass of each watermelon.	1
	• correctly adds the masses of the watermelons. (6 + 7 + 5 = 18 kg)	1
2	Your student: • correctly finds the mass of the apples and oranges. (oranges: 2 × 5 = 10 kg; apples: 3 × 4 = 12 kg)	1
	• gives the correct answer. (apples)	1
3	Your student: • correctly explains that Jack prepares more apple juice than orange juice.	2
4	Your student: • correctly find the cups of cranberry juice made (2 × 2 = 4)	1
	• correctly identifies that 4 cups equal 1 liter and gives the correct answer. (yes)	1
	Total	**8**

Use this table as a guide to help you relate your student's scores to his/her performance levels.

Level	Score
	7-8
	3-6
	0-2

STEAM Project Work (Student Book, Chapter 8, page 142)

- Your student is given an opportunity to make connections between science and mathematics in this project work.
- At the end of **Chapter 8**, your student should be able to complete **Part 1** and **Part 2**.
- **Part 1** requires your student to create a list of materials he/she will need to carry out his/her experiment about mass and size (volume). Allow your student time to plan how to categorize the objects by their mass and size.
- **Part 2** requires your student to record the procedures of the experiments in how he/she can measure mass or size (volume) of the objects.

Chapter Practice (Student Book, pages 143 to 146)

- Have your student work on **Chapter Practice** in the Student Book independently to help him/her consolidate and extend understanding of the chapter.
- You may find a summary of the chapter learning objectives and the difficulty level of the questions below.
- Teaching prompts are provided for Level 2 questions.
- When your student is ready, have him/her work on **Additional Practice 3B, Chapter Practice**.

Chapter Practice Answers
(Student Book, pages 143 to 146)

1. Option D

2. Option C

3.

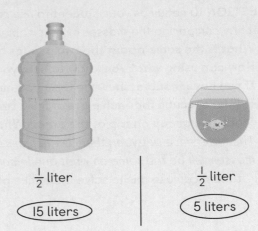

$\frac{1}{2}$ liter	$\frac{1}{2}$ liter
15 liters	5 liters

4. 3

5. 6; 2

6. 6 − 2 = 4; 4

Question	Level	Chapter 8 Learning Objective(s)	Section(s)	Day(s)
1	1	Measure and estimate the mass of objects to the nearest kilogram.	8A	2
2	1	Measure and estimate the mass of objects to the nearest gram.	8B	3
3	1	Measure and estimate liquid volumes to the nearest liter.	8C	4
4	1	Measure and estimate the mass of objects to the nearest kilogram.	8A	2
5	1	Measure and estimate the mass of objects to the nearest kilogram. Solve word problems involving mass.	8A, 8D	2, 5
6	1	Measure and estimate the mass of objects to the nearest kilogram. Solve word problems involving mass.	8A, 8D	2, 5
7	1	Measure and estimate liquid volumes to the nearest liter.	8C	4
8	1	Measure and estimate liquid volumes to the nearest liter. Solve word problems involving liquid volume.	8C, 8D	4, 5
9	2	Measure and estimate the mass of objects to the nearest gram. Solve word problems involving mass.	8B, 8D	3, 5
10	2	Measure and estimate the mass of objects to the nearest gram. Solve word problems involving mass.	8B, 8D	3, 5

QUESTION 9 requires your student to solve a two-step word problem involving mass in grams.

🗨 What is given in the problem? What do you know and what can you determine from what you know? How will you begin? What must you find out? How might you model the problem to help you see which operation you will use?

QUESTION 10 requires your student to use reasoning to find the mass of one object by comparing the masses of other objects.

🗨 What is the same about the two groups being weighed? What is different? How can using what you know to help you find what you do not know? If you have trouble, show me this problem with connecting cubes, using a different cube for each piece of fruit, red for apples and yellow for lemons. Stack one group on top of the other. What is different about each group? *The difference between them is the mass of one lemon, so the difference in masses will be the same as what one lemon weighs.*

Your student can use this to solve the entire problem.

Days 10–11 of 12

Chapter Test

• Assign **Chapter Test 8** in **Assessment Guide Teacher Edition** to assess your student's understanding of the chapter.

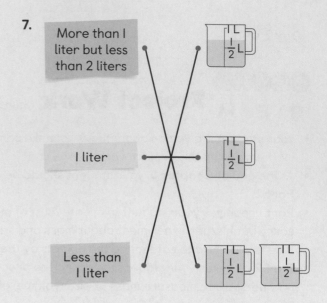

7.

8. 2 × 4 = 8; 8

9. 62 + 62 = 124
124 − 100 = 24; 24

10. (a) Subtract the mass shown on the scale on the left from the mass shown on the scale on the right.
Mass of one lemon = 270 − 190 = 80 g
(b) Subtract the mass of one lemon from the total mass of an apple and a lemon.
Mass of one apple = 190 − 80 = 110 g

Chapter Self-Reflection

Check (✓) to show what I can do.

I Can	😊😊😊 Yes	😊😊 Not Sure	😊 No
measure and estimate the mass of objects to the nearest kilogram.			
measure and estimate the mass of objects to the nearest gram.			
measure and estimate liquid volumes to the nearest liter.			
compare capacities to the benchmark of 1 liter.			
solve word problems involving mass.			
solve word problems involving liquid volume.			

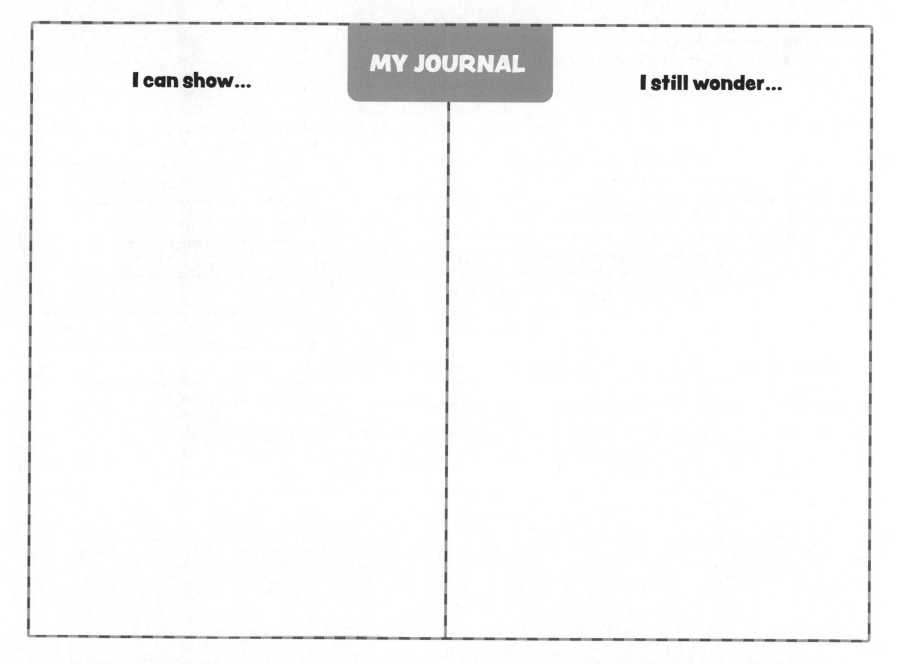

MY JOURNAL

I can show...

I still wonder...

Solve! Heuristics (Student Book, pages 147 and 148)

Heuristic: Act It Out
Go through the four-step problem-solving model to guide your student to solve the problem.

 Step 1 **Understand**

Show the problem and picture only. Have your student read the problem and direct his/her attention to the picture.

🗨 **What do you know?** *There is a 3-liter bucket and a 5-liter bucket, and a tub we need to put exactly 7 liters of water into.* **What do you need to find out?** *How to use the buckets we have to measure 7 liters.* **Is there anything else you know that might help you, even if it is not stated in the problem?** *how to break apart quantities* **What are some helpful ways you might break apart these numbers?** *5 and 2 make 7; 3 and 2 make 5.*

 Step 2 **Plan**

Invite your student to consider the best way to solve the problem using a visual to help him/her understand the problem.

🗨 **How could you start to solve the problem?:** *I could draw it; I could try to do it myself.*

Step 3 **Do**

Give your student a chance to engage in productive struggle to answer the question before looking at the solution in the Student Book. You can use measuring cups instead of liters to act this out, or recycled jars with lines drawn at the 3 and 5 cup marks and a pot for filling with the seven cups.

Do not show the book's solution until your student has generated one of his/her own. Your student may very well generate a different way to solve it, and that is fine. For example, if he/she fills the 3-liter measure once and pours it into the 5-liter measure, then does it again, he/she will be left with 1 liter in the 3-liter container. Pour the 5 liters and the 1 liter into the pot for a total of 6 liters. Then repeat the procedure to get the remaining 1 liter needed. Pour that into the pot for a total of 7 liters in the pot (and 5 liters wasted).

Use the method presented in the Student Book for reflection after he/she has solved it, and ask your student,

🗨 **Which way is most efficient? Which way results in less wasted water?**

Alternative strategy
Heuristic: Draw a Diagram
Encourage your student to share alternative ways to solve the problem. For example, you could draw diagrams to help see the relationships within the numbers:

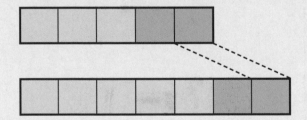

Encourage your student to draw diagrams to solve the next 2 questions.

Encourage your student to look back over the answer to ensure that it makes sense. Then invite your student to consider another way to solve the problem.

💬 **How might you check the answer? Is the answer correct? What is another way to solve the problem?**

QUESTION 1 requires your student to find a way to measure exactly 4 liters of water using only a 5-liter container and a 7-liter container.

💬 **What do you know?** *2 containers, one with 7-liter capacity and one with 5-liter capacity, and an empty aquarium that must be filled with 4 liter of water.* **What do you need to find?** *how to get exactly 4 liter* **How can knowing how to break apart numbers help you solve this?** *There are 5 liters and 2 liters in 7 liters. We need 2 liters twice, or 4 liters to fill the aquarium.* **How is this problem similar and different from the last example?** *Answers vary.* **What might you do to help see the problem?** *Act it out.* **How might you check your work?** *Measure to see if we got 4 liters in the aquarium.*

QUESTION 2 requires your student to prove that a bag of potatoes has a mass of 7 kg using 5-, 3-, and 1-kg weights.

💬 **What do you know?** *We have a 5-kg mass, a 3-kg mass, a 1-kg mass, and a bag of potatoes that Owen claims are 7 kg.* **What do you need to find out?** *if Owen's claims true* **What do you know that might help you?** *Balance scales show us if one side is heavier than the other, and I know how to decompose 8. (5 + 3 = 8; 7 + 1 = 8)*

Caution

Changing context can be quite difficult for your student. Your student might miss the fact that this problem is solved exactly as the others: by breaking apart a number, in this case 8.

Solve! Heuristics Answers
(Student Book, page 148)

1. Fill up the 7-liter container.
   Pour all the water into the 5-liter container and the remaining 2 liters of water into the aquarium.
   Empty the 5-liter container.
   Repeat the above steps to get 4 liters of water in the aquarium.

2. Put the 5-kg and 3-kg masses on one side of the balance. Put the 1-kg mass and the bag of potatoes on the other side of the balance. If the balance does not tilt, the bag of potatoes has a mass of 7 kg.

Alternative strategy
Heuristic: Draw a Diagram

As with the previous example, your student can draw a bar model to help see the relationships between the measuring cups he/she has and the amount of water needed to solve the problem.

Alternative strategy
Heuristic: Draw a Diagram

As with the previous example, your student can draw a bar model to help see the relationship between the total mass of the weights and the numerical decomposition he/she needs to solve this problem.

9 DATA

Chapter Overview

In this chapter, your student's foundational knowledge to read, interpret, and create various graphs and line plots using I to I scales in both vertical and horizontal forms from Grade 2 will be extended to his/her understanding in picture graphs and bar graphs with scales other than I and line plots with measurements to the nearest quarter-inch. Your student will:

• read and **interpret picture graphs** with scales other than I.

Five children read a total of 80 books.
The picture graph below shows the number of books each of them read. How many books did each child read?

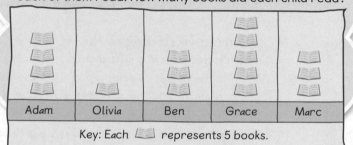

Key: Each 📖 represents 5 books.

Learn

(a) How many books did Adam read?

Adam read __20__ books.

$4 \times 5 = \underline{20}$
4 📖 represent __20__ books.

(b) How many books did Grace read?

__5__ × 5 = __25__

Grace read __25__ books.

(c) How many more books did Ben read than Olivia?

__2__ × 5 = __10__

Ben read __10__ more books than Olivia.

Ben has 2 more 📖 than Olivia.

• create his/her own **picture graphs with scales** other than I.

Ice Cream Flavor	Tally
Vanilla	⊞⊞ IIII
Chocolate	⊞⊞ ⊞⊞ ⊞⊞ ⊞⊞ I
Strawberry	⊞⊞ ⊞⊞ II
Mango	⊞⊞ ⊞⊞ ⊞⊞ III

(a) Draw a picture graph to show the data.

Favorite Ice Cream Flavor

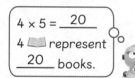

Key: Each 🍦 represents 3 children.

Fill in the blanks.

(b) __6__ more children like mango flavor than strawberry flavor.

(c) There are a total of __60__ children.
20 × 3 = 60

- read and **interpret scaled bar graphs** with scales other than 1.

Vowels In a Paragraph

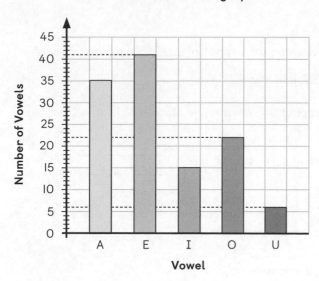

Fill in the blanks.

(a) The vowel A is used ___35___ times in the paragraph.

(b) The vowel O is used ___7___ more times than the vowel I.

(c) The most commonly used vowel is ___E___.

(d) The least commonly used vowel is ___U___.

- create his/her own **bar graphs with scales** other than 1.

Shoe Type	A	B	C	D	E
Number of Pairs	18	10	12	20	25

(a) Use the data in the table to complete the bar graph.

Shoes Sold at Happy Shoes Store

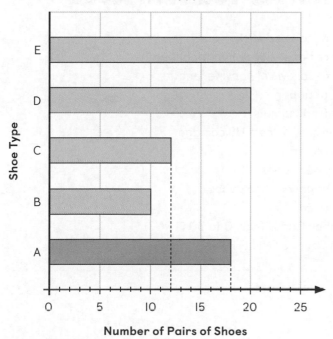

Fill in the blanks.

(b) The store sold ___8___ more pairs of Type A shoes than Type B shoes.

(c) The store sold ___13___ fewer pairs of Type C shoes than Type E shoes.

- read a **line plot** with fractions.

Complete the line plot.

Length of Screws

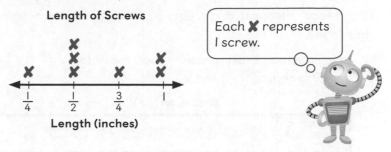

Each ✖ represents 1 screw.

Length (inches)

- measure to the nearest $\frac{1}{4}$ inch and record measurement data with **fractions on a line plot**.

(a) Use an inch ruler to measure the width of the building blocks.

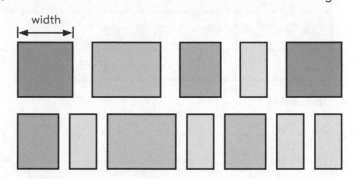

width

(b) Make a line plot to show the data.

Width of Building Blocks

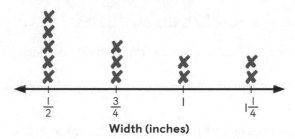

Width (inches)

Key: Each ✖ represents 1 building block.

Key Ideas

- We can read, interpret, and create picture graphs with scales other than 1.

    (b) Complete the picture graph to show the data.
    Use ⬭ to represent 2 shapes.

    Shapes on the Wall

Rectangle	⬭ ⬭ ⬭ ⬭ ⬭ ⬭ ⬭ ⬭ ⬭ ⬭
Hexagon	⬭ ⬭ ⬭ ⬭ ⬭
Triangle	⬭ ⬭ ⬭ ⬭ ⬭
Circle	⬭ ⬭ ⬭ ⬭ ⬭ ⬭

    Key: Each ⬭ represents 2 shapes.

Fill in the blanks.

(c) There are ___4___ different shapes on the wall.

There are ___54___ shapes altogether.

(d) __Rectangle__ is the most common shape on the wall.

(e) The least common shape is __hexagon__.

(f) There are as many __triangles__ as __circles__.

(g) There are ___10___ fewer hexagons than rectangles.

- We can read, interpret, and create bar graphs with scales other than 1.

    (a) Record the number of jellybeans of each color in the table below.

Color	Red	Yellow	Blue	Green	White
Number of Jellybeans	14	24	20	28	24

    (b) Complete the bar graph to show the data.

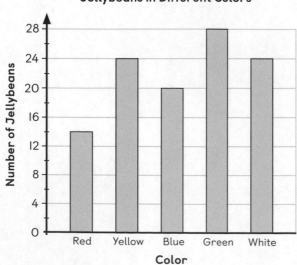

Jellybeans in Different Colors

Fill in the blanks.

(c) There are ___8___ more green jellybeans than blue jellybeans.

28 − 20 = 8

(d) There is an equal number of __yellow__ jellybeans and __white__ jellybeans.

- We can interpret and create line plots.

    Complete the line plot.

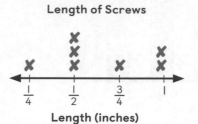

Length of Screws

Length (inches)

Each ✗ represents 1 screw.

Fill in the blanks.

(a) There is an equal number of ___$\frac{1}{4}$___-inch screws and ___$\frac{3}{4}$___-inch screws.

(b) There are ___2___ more $\frac{1}{2}$-inch screws than $\frac{1}{4}$-inch screws.

(c) There are ___5___ screws of length less than 1 inch.

(d) There are ___3___ screws of length more than $\frac{1}{2}$ inch.

Materials You Will Need

- 1 set of colored sticky dots
- 1 set of paper clips of varying lengths
- 1 set of screws of varying lengths
- slips of paper
- 3 stuffed animals
- 3 coin sets or real US coinage
- 1 inch ruler
- 2 number cubes
- 1 set of connecting cubes
- 1 set of counters
- Number Cards from 0 to 30 (TR03)
- Inch Square Grid (TR24)

Chapter at a Glance

	Day	Learning Objective(s)	Vocabulary	Resource(s)	Material(s)
Chapter Opener / Recall Student Book, pp. 149–152	1 of 11				• 2 coin sets or real US coinage
Section 9A **Picture Graphs** Student Book, pp. 153–158	2 of 11	• Read and interpret picture graphs. • Create picture graphs.		• **Additional Practice 3B,** Exercise 9A • **Reteach 3,** Exercise 9A • **Extension 3,** Exercise 9A • **Mastery and Beyond 3B,** Chapter 9, Practice 1	• slips of paper • 3 stuffed animals • 1 coin set or real US coinage • 1 set of counters • 1 copy of Number Cards from 0 to 30 (TR03)
Section 9B **Bar Graphs** Student Book, pp. 159–166	3 of 11	• Read and interpret bar graphs. • Create bar graphs.		• **Additional Practice 3B,** Exercise 9B • **Reteach 3,** Exercise 9B • **Extension 3,** Exercise 9B • **Mastery and Beyond 3B,** Chapter 9, Practice 2	• 1 set of colored sticky dots • 2 number cubes • 1 set of connecting cubes
Section 9C **Line Plots** Student Book, pp. 167–174	4 of 11	• Generate and show measurement data by making line plots. • Interpret line plots.		• **Additional Practice 3B,** Exercise 9C • **Reteach 3,** Exercise 9C • **Extension 3,** Exercise 9C • **Mastery and Beyond 3B,** Chapter 9, Practice 3	• 1 set of paper clips of varying lengths • 1 set of screws of varying lengths • 1 inch ruler • 1 copy of Inch Square Grid (TR24)
Chapter Wrap Up / **Performance Task** Student Book, pp. 175–178	5 of 11				
STEAM Project Work Student Book, p. 142	6 of 11				
Chapter Practice Student Book, pp. 179–184	7–8 of 11			• **Additional Practice 3B,** Chapter Practice	

© 2022 Marshall Cavendish Education Pte Ltd

Chapter Test	Day	Learning Objective(s)	Vocabulary	Resource(s)	Material(s)
	9–10 of 11			• **Assessment Guide Teacher Edition,** Chapter Test 9	
Solve! Heuristics Student Book, pp. 185–186	11 of 11				• 1 set of counters

Chapter Opener (Student Book, page 149)

Consider the picture and the questions on the page. Discuss them with your student. Prompt him/her to consider the information given in the picture and what is being asked. You may wish to ask the following questions:

💬 **What do you notice about the picture? What are the students doing? How do you know? What is everything you know from the information on the chart? What do smiley faces tell us?** *Smiley faces represent students.* **What do you know from the chart about how many students each smiley face represents?** *The chart says that each smiley face represents 3 students.* **Based on the number of smiley faces on the chart, how many students like orange juice?** *18 students like orange juice.* **How do you find that information?** *Multiply six smiley faces by 3 since the key tells us that each smiley face represents 3 students.* **How many different drinks do they like?** *4* **How could we find out the answer to the teacher's question?** *There are 10 smiley faces representing 30 students. We would have to know how many students are in her class. If there are 30 students in the class, the answer to her question is "Yes".* **Which drink is most popular?** *orange juice* **Why do you say that?** *It has the most smiley faces.* **How many more students prefer orange juice to milk?** *18 − 6 = 12, 12 more students prefer orange juice to milk.*

For Additional Support

After a period of productive struggle, if your student is unable to interpret the picture graph, draw a copy of it exactly on a piece of paper. Suggest using a yellow counter for smiley face, placing them on top of each drawing methodically. Then allow your student to point to the key, where it shows that each smiley face represents 3 students.

Have your student skip count and write the number that each set of data represents. To make it more visual, you may wish to prompt your student to incorporate tally marks as he/she counts.

Digging Deeper

💬 **Do you think this chart is a fair representation of the drinks a class of 30 would like? Why or why not? How would you change it?** *I would change the label for orange juice to say juice because I do not think that many people like orange juice.* **Thinking about your friends, what would you say is the most popular drink?** *Answers vary.*

Teaching Tip

If your student is unfamiliar with the graphs, tables, and charts in the **Opener** and **Recall**, stop and take a day to rebuild a more firm foundation. Generate data from anything known and readily quantifiable by your student, such as the number of soft toys or baseball cards in a collection he/she possesses. After your student has tallied, charted, and plotted the data he/she collects from his/her own personal collection, use the **Chapter Opener** and **Recall** to determine if he/she is ready to move on. As always, using concrete and pictorial methods first will advance thinking. In this case, you may wish to have your student use magnets on a magnetic whiteboard to collect and display data in a more concrete fashion.

Recall (Student Book, pages 150 to 152)

Materials
• 2 coin sets or real US coinage

Before moving on to the problems on pages 150 to 152 of the Student Book, make sure your student is familiar with the prerequisite knowledge needed in this chapter. He/She will need to be able to read and produce line plots, bar graphs, picture graphs, and tally charts. He/She should be able to take raw data and represent it on any of these graphs. You may wish to use the data generated in the suggested game to produce the different types of graphs.

If that proves too time consuming, take two handfuls of coins and place them on the table in front of your student. Have your student organize the coins by type, then chart the data in different ways until you have covered each type represented in the **Recall**.

Make it a Game!

Encourage your student to choose any question he/she wishes to ask his/her family and friends. For example, what is your favorite breakfast food? Then send an email to as many people as he/she can think of, asking the question in a survey form. Have your student arrange the data in a graph and generate several questions to ask that are similar to those in **Recall**. Your student should create an answer key so everyone who answers the questions can "check" their work. (In reality, you will see whether your student understands the concepts by his/her answers.) You may wish the ask the following questions:

💬 **What are some different ways you can represent this data?** *line plot, picture graph, or bar graph* **What questions would you like to ask?** *Answers vary.*

Then have your student present his/her data to the family and see whether they can figure out the answers to the questions! Those who get them all correct win bragging rights.

After this review, your student should be able to complete the tasks on pages 150 to 152 of the Student Book independently.
• **QUESTION 1** assesses your student's ability to complete a picture graph using data in a tally chart. Then interpret the data based on the picture graph.
• **QUESTION 2** assesses your student's ability to interpret data from a bar graph.
• **QUESTION 3** assesses your student's ability to create a line plot from data given in a table.
• **QUESTION 4** assesses your student's ability to write fractions on a number line.

Recall Answers
(Student Book, pages 150 to 152)

1. **(a)**

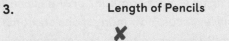

Walk	◯◯◯◯◯
Bike	⬤⬤⬤
Car	⬤◯◯◯◯
School Bus	◯◯◯◯◯◯◯◯

Key: Each ⬤ represents 1 child.

  (b) 6
  (c) bike
  (d) 9

2. **(a)** 5
  (b) Math
  (c) 7
  (d) 16

3.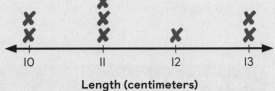

Length of Pencils

Length (centimeters)

4.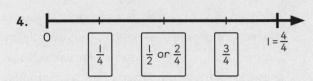

9A Picture Graphs

Learning Objective(s)
- Read and interpret picture graphs.
- Create picture graphs.

Material(s)
- slips of paper
- 1 set of counters
- 1 copy of Number Cards from 0 to 30 (TR03)
- 3 stuffed animals
- 1 coin set or real US coinage

PICTURE GRAPHS (Student Book, pages 153 to 158)

Lesson Opener

Task (Student Book, page 153)

Show your student the **Lesson Opener** and cover the rest of the page. Discuss the question with your student. Do not show your student how to do the task and allow him/her to explore in the reading and interpreting of picture graphs.

Refer your student to **Learn** and **Learn Together** in the Student Book for reflection after your student has explored the concepts. Use questions to build understanding and direct instruction to refine understanding.

Lesson Development
Learn (Student Book, page 153)

Continuing to hide the rest of the page, discuss the picture graph with your student. Thoroughly investigate what he/she can interpret from it. Since the scale is 5, your student should be able to easily skip count to determine the number of books each child read and compare them. You may wish to ask these questions:

💬 **What is the scale? What does each little book stand for?** *5 books* **How do you know?** *It says at the bottom of the graph.* **How can you tell whether the children actually read 80 books in all?** *Skip count by 5s for all the little pictures of books; count them all and multiply by 5; count and multiply each column by 5, then add the column totals together.* **Who read the most books?** *Grace* **Why do you say that?** *Her column is the tallest.* **How many books did Grace read?** *25* **How do you know?** *There are 5 pictures of books and each picture represents 5 books, 5 × 5 = 25.* **How can you tell who read the least?** *Olivia, because her column is the shortest.* **How might you compare what each child read?** *Find how many pictures of books are in each column and subtract.*

© 2022 Marshall Cavendish Education Pte Ltd

Focus Question

💬 **How do you interpret and share information from picture graphs?** Invite your student to ponder this question as you go through the lesson. Revisit this question when you reach the end of the lesson to check his/her understanding.

Teaching Tip

Your student will learn to read a picture graph based on information given in the key, then interpret the data to solve problems. Your student will also create picture graphs based on raw data and data presented in tally charts.

New to Grade 3 is a scale representing the number of each object. Your student will have to multiply the number of icons in a column by the number each icon represents in order to find the total quantity in each column. Thus, you will find plenty of clever review for multiplication facts hidden within the pages of this chapter.

If your student needs it, you may wish to extend various problems for multiplication review after your student solves them. To provide this opportunity, simply alter the data and/or change the key. You also may wish to change information in the keys to target the multiplication facts your student finds most challenging.

💬 **What if each circle represented 7 students instead? How many students would like oranges best in that case?** *Questions and answers will vary according to each problem set.*

💬 **How many books did Adam read?** *20* **How do you know?** *There are 4 pictures of books and each picture represents 5 books, 4 × 5 = 20.* **How might we find out how many more books Ben read than Olivia?** *We can see that Ben has two more pictures of book than Olivia. Each represents 5 books, 2 × 5 = 10 so Ben read 10 more books than Olivia.*

After you are certain your student understands how to read the chart, use the scale, and interpret the data, uncover the rest of the page and have your student answer the questions.

💬 **What are the mascots thinking? Do you agree or disagree? Why?**

Learn Together (Student Book, pages 154 to 156)

In this section, your student will learn to represent data on a tally chart, use that to create a picture graph, and solidify understanding about interpreting and using data represented on a picture graph. Invite your student to observe each picture before proceeding with the problems in **Learn Together**.

Through questioning, lead your student to interpret the picture graph in **Learn Together**. As you go through the problems with your student, you may wish to ask the following questions:

💬 **What is the scale on this graph? How do you know? Where does it tell you that? What can you tell right away from this picture graph?** *Which is greater/less.* **Compare the data.**

After your student has explored the concepts in the **Lesson Opener**, **Learn**, and **Learn Together**, you may wish to ask these questions to encourage further reflection:

💬 **What is your favorite thing about picture graphs? How do picture graphs make it easy to process information? What do you find most difficult about representing data?**

You may wish to have your student summarize his/her learning in a math journal. Invite your student to create his/her own picture graph from data he/she collects. Please see the **Do More at Home** box for ideas.

- **QUESTION 1** requires your student to interpret information from a picture graph.
  💬 **What is the title of the graph?** *Insects in Jane's Garden* **What does each triangle represent?** *3 insects* **How do you know?** *The key tells us.* **How many more ___ are there than ___? How do you know?** *Answers vary.*

- **QUESTION 2** requires your student to create a tally chart and a picture graph based on the given shapes.
  💬 **What mathematical tools or strategies have you used before that could help you with this problem?** *use counters; look for patterns as a strategy* **Do you observe any patterns that might make counting the shapes easier for you?** *I can see 4 rows of 5 yellow rectangles right away so that is 4 × 5, or 20 yellow rectangles; I see 3 rows of 4 green circles; etc.* **How will you record it in the tally chart?** *I can bundle each group of five, then put a line for any extras, and write the total in the second column.* **What does each stick represent in a tally? / What does each bundle represent?** *5* **What is the scale for the picture graph?** *Each cloud represents 2 shapes.* **How many clouds will you use to represent rectangles on the picture graph and why?** *10 because 10 × 2 = 20 and there are 20 rectangles.*

Learn Answers

(Student Book, page 153)

(a) 20; 20; 20
(b) 5; 25; 25
(c) 2; 10; 10

For Additional Support

Your student should be ready to grasp the pictorial nature of graphs in this chapter, but sometimes may need to physically build a few of the picture graphs before being able to understand the information in them. If this is the case for your student, make sure he/she also draws a reasonable representation of what he/she built, and that it matches the data represented in the book. Moving through the concrete-pictorial progression will help your student understand the abstract information he/she can gather from graphs and charts.

Learn Together Answers

(Student Book, pages 154 to 156)

1. **(a)** 6
   (b) dragonflies
   (c) dragonflies; ladybugs
   (d) 75

2. **(a)**

Shape		Tally	Number
Rectangle	▭	卌 卌 卌 卌	20
Hexagon	⬡	卌 卌	10
Triangle	△	卌 卌 Ⅱ	12
Circle	◯	卌 卌 Ⅱ	12

(b)

Shapes on the Wall

Rectangle	◎◎◎◎◎◎◎◎◎◎
Hexagon	◎◎◎◎◎
Triangle	◎◎◎◎◎◎
Circle	◎◎◎◎◎◎

Key: Each ◎ represents 2 shapes.

(c) 4; 54
(d) Rectangle
(e) hexagon
(f) triangles; circles
(g) 10

Lesson Debrief

- Conclude the lesson and facilitate your student's reflection by asking him/her to answer the **Focus Question** and share his/her thinking.
- Extend the discussion by posing the following questions.
  - 💬 **What is a picture graph?** *A visual representation of a set of data.* **How do we read picture graphs?** *Look at the title and the key, and then figure out the quantities the pictures represent.* **What is important to know when creating a picture graph?** *the data given* **Where can you find information in a picture graph?** *We can look at the key to find out how many each picture represents, and use that to figure out the quantity in each column; we can use the columns to compare information; we can read the title to know what the graph is about.* **How can you use a picture graph to share information?** *We can decide based on the data and the key how many pictures we should put in each column of the graph.*

Reflect and Connect

- Allow time for your student to reflect on what he/she has learned and ask questions about what he/she may be unsure of.
- Encourage him/her to share anything that was confusing or difficult, and how thinking about it differently and perseverance helped the process of learning.
- Ask your student to answer a reflection question or draw a picture to show his/her reflection. You may offer these prompts:
  - 💬 **What have you learned about reading and understanding picture graphs? What is important to know about reading picture graphs? What would you tell someone who does not know how to represent groups on a picture graph? What is important to know?**

What to look for:
- ability to understand what each picture graph is about
- ability to find the key and the scale for each picture graph
- ability to read a picture graph to determine what each row or column represents and compare sets of data
- ability to create a tally chart given a set of raw data
- ability to represent raw data from a tally chart on a picture graph

Practice On Your Own (Student Book, pages 157 and 158)

- **QUESTION 1** assesses your student's ability to read a picture graph with a scale and interpret information from the picture graph.
- **QUESTION 2** assesses your student's ability to translate data in a given tally chart to a picture graph and interpret information from the graph.

Practice On Your Own Answers
(Student Book, pages 157 and 158)

1. (a) 12
   (b) melon
   (c) 8
   (d) 80; 20 × 4 = 80

For Additional Support

Your student who still struggles can practice making real-life picture graphs. Give a small handful of nickels or dimes to your student for each of his/her three favorite stuffed animals, then have him/her make a picture graph showing how much money each stuffed animal has, using the real coins. Encourage your student to compare quantities between stuffed animals and figure out how much money they have in all.

More Resources

- Refer to **Do More at Home** below and **Reteach 3**, **Exercise 9A** if your student needs additional support.
- When your student is ready, have him/her work on **Additional Practice 3B**, **Exercise 9A**.
- To provide your student with a challenge, have him/her work on **Extension 3**, **Exercise 9A**.
- You may also assign **Mastery and Beyond 3B**, **Chapter 9**, **Practice I** to provide further support and development to sustain learning.

Do More at Home

Here are a few ideas to solidify the concept of gathering data and representing it in everyday life:

1) Invite your student to gather data and make a picture graph about the people in your family regarding a preference (for example, who likes which pizza toppings) or a quantity (for example, the number of shoes each family member has).
2) Give your student a variety of objects you can easily find or make in quantity, for example, pattern blocks, or different varieties of dried beans, or different types of pasta noodles, or different kinds of pebbles or coins.

    Encourage your student to organize the data in a tally chart, then create a picture graph with a scaled key. Your student should then make four problems for you to solve, along with an answer key for you to "check" your work (and see if your student did his/her work correctly).

2. (a)

Favorite Ice Cream Flavor

Vanilla	🍦🍦🍦
Chocolate	🍦🍦🍦🍦🍦🍦
Strawberry	🍦🍦🍦🍦
Mango	🍦🍦🍦🍦🍦

Key: Each 🍦 represents 3 children.

(b) 6
(c) 60; 20 × 3 = 60

Digging Deeper

Invite your student to make a tally chart and picture graph representing any set of data that is of interest, and then ask you questions about it to see whether you can get them right.

If your student cannot think of anything to make a graph, he/she might enjoy creating a graph entitled **My Zoo**:

Using Number Cards (TR03) of even number (or only cards that are multiples of a certain chosen number) and slips of paper with various animal names written on them, invite your student to choose four slips of paper to determine the animals in his/her zoo, along with four even numbers to give the quantity of each animal.

Your student will use that data to create a picture graph representing the animals in his/her zoo, with the key that each picture represents two animals—or whichever factor the number cards are multiples of. Make use of the opportunity to throw in a little practice with multiplication.

Lastly, encourage your student to create questions based on his/her picture graphs for you to answer.

9B Bar Graphs

Learning Objective(s)
- Read and interpret bar graphs.
- Create bar graphs.

Material(s)
- 1 set of colored sticky dots
- 1 set of connecting cubes
- 2 number cubes

BAR GRAPHS (Student Book, pages 159 to 166)

Lesson Opener

Task (Student Book, page 159)

Show your student the **Lesson Opener** and cover the rest of the page. Discuss the question with your student. Do not show your student how to do the task and allow him/her to explore in the reading and interpreting of bar graphs.

Refer your student to **Learn** and **Learn Together** in the Student Book for reflection after your student has explored the concepts. Use questions to build understanding and direct instruction to refine understanding.

Lesson Development

Learn (Student Book, pages 159 and 160)

Taking care to continue to hide the rest of the page, invite your student to discuss the bar graph with you. Do not show your student what the mascot thinks until he/she has figured out that the dotted lines show numbers that lie halfway between the grid lines. You may wish to ask these questions:

💬 **What information can you tell at a glance?** *What the graph is about, and the fact that Class C won.* **Why do you say that?** *The title tells us what the graph is about and Class C's bar is the tallest.* **How can you tell who lost?** *Class E, because its bar is the shortest.* **How will we figure out the number of points each class scored?** *The side axis tells us the number of points.* **How many points does each grid line represent?** *2 points* **How do you know?** *The numbers up the side are skip counting by twos.* **How might you compare bars?** *Measure each bar and subtract.* **Why are there some dotted lines?** *Those bars fall in between grid lines.* **How will you tell how many points those bars represent?** *Look at the grid line before and after and figure out what is in the middle. In this case, each half is one point.* **How many points did Class D score?** *11* **How do you know?** *11 is halfway between 10 and 12.* **Which class scored the most points, and how much was that?** *Class C scored 19 points.* **How do you know?** *Class C's bar is tallest and halfway between 18 and 20.* **How might we find out how many points were scored altogether?** *We can figure out the points each bar represents and add them altogether.*

© 2022 Marshall Cavendish Education Pte Ltd

Focus Question

💬 **How do you interpret and share information from bar graphs?**

Invite your student to ponder this question as you go through the lesson. Revisit this question when you reach the end of the lesson to check his/her understanding.

Teaching Tip

In this lesson, you will help your student learn to read a bar graph based on information given on the axes of the graph, then interpret the data to solve problems. Your student will also create bar graphs based on raw data and data presented in charts.

New to Grade 3 are scales on the horizontal or vertical axes so that each grid line increases by more than one. Your student will also read and interpret data that falls between the lines to determine the value of each given bar in the bar graph.

You may wish to emphasize the reasons for scales in graphs. On a whiteboard, invite your student to represent just one of the bars from one of the bar graphs in this lesson. When each grid line represents 1, he/she will see quickly how unwieldy the data becomes.

Learn Answers
(Student Book, pages 159 and 160)

(a) 11
(b) C; 19
(c) 9; 13; 19; 11; 8; 60; 60

After your student has determined that the dotted lines show scores that lie between the grid lines, uncover the rest of the page and have your student answer the questions.

💬 **How did the mascot think about this?** *The mascot figured out the numbers halfway between the grid lines.*

Activity! (Student Book, page 160)

Invite your student to make some observations about the different orientation of the bar graph as he/she creates it from the same data in **Learn**.

💬 **What is the same about this horizontal graph?** *The two sides still say Classes and Number of Points; the title is exactly the same; the scale is the same since each grid line increases by two.* **What is different about this horizontal graph?** *The two sides switched places.* **How do you think the information on this horizontal graph will look different?** *The bars will run long instead of tall.* **Do you notice anything that you find odd about the horizontal graph?** *The classes start at A from the bottom and go to E at the top.* **Which data would you like to add first?** *Answers vary. Allow your student to start with any class, but carefully place it next to the appropriate class letter.* **How did you identify the odd points on the horizontal graph?** *with a dotted line to the bottom of the graph* **Is the information on the horizontal graph different from the information on the vertical graph?** *No, it is exactly the same.* **Are the total points scored the same or different?** *the same* **How will you prove it to me?** *Answers vary. Your student must convince you that the data is not altered by presenting it in a different orientation.*

For Additional Support

If your student does not understand the word *horizontal*, remind him/her that a *horizon*, the line where earth meets sky, runs across our vision from left to right—and so does a horizontal bar graph.

Activity! Answer

(Student Book, page 160)

Points Scored in a Spelling Bee

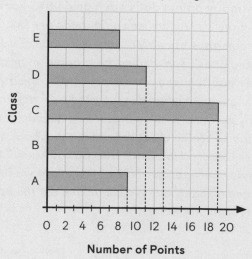

Learn Together (Student Book, pages 161 and 162)

In this section, you will help your student solidify understanding about representing data in bar graphs. Invite your student to carefully observe each bar graph before proceeding with the problems in **Learn Together**.

Through questioning, lead your student to interpret the bar graph in **Learn Together**. As you go through the problems with your student, you may wish to ask the following questions:

🗨 **Where do you find the information that tells you about this graph? What information do the numbers at each grid line give you? What can you see at a glance in this graph? When data for a bar ends between grid lines, what should you do to tell the quantity the bar represents?** *Draw a dotted line.*

After your student has explored the concepts in the **Lesson Opener**, **Learn**, and **Learn Together**, you may wish to ask these questions to encourage further reflection:

🗨 **What is different about bar graphs from picture graphs? What do you want to remember about bar graphs that you did not realize before?**

You may wish to have your student summarize his/her learning in a math journal. Invite your student to choose a bar graph from the Student Book, or create one for himself/herself, and explain the features of a bar graph.

- **QUESTION 1** requires your student to interpret information from a bar graph.
  - 🗨 **What is the title of the graph?** *Vowels in a Paragraph* **What is the scale of this graph?** *It has a scale of 5.* **How do you know?** *The number of vowels goes up by 5 for each marked line.* **What else do you observe about the scale on the side?** *There are smaller intervals between the numbers. Each small interval stands for 1; it is like a number line.* **How many more times does E appear than A?** *6* **How do you know?** *The line for E runs to 41 and the line for A is at 35.* **What else do you observe?** *E occurs most often and U occurs least often.*

  - 😀 Invite your student to think more deeply about the data presented in the bar graph.
  - 🗨 **What else can you say about the number of times each vowel was used?** *E is the most frequently used letter, followed by A; I, O, and U are not frequently used. A and E together occur twice as often as I, O, and U together.* **What else can you observe?** *Only two vowels hit a line exactly, but I can see the value of each bar because of the smaller lines.* **What makes the graph easy to read?** *The lines and broken lines help us read it; the different colors show different data points.* **Why do you think that some vowels are used less frequently?** *Answers vary.*

- **QUESTION 2** requires your student to complete a horizontal bar graph using the given data.
  - 🗨 **What is the scale for this graph?** *It has a scale of 5.* **How is this similar and different from the previous graph?** *Both graphs have a scale of 5 and small intervals between the numbers. Each small interval stands for 1 in both graphs. The previous graph is vertical but this graph is horizontal.* **Of which shoe type does Happy Shoes have sold the most pairs?** *Type E* **Of which shoe type does Happy Shoes have sold the fewest pairs?** *Type B* **How many fewer pairs of Type B are there than Type D?** *10*

Learn Together Answers

(Student Book, pages 161 and 162)

1. (a) 35
   (b) 7
   (c) E
   (d) U

2. (a)

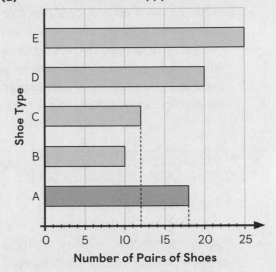

Shoes Sold at Happy Shoes Store

   (b) 8
   (c) 13

Digging Deeper

Letter frequency analysis dates back to the 9th century, when mathematician Al-Kindi used it to break codes. In World War II, the U.S. Army recruited Native Americans to transmit messages in their own languages in order to confound enemy surveillance and prevent Axis powers from cracking codes in widely known English. If you are aware that the letter E occurs 13% of the time in English, for example, you can find a letter or string of symbols occurring with that same frequency and substitute them to decipher messages.

🗨 **Is it usually true that E occurs most and U occurs least? I wonder if it is different for fiction or nonfiction. What are some ways we could investigate this? I wonder if it is also true for different languages that use the same alphabet, like Spanish. What ideas do you have to find out?** *The data presented in this graph generally reflects the frequency of vowel occurrence in English.*

Lesson Debrief

- Conclude the lesson and facilitate your student's reflection by asking him/her to answer the **Focus Question** and share his/her thinking.
- Extend the discussion by posing the following questions.
    - 💬 **Where can you find information in a bar graph?** *We can look at the title, the labels on the horizontal and vertical axes, the scale, and the bars themselves to find out the value of each bar. We can then compare data.* **How can you use a bar graph to share information?** *We can decide based on the data in a table how to build the bars of the graph. We must decide what scale to use and how to label our graph.* **How is a bar graph helpful?** *Bar graphs are useful to help us see and compare data quickly.* **When might you use a bar graph instead of a picture graph?** *We might use a bar graph to represent bigger numbers, so we do not have to count the pictures and multiply to get the values.*

Reflect and Connect

- Allow time for your student to reflect on what he/she has learned and ask questions about what he/she may be unsure of.
- Encourage him/her to share anything that was confusing or difficult, and how thinking about it differently and perseverance helped the process of learning.
- Ask your student to answer a reflection question or draw a picture to show his/her reflection. You may offer these prompts:
    - 💬 **What have you learned about reading and understanding bar graphs? What is important to know about reading bar graphs? What would you tell someone who does not know how to represent data on a bar graph? What is important to know?**

What to look for:
- ability to read the bar graph to know what it is about
- ability to tell from the numbers on the grid lines how to interpret the data in the bar graph
- ability to collect raw data and represent it on a bar graph
- understanding that data falling between grid lines can be interpreted exactly according to where the bar ends, sometimes, the bar provides a dotted line, so we can more easily see where the data ends

For Additional Support

Learn Together Question 2 will be difficult for your student because he/she must use data in a table to create a horizontal bar graph. Use this as an opportunity to practice problem-solving. Your student who finds this task overwhelming might be helped by using connecting cubes to create the bar graphs physically before drawing them.
- 💬 **What mathematical tools or strategies have you used before that could help you with this problem?** *We might use connecting cubes.*

Practice On Your Own (Student Book, pages 163 to 166)

- **QUESTION 1** assesses your student's ability to read a bar graph with a scale of 10 and interpret information from the bar graph.
- **QUESTION 2(a)** assesses your student's ability to collect and sort data and then record the data in a table.
- **QUESTION 2(b)** assesses your student's ability to represent the data from the table in (a) in a bar graph with a given scale.
- **QUESTIONS 2(c)** and **(d)** assess your student's ability to interpret information from the bar graph in (b).
- **QUESTION 2(e)** assesses your student's ability to collect and sort data and then record the data in a table.
- **QUESTION 2(f)** assesses your student's ability to represent the data from the table in (e) in a bar graph with an appropriate scale.

👀 How is the new graph different from the bar graph in (b)? Invite your student to take a closer look at the bar graphs in (b) and (f).

💬 **What else can you say about the difference between these graphs?** *Answers vary.* **What are you asked to do?** *Record the number of jars of jellybeans by color.* **What did the first graph show?** *the number of jellybeans by color* **What should you put in the blank on the left side of the bar graph?** *jars* **What is the scale of this bar graph?** *It has a scale of 2.*

Caution

Question 2(a) requires two steps to solve: 1) count the number of jellybeans in one jar of each particular color and 2) multiply by the number of jars of that color. Your student might not think it through to get from the raw data to recording the information on the table. You may wish to ask the following questions:

💬 **What should you do when you are stumped?** *Use the three-step problem-solving method.* **What are the three problem-solving steps?** *Understand the problem; carry out your plan; check your work.* **Which step is first?** *Understand the problem.* **What should you ask yourself?** *What do I know and what do I need to find out?*

In Question 2, if your student rushes in reading, he/she may neglect to see that 2(e) and 2(f) use the data from the number of jars of jellybeans for each color as opposed to the total number of jellybeans of each color. Simply highlight the phrase your student missed ("jars of jellybeans") and make him/her redo the problem.

Practice On Your Own Answers
(Student Book, pages 163 to 166)

1. (a) March
   (b) $20
   (c) $15; 40 − 25 = 15
   (d) $75; 45 + 25 + 5 = 75

2. (a)

Color	Red	Yellow	Blue	Green	White
Number of Jellybeans	14	24	20	28	24

(b)

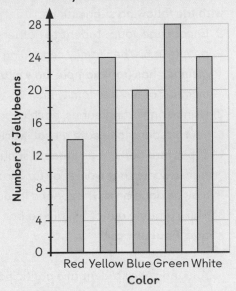

Jellybeans in Different Colors

(c) 8; 28 − 20 = 8
(d) yellow; white
(e)

Color of Jellybeans	Red	Yellow	Blue	Green	White
Number of Jars of Jellybeans	7	6	5	4	3

(f)

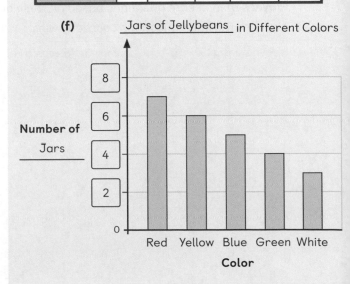

<u>Jars of Jellybeans</u> in Different Colors

More Resources

- Refer to Do More at Home below and **Reteach 3**, **Exercise 9B** if your student needs additional support.
- When your student is ready, have him/her work on **Additional Practice 3B**, **Exercise 9B**.
- To provide your student with a challenge, have him/her work on **Extension 3**, **Exercise 9B**.
- You may also assign **Mastery and Beyond 3B**, **Chapter 9**, **Practice 2** to provide further support and development to sustain learning.

Do More at Home

Extend the concept of gathering data and representing it to everyday life with the following suggestions:

1) Encourage your student to gather data and make a graph about the people in his/her family regarding a quantity of something each family member has (for example, how many different colors of T-shirts each member of his/her family has).

2) Using connecting cubes, each cube having two connection points, invite your student to create a real-world 3-D bar graph by organizing the cubes into bars. Your student should give his/her graphs an appropriate title, a scale that works for larger quantities, and titles for the axes. This may be done on a whiteboard if you prefer.

3) Make a game out of building a bar graph about the weather using the title, **Foul or Fair?**

You and your student are participants of this activity. On a pair of number cube, place four different colored sticky dots on the sides. Use blue for cloudy, yellow for sunny, white for snowy, and red for stormy. Be sure to place duplicates of 2 of the colors on each player's number cube, but make the duplicate colors different for each player. Each player rolls his/her number cube 30 times and records by tally how many times he/she rolls each color. The players will create bar graphs showing the following data: weather frequency in a month for each weather type, adjust the scale to 5 days per line, and outline the bar for snowy weather in black or build with white connecting cubes. Players then create questions based on their bar graphs. Whoever answers the most questions correctly wins!

9C Line Plots

Learning Objective(s)
- Generate and show measurement data by making line plots.
- Interpret line plots.

Material(s)
- 1 set of paper clips of varying lengths
- 1 inch ruler
- 1 set of screws of varying lengths
- 1 copy of Inch Square Grid (TR24)

LINE PLOTS (Student Book, pages 167 to 174)

Lesson Opener

Task (Student Book, page 167)

Show your student the **Lesson Opener** and cover the rest of the page. Discuss the question with your student. Do not show your student how to do the task and allow him/her to explore the concept of line plots and how to share data using line plots.

Refer your student to **Learn** and **Learn Together** in the Student Book for reflection after your student has explored the concepts. Use questions to build understanding and direct instruction to refine understanding.

Lesson Development

Learn (Student Book, pages 167 and 168)

Invite your student to consider how to measure the screws and quantify each according to length on a line plot. Allow for a time of productive struggle as your student attempts to gather and represent data in this way. You may wish to ask these questions:

💬 **It says the screw shown here is shorter than an inch. How can you tell if that is true?** *The line ends at 1 inch, and the screw only goes to $\frac{1}{4}$ inch. So it is true.* **What are all those numbers?** *They are fractions representing $\frac{1}{4}$ inch, $\frac{1}{2}$ inch, $\frac{3}{4}$ inch, and 1 inch. Write the length in the space.*

Show page 168, keeping the mascot's thinking bubble hidden by a sticky note.

💬 **What about this line plot on page 168? What can you say about it?** *It says the length of the screws in inches, and it has one screw of $\frac{1}{4}$ inch marked, three screws of $\frac{1}{2}$ inch marked, and one screw of $\frac{3}{4}$ inch marked.* **So far, is that what we measured?** *yes* **Is the line plot complete? If not, what's missing?** *No. It is missing the data for 1-inch screws. There are two of them.* **How do you think you should show that?** *Put two x marks above the 1-inch mark on the line.* **Why?** *Because the other data points show the exact number of screws and they are marked in this way.* **How is this different from a picture graph?** *In a picture graph, each picture can represent several actual objects. In a line plot, it seems that each x represents only one.* **Do you think that this is true all the time?** *Not sure; we will have to find out.*

Focus Question

💬 **How do you interpret and share information from line plots?**
Invite your student to ponder this question as you go through the lesson. Revisit this question when you reach the end of the lesson to check his/her understanding.

Teaching Tip

In this lesson, your student will learn to read, interpret, and generate line plots. Your student will also create line plots based on raw data and data presented in charts.

This lesson is a practical opportunity to work with fractions and practice measuring objects to the quarter-inch. Your student may enjoy the brain break of working with measurement while learning to represent data in a different way.

Learn Answers

(Student Book, pages 167 and 168)

$\frac{1}{4}$

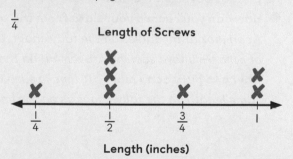

Length of Screws

Length (inches)

(a) $\frac{1}{4}, \frac{3}{4}$

(b) 2

(c) 5

(d) 3

After your student has explored the concepts and answered the **Learn** Questions, uncover the mascot's speech bubble.

🗨 **What is the mascot thinking about this?** *Each x represents a screw.*

Learn Together (Student Book, pages 169 and 170)

In this section, your student will measure and record the lengths of the pencils in a tally chart, then represent the data in a line plot. Invite your student to observe each picture before proceeding with the problems in **Learn Together**.

Through questioning, lead your student to represent the data in a line plot in **Learn Together**. As you go through the problems with your student, you may wish to ask the following questions:

🗨 **How long is the pencil? How do you locate the length of the pencil on a line plot? How are fractions on a line plot carefully marked? Where do we collect data for a line plot?** *from a tally chart* **How do we plot data on a line plot?** *with an x*

After your student has explored the concepts in the **Lesson Opener**, **Learn**, and **Learn Together**, you may wish to ask these questions to encourage further reflection:

🗨 **What can you tell me about line plots? What does each plot on a line plot represent?**

You may wish to have your student summarize his/her learning in a math journal. Invite your student to choose a line plot from the Student Book or create a new one, and explain the features of a line plot.

- **QUESTION 1** requires your student to read the length of each pencil in inches.
  - 🗨 **What do you find difficult about measuring to the quarter-inch?** *Answers vary.* **Why do we write it like that?** *Because it is two inches plus a quarter-inch, so we write $2\frac{1}{4}$.*

- **QUESTIONS 2** requires your student to measure lengths to halves and fourths of an inch and record the results in a tally chart. Then create a line plot to represent the data.
  - 🗨 **How can you record your data from the tally chart on the line plot?** *I can look at the tallies on the tally chart, then put the same number of x marks above each measurement on the line plot.* **How do you know where to put each x mark?** *If I make sure that I use the data from the same length on the tally chart as on the line plot, I should be doing it right.*

Learn Together Answers

(Student Book, pages 169 and 170)

1. **(a)** $2\frac{1}{4}$

   (b) $1\frac{3}{4}$

2. **(a)**

Length (inches)	$1\frac{1}{4}$	$1\frac{3}{4}$	2	$2\frac{1}{4}$	$2\frac{1}{2}$
Tally	I	II	IIII	I	I

   (b)

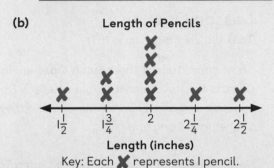

Length of Pencils

Length (inches)

Key: Each ✖ represents 1 pencil.

Lesson Debrief

- Conclude the lesson and facilitate your student's reflection by asking him/her to answer the **Focus Question** and share his/her thinking.
- Extend the discussion by posing the following questions.
  - 💬 **What is a line plot?** *A representation of a set of data showing one x for every data point along a line.* **What is important to know when creating a line plot?** *the data given* **Where can you find information on a line plot?** *We can look at the title and the label to find out what the plot represents, and see the number of x marks at each data point to compare data.* **How can you use a line plot to share information?** *We can represent quantities of data at each data point in the plot with x marks.* **Why would you use a line plot instead of a different graph?** *A line plot is a quick way to show simple quantities.*

Reflect and Connect

Allow time for your student to reflect on what he/she has learned and ask questions about what he/she may be unsure of.

- Encourage him/her to share anything that was confusing or difficult, and how thinking about it differently and perseverance helped the process of learning.
- Ask your student to answer a reflection question or draw a picture to show his/her reflection. You may offer these prompts:
  - 💬 **What have you learned about reading and understanding line plots? What is important to know about making line plots? What would you tell someone who does not know how to read or show information on a line plot? What is important to know?**

What to look for:
- ability to gather data, create a line plot using mixed numbers, and represent the data on the line plot
- ability to read and interpret data from a line plot to answer questions

Practice On Your Own (Student Book, pages 171 to 174)

- **QUESTION 1 (a)** assesses your student's ability to represent the measurements from a tally chart using a line plot.
- **QUESTIONS 1 (b)** to **(e)** assess your student's ability to interpret data from the line plot.
- **QUESTION 2 (a)** assesses your student's ability to use an inch ruler to measure the width of a shape to halves and fourths of an inch.
- **QUESTION 2 (b)** assesses your student's ability to record the measurements in (a) on a line plot to show the data.
- **QUESTIONS 2 (c)** to **(f)** assess your student's ability to interpret data from the line plot.

Practice On Your Own Answers

(Student Book, pages 171 to 174)

1. (a)

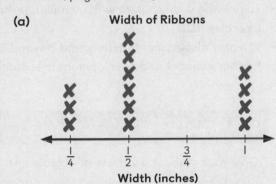

Width of Ribbons
Width (inches)
Key: Each ✗ represents 1 roll of ribbon.

(b) 3
(c) 2
(d) 9
(e) 13

2. (b)

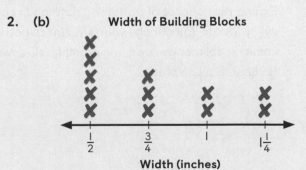

Width of Building Blocks
Width (inches)
Key: Each ✗ represents 1 building block.

(c) 4
(d) $\frac{1}{2}$; $1\frac{1}{4}$
(e) 2; 5
(f) 7

Think!

- **QUESTION 3** assesses your student's ability to reason about the scale on a line plot, and then interpret data from the line plot.

Caution

Your student who may lack sufficient practice measuring and recording measurements to the nearest quarter-inch might have a difficult time marking the measurements on the horizontal axis of the line plot.

Please see the **For Additional Support** box above for ideas on how to remediate the gap.

More Resources

- Refer to **Do More at Home** below and **Reteach 3, Exercise 9C** if your student needs additional support.
- When your student is ready, have him/her work on **Additional Practice 3B, Exercise 9C**.
- To provide your student with a challenge, have him/her work on **Extension 3, Exercise 9C**.
- You may also assign **Mastery and Beyond 3B, Chapter 9, Practice 3** to provide further support and development to sustain learning.

Do More at Home

Give your student a variety of objects he/she can measure to the nearest quarter-inch, for example, screws or paper clips of different sizes. Invite your student to measure each size of the given object, count them, organize the data in a tally chart, then create a line plot representing the data. Your student should make a few problems for you to solve, as well as an answer key so you can "check" your work—and that of your student!

Extend the concept of gathering data and representing it in a line plot to everyday life. Encourage your student to gather data by measuring some common objects you own, for example, silverware, and represent his/her findings in a line plot.

Think! Answers

3.

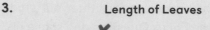

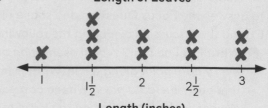

Length (inches)
Key: Each ✗ stands for 1 leaf.

4 leaves are shorter than 2 inches. There are 4 intervals between 1 and 3, so the tick mark in the middle must be 2. From the line plot, I count 4 leaves that are shorter than 2 inches.

Digging Deeper

Encourage your student to make a tally chart and line plot representing any set of data that is of interest, and then ask you questions about it to see whether you can get them right.

Chapter Wrap Up

Before your student works on **Performance Task**, help him/her recap the key learning objectives and develop a concept map to reflect the concepts and skills of the chapter. Use the following key terms to start constructing the concept map:

- Picture graphs
- Bar graphs
- Line plots

Encourage your student to complete the **Chapter Self-Reflection** on page 179 as a form of self-reflection.

Performance Task (Student Book, pages 175 to 178)

Refer your student to the **Performance Task** to consolidate and deepen his/her understanding of the chapter through tasks that require him/her to show, explain, and/or apply thinking. You may use the rubric on page 176 to encourage your student to set his/her own goals.

QUESTION (a) requires your student to read and interpret a bar graph to find the total number of students who took part in a survey.

🗨 **What information can you find on the graph? How do you calculate totals? Can you tell the total number of classmates who took part in the survey from Oliver's graph? Why or why not?**

QUESTION (b) requires your student to read the value of a bar between two numbers on the scale

🗨 **What information do you have? How can you carry out the task? What helps you justify your reasoning?**

QUESTIONS (c) and **(d)** require your student to read and interpret a bar graph to find the number of students who read a given number of books.

🗨 **Does your reasoning make sense in this situation? Why or why not?**

QUESTION (e) requires your student to read and interpret a bar graph to find the total number of books read in the month.

🗨 **What is your strategy for approaching this part of the problem? What information do you need to solve it? Where can you find that information? What is a possible tripping point where someone might make a mistake?**

QUESTION (f) requires your student to reason if the bar graph correctly shows the information given in the table and explain his/her answer.

🗨 **Does Oliver's graph match his data? Why or why not?**

Performance Task Answers

(Student Book, pages 175 to 178)

(a) 23
(b) 7
(c) 2
(d) 6
(e) 47
(f) Total number of students (from the table)
= 2 + 7 + 11 + 5 = 25
Total number of students (from the bar graph) = 7 + 11 + 5 = 23
The bar graph shows only data from 23 students. The data for two students are missing. His bar graph is wrong as the bar representing the two students who read 0 books is not shown on the bar graph.

(g)

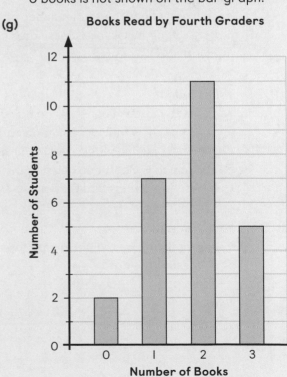

Books Read by Fourth Graders

QUESTION (g) requires your student to model and draw the bar graph to correctly represent the given data.

💬 How will you represent the same data? How will you check your work? How can you be sure you have accurately represented all the data?

Rubric (Student Book, page 178)

Use the scoring guide to help you give feedback on your student's work. Use the comments section to provide information about what was done well and what could be improved. Write words of encouragement to let your student know what he/she has done well.

Scoring Rubric		
	Description	**Point(s)**
(a)	Your student: • correctly finds the number of classmates who took part in the survey. (23)	1
(b)	Your student: • correctly finds the number of classmates who read 1 book each. (7)	1
(c)	Your student: • correctly finds the number of books read by most classmates. (2)	1
(d)	Your student: • correctly finds the number of classmates who read more than 2 books each. (6)	1
(e)	Your student: • correctly finds the total number of books read by Oliver's classmates in the month. (47)	1
(f)	Your student: • correctly determines that the bar graph does not show the correct information. • correctly justifies their reasoning why the bar graph is incorrect. (missing the data for students who read 0 books)	0.5 0.5
(g)	Your student: • correctly draws the bar graph to represent the data.	2
	Total	**8**

Use this table as a guide to help you relate your student's scores to his/her performance levels.

Level	Score
😊 😊 😊	7–8
😊 😊	2.5–6.5
😊	0–2

Project Work (Student Book, Chapter 8, page 142)

- Your student is given an opportunity to make connections between science and mathematics in this project work.
- At the end of **Chapter 9**, your student should be able to complete **Parts 3** and **4**.
- **Part 3** requires your student to record the results of each experiment visually using a graph of his/her choice.
- **Part 4** requires your student to ask questions regarding the mass and size (volume) of objects to achieve the aim of convincing first graders.

Chapter Practice (Student Book, pages 179 to 184)

- Have your student work on **Chapter Practice** in the Student Book independently to help him/her consolidate and extend understanding of the chapter.
- You may find a summary of the chapter learning objectives and the difficulty level of the questions below.
- Teaching prompts are provided for Level 2 questions.
- When your student is ready, have him/her work on **Additional Practice 3B**, **Chapter Practice**.

Question	Level	Chapter 9 Learning Objectives	Section(s)	Day(s)
1	1	Read and interpret picture graphs.	9A	2
2	1	Create picture graphs. Read and interpret picture graphs.	9A	2
3	1	Read and interpret bar graphs.	9B	3
4	1	Create bar graphs. Read and interpret bar graphs.	9B	3
5	2	Read and interpret picture graphs. Generate and show measurement data by making line plots. Interpret line plots. Create bar graphs.	9A, 9B, 9C	2, 3, 4

QUESTION 5 requires your student to create a line plot from a given picture graph, interpret information from the line plot to solve problems, and create a bar graph to show the same data.

💬 **What is the difference between the data on the picture graph and the way it will be presented on the line plot?** *On the picture graph each point represents 3 students. On the line plot each point represents 1 student.* **How do you know?** *The key tells us.* **How will you figure out the scale to use on your grid lines for the bar graph?** *I can look at the key on the picture graph or I can figure it out based on the multiples.*

Chapter Practice Answers

(Student Book, pages 179 to 184)

1. **(a)** 8
   (b) 24
   (c) 16
   (d) 72

2. **(a)**

Favorite Part of School Play	
Costumes	🙂🙂
Singing	🙂🙂🙂🙂
Dancing	🙂🙂🙂
Acting	🙂

Key: Each 🙂 represents 3 students.

   (b) singing
   (c) 3
   (d) 30

3. **(a)** brown
   (b) gray
   (c) 3; 6 − 3 = 3
   (d) 23; 6 + 9 + 3 + 5 = 23

Chapter Test

- Assign **Chapter Test 9** in **Assessment Guide Teacher Edition** to assess your student's understanding of the chapter.

4. (a)

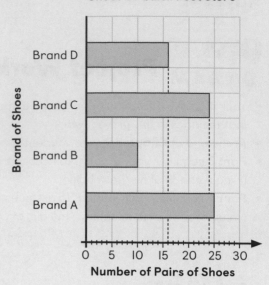

Shoes at Quick Feet Store

(b) 75; 25 + 10 + 24 + 16 = 75
(c) 9; 25 − 16 = 9

5. (a)

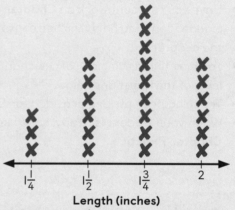

Length of Little Finger

Key: Each ✗ represents 1 student.

(b) $1\frac{3}{4}$

(c) 9

(d) 3; 6 − 3 = 3

(e) 24; 3 + 6 + 9 + 6 = 24

(f)

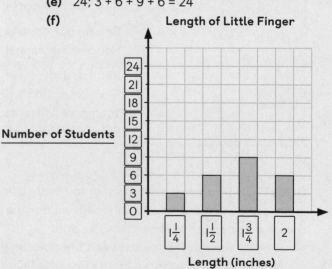

Length of Little Finger

Chapter Self-Reflection

Check (✓) to show what I can do.

I Can	Yes	Not Sure	No
read and interpret picture graphs.			
create picture graphs.			
read and interpret bar graphs.			
create bar graphs.			
generate and show measurement data by making line plots.			
interpret line plots.			

MY JOURNAL

I can show...

I still wonder...

Solve! Heuristics (Student Book, page 185)

Heuristic: Make a List
Go through the four-step problem-solving model to guide your student to solve the problem.

Alternative strategy
Heuristic: Draw a Model
Encourage your student to share alternative diagrams to solve the problem. For example, guide him/her to draw a bar model for the sample problem:

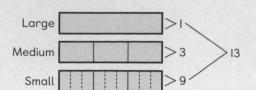

 Step I   **Understand**

Show the problem and picture only. Have your student read the problem and direct his/her attention to the picture.

🗨 **What do you know?** *There is a large box; 3 medium boxes will fit in it and 3 small boxes will fit in each medium box.* **What do you need to find out?** *How many boxes there are in all.*

 Step 2   **Plan**

Invite your student to consider the best way to solve the problem using a visual to help you understand the problem.

🗨 **How could you start to solve the problem?** *make a list; draw a diagram*
If there was one medium box, how many boxes would there be in all? *4*
How do you know? *The medium box plus 3 small boxes is 4 boxes in all.*
How might that look like in a chart? *Support your student to make a rudimentary chart.* **How might you keep track of all the boxes in this problem?** *make a list*

 Step 3   **Do**

Draw the beginnings of the chart in the Student Book on a whiteboard, leaving out the words *medium* and *small*, and the lines to each small box. Invite your student to complete the chart.

🗨 **What pattern do you see?** *It looks like a tree.* **How many boxes are there in all?** *13*

 Step 4   **Look Back**

Encourage your student to look back over the answer to ensure that it makes sense. Then have your student consider another way to solve the problem. Guide your student to check the answer.

🗨 **How might you check the answer? Is the answer correct? What is another way to solve the problem?**

Solve! Heuristics (page 186)

Question 1 requires your student to make a list to find the number of grandchildren Mr. and Mrs. Jones have in all.

💬 **What do you know?** *4 sons with 2 children each* **What do you need to find?** *How many grandchildren there are.* **How can knowing the number of sons help you find the number of grandchildren?** *If we multiply sons by their children, we will find total grandchildren, 4 × 2 = 8.* **What might you do to help see the problem?** *make a list* **How might you check your work?** *Answers vary.*

Question 2 requires your student to make a list to find the number of 2 flavor choices that can be made with 4 flavors.

💬 **How will we make a list for this problem?** *List each flavor and put the other flavors next to each one.* **How many combinations are there?** *12* **Are they all different?** *no* **How might we indicate the duplicates?** *Answers vary.*

Caution

Visualizing this can be quite difficult. Mathematically, there are 12 possible combinations, since each of the four flavors can combine with three other flavors (4 × 3 = 12). Practically, however, there are only 6 combinations due to duplicate combinations. It will be helpful to draw this on a whiteboard and have your student circle each possible combination in the same color. For example, circle both apple-berry and berry-apple in purple, and count it as one possible combination.

Solve! Heuristics Answers

(Student Book, page 186)

1.

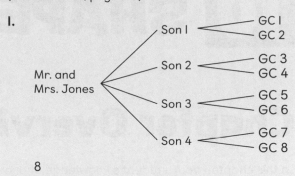

8

Alternative strategy
Heuristic: Draw a Model

Encourage your student to share alternative diagrams to solve the problem. For example, guide him/her to draw a bar model for Question 1:

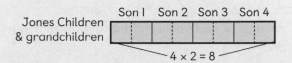

2.

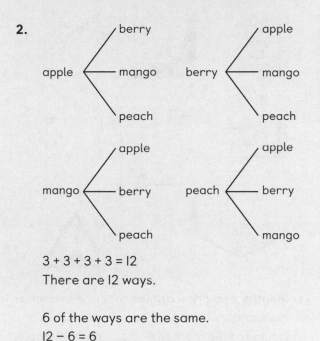

3 + 3 + 3 + 3 = 12
There are 12 ways.

6 of the ways are the same.
12 − 6 = 6
6

Alternative strategy
Heuristic: Use mathematical tools

Invite your student to share how he/she might solve the problem in another way. For example, one might solve this problem by using different colored counters for each flavor in order to visually eliminate duplicate combinations quickly.

Chapter 10 SHAPES

Chapter Overview

In this chapter, your student's knowledge of drawing, sorting, and partitioning 2-D shapes from Grade 2 will be extended to understanding angles regardless of orientation in space, right triangles, triangles with angles larger or smaller than right triangles, and various types of quadrilaterals. By the end of the chapter, your student will be able to tell the differences and similarities between rectangles, squares, and rhombuses, and explain how side length and angle type affects the definition of various 4-sided figures. Your student will:

- **recognize and name right angles** in real-world objects and drawings.

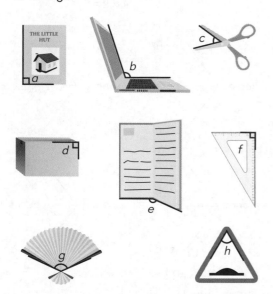

- **identify and draw angles** that are smaller or larger than right angles.
  Compare the marked angles to a right angle.
  Write **smaller** or **larger**.

(a)  _____larger_____ than a right angle.

(b)  _____smaller_____ than a right angle.

- **recognize and sort triangles** by their angles.

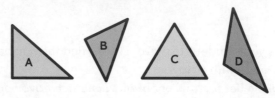

(a) Triangles __A__ and __B__ are right triangles.

(b) Triangle __C__ only has angles smaller than a right angle.

(c) Triangle __D__ has an angle larger than a right angle.

- identify **various quadrilaterals**.

X   y   Z

- **identify and compare** rectangles, squares, and rhombuses.

Compare a square and a rectangle.
How are they alike?
How are they different?

This is a **rhombus**.
It has __4__ equal sides.

- **identify and draw quadrilaterals** other than rectangles, squares, and rhombuses.

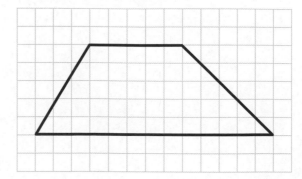

Key Ideas

- We can recognize and identify right angles, angles that are larger than a right angle and angles that are smaller than a right angle in real-world objects and in triangles.

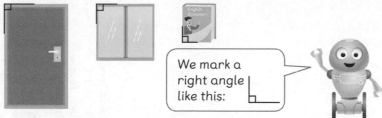

We mark a right angle like this: ⌐

A pentagon is divided into three triangles, A, B, and C.

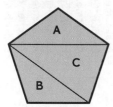

(a) Triangles A and B each have ___2___ angles smaller than a right angle.

Each triangle also has ___1___ angle larger than a right angle.

(b) All angles in Triangle C are __smaller__ than a right angle.

- We can identify, compare, and draw quadrilaterals.

Look at the quadrilaterals below.

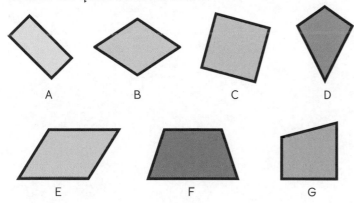

A   B   C   D

E   F   G

Fill in the blanks.

(a) Figure ___B___ has 4 equal sides and no right angles.

It is a __rhombus__.

(b) Figures ___B___, ___D___, ___E___, ___F___, and ___G___ are not rectangles.

(c) Figure ___C___ has 4 right angles and 4 equal sides.

It is a __square__.

(d) Figure ___G___ has right angles, but is not a square or a rectangle.

Draw a quadrilateral that is **both** a rhombus and a rectangle.

Answers vary.

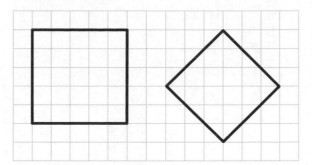

Materials You Will Need

- 1 piece of graph paper
- 1 ruler
- 1 set of index cards
- 1 set of attribute blocks
- 1 set of craft sticks
- 1 set of pattern blocks
- Shape Cutouts (TR35)

Chapter at a Glance

	Day	Learning Objective(s)	Vocabulary	Resource(s)	Material(s)
Chapter Opener / Recall Student Book, pp. 187–188	1 of 13				• 1 set of attribute blocks • 1 set of pattern blocks • 1 copy of Shape Cutouts (TR35)
Section 10A **Angles and Shapes (1):** **Angles and Triangles** Student Book, pp. 189–194	2 of 13	• Identify right angles and angles that are smaller or larger than a right angle. • Identify right triangles.	• right angle • right triangle	• **Additional Practice 3B,** Exercise 10A (1) • **Reteach 3,** Exercise 10A (1) • **Extension 3,** Exercise 10A (1) • **Mastery and Beyond 3B,** Chapter 10, Practice 1	• 1 set of craft sticks
Section 10A **Angles and Shapes (2):** **Angles and Quadrilaterals** Student Book, pp. 195–200	3 of 13	• Identify quadrilaterals with shared attributes. • Distinguish between types of quadrilaterals based on the side lengths and the types of angles. • State the relationship between rectangles, squares, and rhombuses.	• rhombus	• **Additional Practice 3B,** Exercise 10A (2) • **Reteach 3,** Exercise 10A (2) • **Extension 3,** Exercise 10A (2) • **Mastery and Beyond 3B,** Chapter 10, Practice 2	• 1 set of index cards
Chapter Wrap Up / **Performance Task** Student Book, pp. 201–203	4 of 13				• 1 ruler
STEAM Project Work Student Book, pp. 204	5 of 13				
Chapter Practice Student Book, pp. 205–208	6–7 of 13			• **Additional Practice 3B,** Chapter Practice	
Chapter Test / **Cumulative** **Assessment / End-of-Year Assessment**	8–13 of 13			• **Assessment Guide Teacher Edition,** Chapter Test 10 • **Assessment Guide Teacher Edition,** Cumulative Assessment 4 • **Assessment Guide Teacher Edition,** End-of-Year Assessment	• 1 piece of graph paper

Chapter Opener (Student Book, page 187)

Consider the picture and the question on the page. Discuss them with your student. Prompt him/her to consider the information given in the picture and what is being asked. You may wish to ask the following questions:

💬 **What do you notice about the picture?** *There are shapes on the wall and pattern blocks on the table.* **What sorts of shapes do you see?** *square; rectangle; triangle; rhombus; trapezoid; hexagon; pentagon* **How do you know what makes a particular shape?** *the number of sides and angles; whether or not the sides are of equal length* **What is an angle?** *The place where two sides of a shape meet to form a corner.* **What is a quadrilateral?** *a shape with 4 sides* **Which shapes are quadrilaterals?** *squares; rectangles; rhombuses; trapezoids*

For Additional Support

Your student who struggles will often benefit from inserting a pictorial step into the learning progression. If identifying 2-D shapes is difficult, have your student draw them on a whiteboard while identifying their attributes.

💬 **How do you know this is a triangle?** *It has 3 sides and 3 angles.* **How do you know this is a quadrilateral?** *It has 4 sides and 4 angles.* **How many different ways can you make this shape out of other shapes?** *Hexagons can be composed of 6 triangles, or 2 trapezoids, or 1 rectangle and 2 triangles.*

Digging Deeper

Choose two different quadrilaterals to compare, for example, rhombuses and rectangles.

💬 **What is the same about these two different quadrilaterals?** *They both have 4 sides and 4 angles.* **What is different about these two different quadrilaterals?** *the length of their sides* **Can you make a rule to help you identify quadrilaterals?** *All quadrilaterals have 4 sides and 4 angles. Some special quadrilaterals have 4 equal sides, as in the case of rhombuses, or 4 right angles, as in the case of rectangles—and squares have both equal sides and 4 right angles!*

Teaching Tip

Kick off this chapter by allowing your student to play with 2-D shapes, creating an elaborate scene or picture from them. If you do not have attribute blocks, cut out a host of different shapes using Shape Cutouts (TR35) and allow your student to use those. Keep them accessible for the remainder of Chapter 10.

💬 **Which shapes did you use? Which shapes are quadrilaterals? What is a quadrilateral? How do you tell which shape is which?** *by number of sides or angles, etc.*

Recall (Student Book, page 188)

Material(s)
- I set of attribute blocks
- I set of pattern blocks
- I copy of Shape Cutouts (TR35)

Before moving on to the problems on page 188 of the Student Book, extend the suggested activity from the **Teaching Tip** to include review of the concepts covered in the **Recall**.
- Invite your student to build a specific picture and tell you the shapes he/she used to make it.
- Have your student choose all the shapes with 4 angles and compare them.
- Invite your student to count the number of angles in a pentagon or hexagon.
  - 💬 **How can we determine what a specific shape is?** *By sides, corners, and if the sides are of equal length, etc.*

Make it a Game!

In Great Shape

Using attribute or pattern blocks or Shape Cutouts (TR35), take turns with your student to select a shape from a bowl while your eyes are blindfolded. After your student chooses the shape, ask two questions from the following list:

💬 **What other shapes can make up this figure? How many angles make this shape? How many sides does this shape have? What is the name of this shape? How do you know if this shape is a quadrilateral or not?**

Your student earns a point for each correct answer. Switch places and the first player who earns 10 points wins the game.

After this review, your student should be able to complete the tasks on page 188 of the Student Book independently.
- **QUESTION 1** assesses your student's ability to identify squares, rectangles, and triangles in each composite figure.
- **QUESTION 2** assesses your student's ability to recognize and identify the number of angles in each figure.
- **QUESTION 3** assesses your student's ability to identify quadrilaterals as shapes with 4 sides and 4 angles.

Recall Answers
(Student Book, page 188)

1. **(a)** triangle; square
   (b) rectangle; triangle

2. **(a)** 3
   (b) 4

3.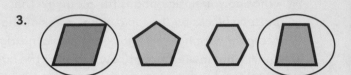

10A Angles and Shapes (1)

Learning Objective(s)
- Identify right angles and angles that are smaller or larger than a right angle.
- Identify right triangles.

Vocabulary
- right angle
- right triangle

Material(s)
- 1 set of craft sticks

ANGLES AND TRIANGLES (Student Book, pages 189 to 194)

Lesson Opener

Task (Student Book, page 189)

Show your student the **Lesson Opener** and cover the rest of the page. Discuss the question with your student. Do not show your student how to do the task and allow him/her to explore similarities about the angles on the door, the window, and the book.

Refer your student to **Learn** and **Learn Together** in the Student Book for reflection after your student has explored the concepts. Use questions to build understanding and direct instruction to refine understanding.

Lesson Development

Learn (Student Book, page 189)

After discussing the angles, show your student the Learn on page 189 of the Student Book and read it together. You may wish to ask these questions:

What is a vertex? *A corner; the point where two lines meet.* **What does it mean to fit a square perfectly? How do you see it?** *Answers vary.*

Look for and help your student make a connection between the corner of the book and the angle of the door and window, even though they are oriented differently.

Draw your student's attention to the robot.

What is the mascot saying? *We mark a right angle with a little box.* **Why do you think they mark a right angle like this, with a small box?** *A right angle indicates an angle that can perfectly fit a square, and the symbol for it is a perfect little square.*

Focus Question

How do you describe angles and triangles?

Invite your student to ponder this question as you go through the lesson. Revisit this question when you reach the end of the lesson to check his/her understanding.

Teaching Tip

In this chapter, you will help your student learn key characteristics of angles, triangles, and quadrilaterals. You may wish to highlight the concepts presented here in everyday life, particularly if your student is not adept at naming shapes and decomposing them as presented in the **Recall**. Encourage your student to look for various types of triangles and note intersections of lines that form angles as you go about your day. For example, while walking, you might look at a tree, then invite your student to find angles that are greater or less than right angles, and further find where right angles occur most. You may wish to ask these questions:

How can you tell if an angle is a right angle? Describe it. Do you see more right angles naturally occurring or man-made?

As your student solidifies understanding of vertices, sides, etc., encourage him/her to include these in distinguishing various shapes. By informally applying these concepts, your student will be able to move forward confidently in the concrete-pictorial-abstract learning progression.

Activity! (Student Book, page 190)

The purpose of this activity is to prove to your student that right angles are formed at the corners of perfect squares. Allow your student to physically fold a paper and check for right angles, as well as discover many such angles around the study room.

🗨 **What is true of right angles?** *They can be measured with anything that has a perfectly square corner because they fit a square perfectly.* **What makes right angles different from other angles that are not right angles?** *The other angles are smaller or larger than right angles.* **How do you know?** *We can measure them using a tool that we make ourselves from a carefully folded paper.* **If you make the tool yourself, what must you be careful to do?** *I must carefully fold the paper so that the corner is square.* **What other tools might you use?** *Anything that has a square corner will work as a tool.*

😀 Invite your student to consider if the paper must be folded into equal parts to get a right angle.

🗨 **What are some ways you could find out?** *I could fold a paper with unequal parts and see if that works.* **Try it!**

Your student should determine that the size of the parts does not matter, but the lines must be straight to make a right angle. Your student could fold a paper into two or more unequal horizontal strips, but if the lines are parallel and the cross fold is perpendicular, he/she will produce a right angle.

🗨 **What is important in order to make a right angle?** *I have to make sure my lines are perfectly lined up; the size of the folds does not matter.*

Learn Together (Student Book, pages 191 and 192)

In this section, your student will learn to observe angles that are larger or smaller than right angles, and will classify triangles by angle type. Invite your student to observe each picture before proceeding with the problems in **Learn Together**. Take care to hide the robot's speech bubble in Question 2, and give your student some time to generate that thought before showing it.

Through questioning, lead your student to identify the angles that are smaller or larger than a right angle and describe triangles using different types of angles in **Learn Together**. As you go through the problems with your student, you may wish to ask the following questions:

🗨 **Why do we call these triangles?** *Tri means "three." A triangle is a shape with three angles.* **What sorts of different triangles do you see? What are a few ways to describe triangles by the angles that are contained inside them?** *Right triangles; triangles larger or smaller than right.* **Which other shapes can you make using only triangles?** *Answers vary.*

Activity! Answers

(Student Book, page 190)

(b) Answers vary.

For Additional Support

Your student will need to play with angles physically in order to understand the differences among them. **Activity** on page 190 of the Student Book will help your student get much needed practice and ground his/her understanding in real-world experience.

Make sure your student sees angles in a variety of orientations, not just upright. Point out naturally occurring angles in various locations and orientations.

🗨 **Is this an angle too? Why or why not? How do you know if it is an angle when it opens in the opposite direction?** *An angle is formed wherever two lines meet at a point. It does not matter which direction the opening of the angle is facing.*

Digging Deeper

Help your student practice creating and identifying different angles with a ruler on a whiteboard. Draw any two lines that meet at a vertex. Your student can check to see if the angles are right angles or not, then indicate that by drawing either a small square or an arc inside the vertex. Be sure to vary the orientation of the angles. To make this activity more fun, switch places.

Variation: cross any two lines and indicate the type of angles formed by them.

🗨 **If one angle is right, what is true of the other angles formed at the spot where the lines cross?** *They are all right.* **If one angle formed by the crossing lines is larger than a right angle, what will be true of the other angles?** *One will also be larger, and the other two will be smaller.* **Is there a pattern?** *Yes; opposite angles are either both smaller or both larger than right angles.*

After your student has explored the concepts in the **Lesson Opener**, **Learn**, and **Learn Together**, you may wish to ask these questions to encourage further reflection:

🗨 **What can you say about angles? What are some important things to know about triangles? Where are some places you have seen angles or triangles before that you did not notice?**

You may wish to have your student summarize his/her learning in a math journal. Have your student write two important things to know about triangles, then draw a picture to show what he/she means.

• **QUESTION 1** requires your student to identify if the marked angle on a real-life object is smaller or larger than a right angle.

🗨 **Are these angles right angles?** *no* **How do you know?** *They are not marked as right angles.* **How can you prove if the markings are correct?** *You can use a tool with a corner that is exactly square to see if they are larger or smaller than right angles.*

• **QUESTION 2** requires your student to identify that a triangle has 3 sides and 3 angles.

🗨 **What makes a triangle?** *It has 3 sides and 3 angles.* **How do you think we started to use the word triangle?** *The word means "3 angles." All triangles have 3 angles.* **Describe these two triangles by the angles they contain.** *One contains all angles that are smaller than a right angle. The other contains one right angle.* **How do you know that?** *The angles are marked, and also, I can see it by exactly fitting a square corner in the right angle.* **Do you think we should have a special name for a triangle that contains one special angle like a right angle?** *Answers vary.* **What do we call a triangle with one right angle?** *a right triangle*

• **QUESTION 3** requires your student to identify the triangles based on their angles.

🗨 **What is the definition of a right triangle?** *It is a triangle with one right angle.* **Do these triangles have any clues to help you know if they are right triangles or not?** *no; none of the angles is marked.* **What is another way to find out if a triangle is a right triangle or not?** *Check to see if one of the angles is right by using a tool with a corner that is exactly square.*

• **QUESTION 4** requires your student to describe the angles in three triangles that are divided from a pentagon.

🗨 **What is this shape?** *Since it has five sides, it is a pentagon.* **Do these triangles have any clues to help you know if they are right triangles or not?** *no; none of the angles is marked.* **What is another way to find out if a triangle is a right triangle or not?** *Check to see if one of the angles is right angle by using a tool with a corner that is exactly square.* **What is true about the triangles in this figure?** *There are no right triangles.*

Learn Together Answers

(Student Book, pages 191 and 192)

1. (a) larger
   (b) smaller

2. 3; 3

3. (a) A; B
   (b) C
   (c) D

4. (a) 2; 1
   (b) smaller

For Additional Support

If your student generally needs more support to create a picture for mental math in his/her mind's eye, be sure to provide physical triangles and make your student draw the triangles you are discussing. Doing so helps your student retain a visual mental picture as well as manipulate the shapes mentally. Make sure your student encounters right triangles in a variety of orientations to promote greater mental flexibility.

Teaching Tip

Geometry requires your student to see shapes and figures in the mind's eye, and manipulate the orientation in space of those figures. Begin to practice this now with your student by having him/her turn various shapes in different directions physically, then draw triangles on whiteboard in different orientations. Making time for some of the suggested games and extensions in today's lesson will also help introduce the sort of flexible thinking required for future success with geometry.

Lesson Debrief

- Conclude the lesson and facilitate your student's reflection by asking him/her to answer the **Focus Question** and share his/her thinking.
- Extend the discussion by posing the following questions.
  - 💬 **Describe angles. What are some different ways that angles look?** *Some are wide open or obtuse, some are smaller, or acute, some are right. Third grade students will learn how to name right angles in this lesson, but not the other types of angles. Some may observe the differences and put it into their own words.*
  - 💬 **How can angles help you identify shapes?** *The number of angles helps us identify shapes, such as 3 angles make a triangle.* **What other attributes help you identify shapes?** *The number of sides also helps us identify shapes, such as 3-sided figures are triangles.* **What are some places you see angles in real life?** *Answers vary.* **What are some different ways that triangles are constructed?** *Some have an angle that is wide open, some have only smaller angles, some have a right angle.* **How can different types of angles help you describe the triangles?** *Right triangles, triangles with only angles smaller than a right angle, or triangles with an angle larger than a right angle.* **How many of each types of angle are in the triangles?** *There can be two or more angles smaller than a right angle, but only one right angle or one angle larger than a right angle.* **Why there cannot be more than one right angle in a right triangle?** *Because then it would be a square or a rectangle or some other shape. It would have more than three sides, or the sides would not be closed.*

Digging Deeper

Help your student think a little more deeply about patterns in triangles.

- 💬 **If one angle is right, what is true of the sizes of the other angles in the triangle?** *They are both smaller than right.* **Is that always true?** *yes* **Why?** *A triangle must only have three sides, and we must connect them all. So if there is one larger angle, the others will be smaller.* **What if one angle is larger than right?** *The other two angles will also be smaller.* **What different types of angle combinations can you think of and create for triangles using three craft sticks?** *Answers vary.* **What patterns do you observe?** *Answers vary.*

- Allow time for your student to reflect on what he/she has learned and ask questions about what he/she may be unsure of.
- Encourage him/her to share anything that was confusing or difficult, and how thinking about it differently and perseverance helped the process of learning.
- Ask your student to answer a reflection question or draw a picture to show his/her reflection. You may offer these prompts:
  💬 **What do you know about angles? How can you use angles to name triangles?**

What to look for:
- an explanation of how we measure and mark angles to indicate if they are right angles or not
- an explanation of how we know it is a right triangle or not

Practice On Your Own (Student Book, pages 193 and 194)

- **QUESTION 1** assesses your student's ability to sort angles with reference to a right angle in real-life objects.
- **QUESTION 2** assesses your student's ability to sort triangles based on the types of angles in each triangle.

Think!

- **QUESTION 3** assesses your student's ability to divide a hexagon into triangles and describe them.

In Question 1, your student will have a hard time visually since the angles are at various orientations in space. You can help your student overcome this by finding various angles in the real world in different orientations, and by drawing different angles at various orientations on a whiteboard.

In Question 3, your student who have a hard time visually may struggle with this more than others. Build a pentagon or hexagon using different types of paper triangles, each of the same size and varying sizes, in order to build confidence and give your student a chance at internalizing a mental picture for geometry.

Practice On Your Own Answers

(Student Book, pages 193 and 194)

1.

Smaller than a right angle	Right angle	Larger than a right angle
c, h	a, d, f	b, e, g

2.

Triangle	Angles smaller than a right angle	Right angle	Angles larger than a right angle
P	✓		
Q	✓		
R	✓		✓
S	✓	✓	

Think! Answers

3.

Answers vary. Example:
There are two different triangles in the hexagon. There are two right triangles in the hexagon.

More Resources

- Refer to **Do More at Home** below and **Reteach 3, Exercise 10A (1)** if your student needs additional support.
- When your student is ready, have him/her work on **Additional Practice 3B, Exercise 10A (1)**.
- To provide your student with a challenge, have him/her work on **Extension 3, Exercise 10A (1)**.
- You may also assign **Mastery and Beyond 3B, Chapter 10, Practice 1** to provide further support and development to sustain learning.

Do More at Home

Here are two activities your student might enjoy that will help solidify understanding about angles and triangles.

1) Organize a hunt for angles hidden in your home with you or an older sibling or friend. Using paper, pencils, craft sticks, and scissors, choose two different rooms in your home in which to find angles. Each of you finds three angles: one right, one larger than a right angle, and one smaller than a right angle. For example, the right angle could come from the spot where two walls meet, and the angle larger than a right angle might come from the angles on a chair. Using the craft sticks to help, make each angle and draw it on a piece of paper. Cut out your three angles and switch cut-outs with the other player. Race to be the first to find all three angles in your opponent's room.

2) Find the least number of triangles you can use to build or draw a pentagon or hexagon using several different types of paper triangles, each of the same size or varying sizes. For example, 6 acute triangles all of the same size will build one hexagon. The player with the least number of triangles for each shape wins. Variation: Earn bragging rights for finding the least number of triangles you can use when using at least one right triangle.

   💬 **How do the types of angles in the triangles you used vary?** *If I want to use the least number of triangles to make a pentagon, I will not have any right triangles.*

10A Angles and Shapes (2)

Learning Objective(s)
- Identify quadrilaterals with shared attributes.
- Distinguish between types of quadrilaterals based on the side lengths and the types of angles.
- State the relationship between rectangles, squares, and rhombuses.

Vocabulary
- rhombus

Material(s)
- 1 set of index cards

ANGLES AND QUADRILATERALS (Student Book, pages 195 to 200)

Lesson Opener
Task (Student Book, page 195)

Show your student the **Lesson Opener** and cover the rest of the page. Discuss the questions with your student. Do not show your student how to do the task and allow him/her to explore different types of quadrilaterals.

Refer your student to **Learn** and **Learn Together** in the Student Book for reflection after your student has explored the concepts. Use questions to build understanding and direct instruction to refine understanding.

Lesson Development
Learn (Student Book, page 195)

After discussing the **Lesson Opener**, show your student the **Learn** on page 195 of the Student Book, hide from the second line of text down, including the vocabulary word quadrilateral. Have your student complete the first line of text. You may wish to ask these questions:

🗨 **What is your best guess as to what we would call a figure with 4 sides?** *Answers vary.*

Five-sided figures are pentagons and 6-sided figures are hexagons, so your student might generate something along those lines.

Uncover the second line of text and prompt your student to read it aloud.

🗨 **What do we call 4-sided figures?** *quadrilaterals* **What about figure W? Is it a quadrilateral?** *no* **Why not?** *It has 5 sides.*

Uncover the rest of page 195.

🗨 **How did you do?** *Answers vary.*

Focus Question

🗨 **How can angles describe quadrilaterals?**

Invite your student to ponder this question as you go through the lesson. Revisit this question when you reach the end of the lesson to check his/her understanding.

Teaching Tip

The last day of this lesson moves your student from triangles to 4-sided figures, called quadrilaterals. Keep a good mixture of concrete and pictorial activities, but focus on the pictorial. Drawing (and have your student draw) the various quadrilaterals presented in this lesson will solidify understanding and ability to remember the different types, as well as the similarities and differences they hold.

Learn Answers
(Student Book, page 195)

4; 4; 5

For Additional Support

Your student will need to play with physical representations of shapes in order to begin to compare and understand the differences among them. Give your student time to do this. Once he/she is able to draw various quadrilaterals and explain similarities and differences among and between them, he/she is ready to move on.

🗨 **How are these similar? How are they different? What is important to know about this shape?** *Answers will vary depending on the shapes chosen.*

Learn Together (Student Book, pages 196 to 198)

Your student will explore quadrilateral shapes and learn about rhombuses in this section. Invite your student to observe each picture before proceeding with the problems in **Learn Together**. Hide the robots' speech bubbles until your student has a chance to generate understanding on his/her own.

Through questioning, lead your student to distinguish between types of quadrilaterals based on the side lengths and the types of angles in **Learn Together**. As you go through the problems with your student, you may wish to ask the following questions:

🗨 **How are squares similar to other rectangles and rhombuses? What makes squares special?** *same side lengths* **When identifying quadrilaterals, what are some key features to consider?** *angles and side length*

After your student has explored the concepts in the **Lesson Opener**, **Learn**, and **Learn Together**, you may wish to ask these questions to encourage further reflection.

🗨 **Which quadrilaterals can you name? What makes a quadrilateral? What distinguishes one quadrilateral from another? What is something new that you did not know before?**

You may wish to have your student summarize his/her learning in a math journal. Have your student put a drawing of each type of quadrilateral studied today into his/her math journal, with an explanation of how we determine types of quadrilaterals and how they are similar or different.

- **QUESTION 1** requires your student to compare a square and a rectangle.
  🗨 **What are these two shapes?** *a square and a rectangle* **What is true about both of these two shapes?** *The pictures show they have 4 right angles.* **How are these two shapes different?** *side lengths* **How is a square a special rectangle?** *A square is a rectangle because it has 4 right angles. But it is a special rectangle because its sides are all the same length.*

😊 Invite your student to think more deeply how squares and rectangles are similar and different.

  🗨 **How are these similar?** *They both have 4 right angles.* **How are they different?** *The square has 4 sides of equal lengths while the rectangle does not.* **What is true about the side lengths of the rectangle?** *Two sets of sides are the same lengths as each other, but not as the other set of sides.*

- **QUESTION 2** requires your student to understand that a rhombus has a shared attribute of 4 equal sides with a square. Highlight what a "rhombus" is.
  🗨 **What are these two shapes?** *a square and a rhombus* **What is true about these two shapes?** *The pictures show they each have 4 equal sides.* **How are these two shapes different?** *Squares have right angles, while rhombuses do not.* **How is a square a special kind of rhombus?** *A square is a rhombus because it has 4 sides that are all the same length. But it is a special rhombus because it has 4 right angles, which many rhombuses do not have.*

Learn Together Answers

(Student Book, pages 196 to 198)

1. 4; 4

2. 4; 4

3. (a) B; rhombus
   (b) B; D; E; F; G
   (c) C; square
   (d) G

4. Answers vary.

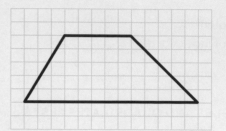

😊😊 Invite your student to think more deeply how squares and rhombuses are similar and different.

🗨 **How are these similar?** *They both have 4 equal sides.* **How are they different?** *The square has 4 right angles, while the rhombus does not.* **What is true about the angles of a rhombus?** *Unless the rhombus is also a square, two of its angles will be larger than right angles, and two angles will be smaller than right angles.*

- **QUESTION 3** requires your student to compare quadrilaterals based on the side lengths and the types of angles.

  🗨 **What about figure D? Is there anything special about it?** *It has two sets of equal sides, but not all sides are equal. It has no right angles yet it is a quadrilateral because it has four sides.* **What must a figure have to be a quadrilateral?** *four sides* **If you could sort these quadrilaterals however you liked, how would you sort them?** *by side length; by right angles*

- **QUESTION 4** requires your student to draw a quadrilateral that is not a rhombus or a rectangle.

Lesson Debrief

- Conclude the lesson and facilitate your student's reflection by asking him/her to answer the **Focus Question** and share his/her thinking.
- Extend the discussion by posing the following questions.

  🗨 **Describe the pattern of how angles appear in rhombuses.** *The angles in rhombuses are constant too, with a pair of angles smaller than right angles and another pair larger than right angles.* **What is the only thing that is true about all quadrilaterals?** *They have exactly 4 sides.*

Digging Deeper

Extend your student's understanding by asking:

🗨 **What types of figures are quadrilaterals F and G? How are they similar?** *They are trapezoids, which are quadrilaterals with one set of sides the same distance apart.*

- Allow time for your student to reflect on what he/she has learned and ask questions about what he/she may be unsure of.
- Encourage him/her to share anything that was confusing or difficult, and how thinking about it differently and perseverance helped the process of learning.
- Ask your student to answer a reflection question or draw a picture to show his/her reflection. You may offer these prompts:

  💬 **How do angles help you name certain quadrilaterals? Which ones are they? What else do you need to know to name quadrilaterals?**

What to look for:

- explanation of how we determine types of quadrilaterals and how they are similar or different

Practice On Your Own (Student Book, pages 198 to 200)

- **QUESTION 1** assesses your student's ability to identify quadrilaterals based on the number of sides.
- **QUESTION 2** assesses your student's ability to identify rectangles based on the number of right angles.
- **QUESTION 3** assesses your student's ability to identify rhombuses based on the number of equal sides.
- **QUESTION 4** assesses your student's ability to identify right angles and determine which quadrilaterals are rectangles.
- **QUESTION 5** assesses your student's ability to draw a quadrilateral that is both a rhombus and a rectangle.

Caution

In Question 4c, your student may forget that squares are special types of rectangles.

Practice On Your Own Answers

(Student Book, pages 198 to 200)

1.

A quadrilateral has 4 sides. The pentagon has 5 sides. It is not a quadrilateral.

2.

A rectangle has 4 right angles. The figures do not have 4 right angles.

3. **(a)** 4
   (b) A; B; D
   (c) it does not have 4 equal sides.

4. **(a)**

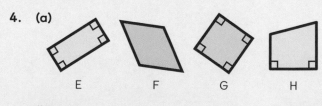

E   F   G   H

   (b) 4
   (c) E; G

5. Answers vary.

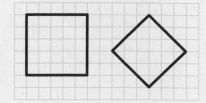

More Resources

- Refer to **Do More at Home** below and **Reteach 3, Exercise 10A (2)** if your student needs additional support.
- When your student is ready, have him/her work on **Additional Practice 3B, Exercise 10A (2)**.
- To provide your student with a challenge, have him/her work on **Extension 3, Exercise 10A (2)**.
- You may also assign **Mastery and Beyond 3B, Chapter 10, Practice 2** to provide further support and development to sustain learning.

Do More at Home

In order to help solidify conceptual understanding regarding various quadrilaterals, the following activities might be helpful.

1) Encourage your student to find quadrilaterals in magazines. Have your student cut out the shapes and sort them in different ways.

   💬 **How many different ways can you sort them? How many different quadrilaterals can you find?**

2) Glue quadrilateral cut-outs to index cards so that you and your student can each have a stack of 10-15 of them. At the count of three, you and your student each turn over a card so both of you can see it. The first person to find a way to match the two cards (by angles, side length, etc.) slaps his/her hand on the pair. If the person who slaps the cards can explain how the cards match, he/she gets the pair. If not, the other player gets to try to state how the cards match in order to win the pair. Play until one player loses all cards.

Chapter Wrap Up

Before your student works on the **Performance Task**, help him/her recap the key learning objectives and develop a concept map to reflect the concepts and skills of the chapter. Use the following key terms to start constructing the concept map:
- Angles and triangles
- Angles and quadrilaterals

Encourage your student to complete the **Chapter Self-Reflection** on page 203 as a form of self-reflection.

Performance Task (Student Book, pages 201 to 203)

Refer your student to the **Performance Task** to consolidate and deepen his/her understanding of the chapter through tasks that require him/her to show, explain, and/or apply thinking. You may use the rubric on page 199 to encourage your student to set his/her own goals.

QUESTION (a) requires your student to reason if the quadrilateral is a square.
🗨 **What strategy did you use to determine your answer? Does your answer make sense?**

QUESTION (b) requires your student to create six different quadrilaterals on geoboards.
🗨 **Is there another way? Have you discovered all the ways you can create a quadrilateral? How many ways do you think there are to answer this question?**

QUESTION (c) requires your student to determine which of the quadrilaterals they drew in (b) is not a square, a rectangle, or a rhombus.
🗨 **How can you know for sure if a shape has equal sides or right angles? Which shapes are easiest to eliminate right away?**

QUESTION (d) requires your student to reason why the quadrilateral they chose in (c) is not a square, a rectangle, or a rhombus.
🗨 **What makes the quadrilateral you chose different from squares, rhombuses, and rectangles?**

Performance Task Answers

(Student Book, pages 201 to 203)

(a) Yes. The quadrilateral has 4 equal sides and 4 right angles.

(b) Answers vary.

(c) Answers vary.

(d) Answers vary.
The quadrilateral has 4 sides and 4 angles. It is not a rhombus or a square because it does not have 4 equal sides. It is not a rectangle or a square because it does not have 4 right angles.

Teaching Tip

Your student can use a tool to help determine if a shape matches the necessary parameters. In the case of Question (c), we can measure the sides with a ruler and check the angles with something we know is a right angle, such as the corner of the ruler.

🗨 **What is the rule for your shape to be a quadrilateral?** *It must have 4 sides and 4 angles.* **Must the sides and angles all match in a quadrilateral?** *no* **What is true of a shape that is not a square, rhombus, or rectangle?** *All 4 sides are not equal, and all 4 angles are not right angles.* **What tool might you use to help you find out if a quadrilateral is square, rhombus, or rectangle?** *a ruler*

Rubric (Student Book, page 203)

Use the scoring guide to help you give feedback on your student's work. Use the comments section to provide information about what was done well and what could be improved. Write words of encouragement to let your student know what he/she has done well.

Scoring Rubric		
	Description	**Point(s)**
(a)	Your student: • correctly identifies and explains why the quadrilateral is a square. (It has 4 equal sides and 4 right angles.)	2
(b)	Your student: • correctly draws six different quadrilaterals.	3
(c)	Your student: • correctly identifies a quadrilateral that is not a square, a rectangle, or a rhombus.	1
(d)	Your student: • correctly explains that the quadrilateral does not have 4 equal sides. • correctly explains that the quadrilateral does not have 4 right angles.	2
	Total	**8**

Use this table as a guide to help you relate your student's scores to his/her performance levels.

Level	Score
😊 😊 😊	7-8
😊 😊	3-6
😊	0-2

STEAM Project Work (Student Book, Chapter 10, page 204)

- Your student is given an opportunity to make connections between art and mathematics as he/she researches maritime signal flags and create a poster to show appreciation for the U.S. Navy veterans.
- At the end of **Chapter 10**, your student should be able to complete **Parts 1** to **3**.
- **Part 1** requires your student to research the maritime signal flags and identify which alphabet and number flags satisfy certain conditions. Allow your student time to conduct the research.
- **Part 2** requires your student to create a poster to show their appreciation for the U.S. Navy veterans. Invite your student to use the maritime signal flags to code their message of appreciation.
- **Part 3** requires your student to share his/her poster with the family and decode each other's messages.

For Additional Support

Your student may find it tedious to recreate each flag. Modify this activity as follows to make it more accessible.

1. Invite your student to choose one favorite flag to recreate, and talk about the shapes he/she needs to do so. You may wish to provide colored paper and encourage your student to make a large flag; for example, the first initial of his/her name, to hang up for display.

2. Make signal cards instead of recreating every flag needed to spell the words of the message your student wishes to send. Simply photocopy the flags. Have your student cut them out and paste them onto index cards to spell out the message, or copy and paste digitally and then print.

3. Talk about the shapes that stand out to your student as he/she works.

Digging Deeper

If your student finds this activity interesting and enjoyable, he/she may like to sort the flags in different ways, and learn a little more about how and why the flags were and are used.

💬 **What are some different ways you might sort these flags, and why?**

Chapter Practice (Student Book, pages 205 to 208)

- Have your student work on **Chapter Practice** in the Student Book independently to help him/her consolidate and extend understanding of the chapter.
- You may find a summary of the chapter learning objectives and the difficulty level of the questions below.
- Teaching prompts are provided for Levels 2 questions.
- When your student is ready, have him/her work on **Additional Practice 3B, Chapter Practice**.

Chapter Practice Answers

(Student Book, pages 205 to 208)

1. **(a)** Option B
   (b) Option A
   (c) Option D

2.

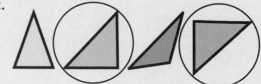

Question	Level	Chapter 9 Learning Objectives	Section(s)	Lesson(s)
1	1	Identify right angles and angles that are smaller or larger than a right angle.	10A	2
2	1	Identify right triangles.	10A	2
3	1	Identify quadrilaterals with shared attributes (rhombuses, including squares).	10A	3
4	1	Identify quadrilaterals with shared attributes (rectangles, including squares).	10A	3
5	2	Identify quadrilaterals with shared attributes. Distinguish between types of quadrilaterals based on the side lengths and the types of angles.	10A	3
6	2	Identify quadrilaterals with shared attributes. Distinguish between types of quadrilaterals based on the side lengths and the types of angles. State the relationship between rectangles, squares, and rhombuses.	10A	3

QUESTION 5 requires your student to identify the different types of quadrilaterals shown on a square grid.

🗨 **How do you determine how many quadrilaterals there are? What are the properties of a rhombus? What are the properties of a rectangle? Which of the quadrilaterals share the properties of both a rhombus and a rectangle? What are they also called? How do you check your answer?**

QUESTION 6(a) requires your student to reason which quadrilateral is a rhombus but not a square.

🗨 **What do you notice about the figures? What is the same about a rhombus and a square? What is different?**

QUESTION 6(b) requires your student to reason if a figure is a quadrilateral and explain his/her thinking.

🗨 **What strategies could help you solve the problem? Does your answer make sense? Why or why not? How do you check your answer?**

Caution

Questions 5a through 5c may be tricky for your student if he/she struggles to separate the shapes in the mind's eye. Please refer to the **Teaching Tip** for ideas on how to help your student if needed.

Teaching Tip

If your student struggles with Question 5, have him/her problem-solve to demonstrate productive struggle.

🗨 **I see you are having a hard time with this. Mathematicians use tools to help themselves unravel tough problems. What do you think might help you get at this problem more easily?**

Allow your student to try a variety of tools or make tools to be able to look at each shape. (For example, tracing each shape individually on graph paper.) You may wish to ask the following questions:

🗨 **What do you notice about this visual?** *It is on a grid.* **How many shapes are there?** *5* **What might help you focus on seeing only one shape at a time?** *Answers vary.* **Is there anything about the grid that could help you determine the length of the sides of the shapes?** *We could use the regular intervals of the grid boxes to count length.* **How are the shapes arranged?** *around the same center point* **How might you use the way they are arranged around the center point as a starting point to help you?** *Count out from the center point.*

3.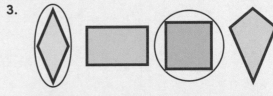

4.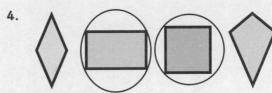

5. (a) 4
   (b) 3
   (c) 2; squares
   (d) Answers vary.

   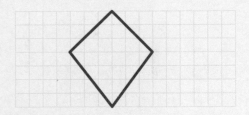

6. (a) Quadrilateral D.
      It is a rhombus because it has 4 equal sides. But it is not a square as it does not have 4 right angles.
   (b) No, it is no longer a quadrilateral. After cutting off a corner, it now has 5 sides instead of 4 sides. A quadrilateral only has 4 sides.

Chapter Test / Cumulative Assessment / End-of-Year Assessment

- Assign **Chapter Test 10** in **Assessment Guide Teacher Edition** to assess your student's understanding of the chapter.
- If you want your student to show his/her work, print out the test in **Assessment Guide Teacher Edition** and have him/her do so on his/her copy.
- Assign **Cumulative Assessment 4** digitally to allow your student to consolidate his/her learning and assess his/her understanding of Chapters 8, 9, and 10.
- Assign **End-of-Year Assessment** digitally to allow your student to consolidate his/her learning and assess his/her understanding of all the chapters learned in Book B.

Chapter Self-Reflection

Check (✓) to show what I can do.

I Can	😊😊😊 Yes	😊😊 Not Sure	😊 No
identify right angles and angles that are smaller or larger than a right angle.			
identify right triangles.			
identify quadrilaterals with shared attributes.			
distinguish between types of quadrilaterals based on the side lengths and the types of angles.			
state the relationship between rectangles, squares, and rhombuses.			

MY JOURNAL

I can show...

I still wonder...

Teacher Resources

You may download the online Teacher Resources and print them for your student as necessary.

TR03 Number Cards (0 to 10)

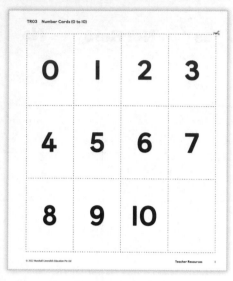

TR03 Number Cards (11 to 20) (Continued)

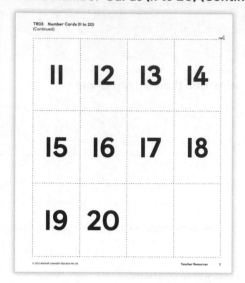

TR03 Number Cards (21 to 30) (Continued)

TR05 Square Grid Paper

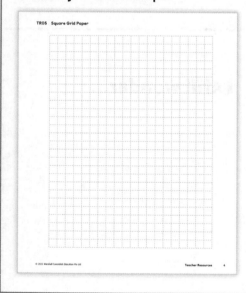

TR19 Square and Triangle Cutouts

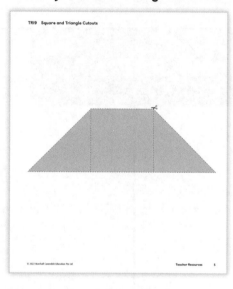

TR20 Grid Paper

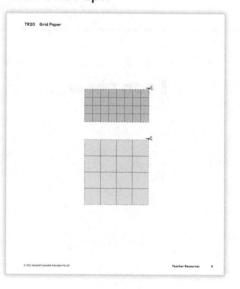

TR21 Tangrams

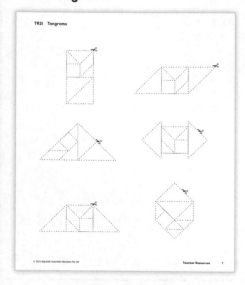

TR22 Paper Squares

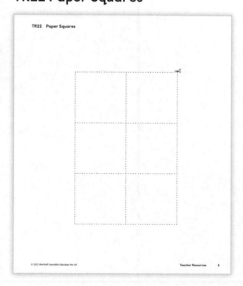

TR23 Centimeter Square Grid

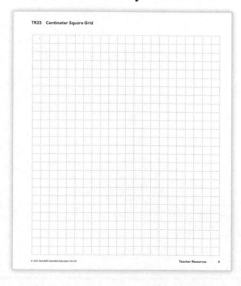

TR24 Inch Square Grid

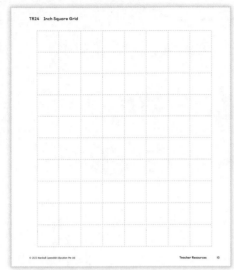

TR25 Playroom Square Grid

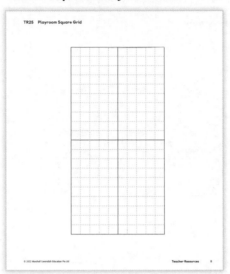

TR26 Rectangular Paper Strips

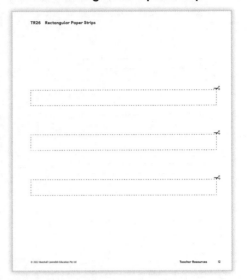

TR27 Unit Fraction Cards

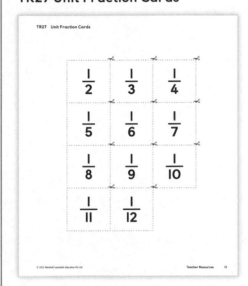

TR28 Ten Frame

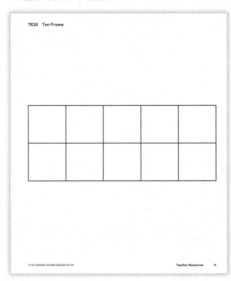

TR29 Paper Square

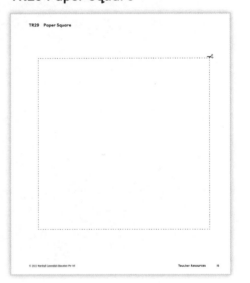

TR30 Fraction Cards

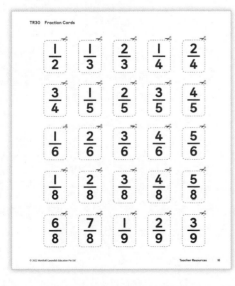

TR31 Fraction Bars

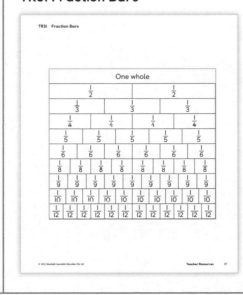

TR32 Fraction Strips

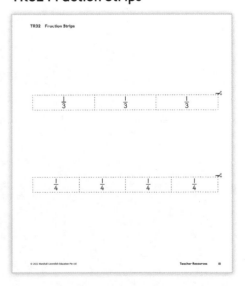

TR33 Number Line Template

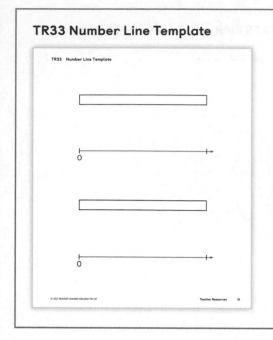

TR34 Blank Scale Faces

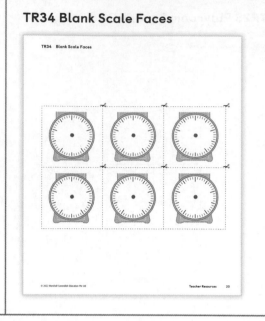

TR35 Shape Cutouts

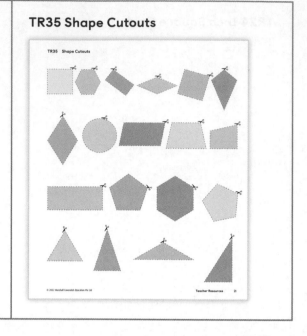

Index

NOTES:

NOTES: